The
Lancashire, Cumbria
Bus Handbook

British Bus Publishing

Body codes used in the Bus Handbook series:

Type:
A	Articulated vehicle
B	Bus, either single-deck or double-deck
BC	Suburban - high-back seated bus
C	Coach
M	Minibus with design capacity of 16 seats or less
N	Low-floor bus (*Niederflur*), either single-deck or double-deck
O	Open-top bus (CO = convertible - PO = partial open-top)

Seating capacity is then shown. For double-decks the upper deck quantity is followed by the lower deck.

Door position:-
C	Centre entrance/exit
D	Dual doorway.
F	Front entrance/exit
R	Rear entrance/exit (no distinction between doored and open)
T	Three or more access points

Equipment:-
L	Lift for wheelchair	TV	Training Vehicle.
M	Mail compartment	RV	Used as tow bus or Engineers vehicle.
T	Toilet	w	Vehicle is withdrawn from service.

e.g. - B32/28F is a double-deck bus with thirty-two seats upstairs, twenty-eight down and a front entrance/exit.
N43D is a low-floor bus with two doorways.

Re-registrations:-
Where a vehicle has gained new index marks the details are listed at the end of each fleet showing the current mark, followed in sequence by those previously carried starting with the original mark.

Regional books in the series:
The Scottish Bus Handbook
The Ireland & Islands Bus Handbook
The North East Bus Handbook
The Yorkshire Bus Handbook
The Lancashire, Cumbria and Manchester Bus Handbook
The Merseyside and Cheshire Bus Handbook
The North and West Midlands Bus Handbook
The East Midlands Bus Handbook
The South Midlands Bus Handbook
The North and West Wales Bus Handbook
The South Wales Bus Handbook
The Chilterns and West Anglia Bus Handbook
The East Anglia Bus Handbook
The South East Bus Handbook
The South West Bus Handbook
The South Central Bus Handbook

Annual books are produced for the major groups:
The 1999 Stagecoach Bus Handbook
The 1999 FirstBus Bus Handbook
The 1999 Arriva Bus Handbook
Editions for earlier years are available. Please contact the publisher.

Associated series:
The Hong Kong Bus Handbook
The Leyland Lynx Handbook
The Model Bus Handbook
The Postbus Handbook
The Toy & Model Bus Handbook - Volume 1 - Early Diecasts
The Fire Brigade Handbook (fleet list of each local authority fire brigade)
The Fire Brigade Handbook - Special Appliances Volume 1
The Fire Brigade Handbook - Special Appliances Volume 2
The Police Range Rover Handbook

Contents

The Lancashire, Cumbria & Manchester Bus Handbook

This second edition of the Lancashire, Cumbria & Manchester Bus Handbook is part of the Bus Handbook series that details the fleets of stage carriage and express coach operators. The operators included in this edition cover those who provide stage and express services in the three former counties and the unitary boroughs. Also included are a number of those operators who provide significant coaching activities.

Quality photographs for inclusion in the series are welcome, for which a fee is payable. The publishers unfortunately cannot accept responsibility for any loss and request you show your name on each picture or slide. Details of changes to fleet information are also welcome.

To keep the fleet information up to date we recommend the Ian Allan publication, Buses, published monthly, or for more detailed information, the PSV Circle monthly news sheets.

Principal Editor: Stuart Martin and Malcolm Jones
Series Editor: Bill Potter

Acknowledgments:
We are grateful to David Donati, Bill Potter, Paul Wigan, Tony Wilson, the PSV Circle and the management and officials of operating companies for their kind assistance and co-operation in the compilation of this book.

The cover picture is by Tony Wilson, rear pictures by Paul Wigan; frontispiece is courtesy Robert Wright & Sons.

ISBN 1 897990 48 0
Published by British Bus Publishing Ltd
The Vyne, 16 St Margaret's Drive, Wellington,
Telford, TF1 3PH
Fax and orderline (+44) (0) 1952 255 669

E-mail sales@britishbuspublishing.co.uk
internet:- http://www.britishbuspublishing.co.uk
© British Bus Publishing, October 1999

ABBOTT'S

Abbott & Sons (Blackpool) Ltd, 95/97 Talbot Road, Blackpool FY1 3QX

w	WFR167K	AEC Reliance 6U3ZR	Plaxton Panorama Elite II	C45F	1972	
w	NFR487M	AEC Reliance 6U3ZR	Plaxton Panorama Elite III	C45F	1973	
	NFR497M	AEC Reliance 6U3ZR	Plaxton Panorama Elite III	C53F	1973	
	PBV637P	AEC Reliance 6U3ZR	Plaxton Supreme III	C53F	1976	
	VFV907R	AEC Reliance 6U3ZR	Plaxton Supreme III	C53F	1977	
	YRN507R	AEC Reliance 6U3ZR	Plaxton Supreme III	C53F	1977	Enterprise, Blackpool, 1997
	HCK847S	AEC Reliance 6U3ZR	Duple Dominant II	C53F	1978	
	JCW517S	Volvo B58-56	Plaxton Supreme III	C53F	1978	
	NCW747T	AEC Reliance 6U3ZR	Duple Dominant II	C53F	1979	
	EFR97W	Leyland Leopard PSU5D/5R	Duple Dominant II	C53F	1981	
	EFR107W	Leyland Leopard PSU5D/5R	Duple Dominant II	C53F	1981	
	MSU611Y	Volvo B10M-61	Duple Laser	C57F	1983	Duple demonstrator, 1983
	A547HBV	Leyland Tiger TRCTL11/3R	Duple Caribbean	C53F	1983	
	A777RBV	Leyland Tiger TRCTL11/3R	Duple Caribbean	C53F	1984	
	B357UCW	Leyland Tiger TRCTL11/3R	Duple Laser	C55F	1984	Duple demonstrator, 1985
	D857XBV	Leyland Tiger TRCTL11/3RZ	Duple 340	C53FT	1987	
	D327VVV	Quest J	Jonckheere Piccolo P35	C33FT	1987	
	F727VAC	Volvo B10M-60	Plaxton Paramount 3500 III	C49F	1988	Volvo demonstrator, 1989
	F787EBV	Ford Transit VE6	Ford	M11	1989	Winder, Blackpool, 1998
	H687XBV	Volvo B10M-60	Plaxton Paramount 3500 III	C57F	1990	
	K617SBV	Volvo B10M-60	Jonckheere Deauville P599	C53FT	1992	
	M307KRY	Volvo B10M-62	Jonckheere Deauville 45	C53FT	1995	
	M337KRY	Volvo B10M-62	Jonckheere Deauville 45	C53FT	1995	

Special event vehicle

	JFV527	Commer B3	Harrington Contender	C41C	1955	Redline, West Bromwich, 1997

Previous registrations
F787EBV   F244XCW, 2428WW, 3346W

Livery:- Grey and red

Abbott's Coaches have provided an express service between Fleetwood, Cleveleys and Manchester for much of the time since the company was formed in the 1930s. However, the main activity is the provision of excursions for those taking a break on the Fylde coast. Pictured at Cleveleys on the Manchester service is Duple Dominant-bodied Leopard, EFR97W.
Bill Potter

ARCHWAY TRAVEL

R M J & M Archer, Unit H Cocker Avenue, Poulton-le-Fylde, Lancashire, FY6 8JU

ONF698R	Leyland Atlantean AN68A/1R	Northern Counties	B43/32F	1977	Town Bus, Poulton-le-Fylde, 1996
RJA719R	Leyland Atlantean AN68A/1R	Northern Counties	B43/32F	1977	Town Bus, Poulton-le-Fylde, 1996
RJA809R	Leyland Atlantean AN68A/1R	Northern Counties	B43/32F	1977	Town Bus, Poulton-le-Fylde, 1996
BNC947T	Leyland Atlantean AN68A/1R	Park Royal	B43/32F	1979	Finglands, 1997
FIL4988	Volvo B10M-61	Jonckheere Jubilee P90	C50/7FT	1984	AG Executive, Pilling, 1997
A20JDA	Bedford YNT	Duple Laser	C53F	1985	Jackson, Chorley, 1992
D122NON	Freight Rover Sherpa	Carlyle	B20F	1987	Town Bus, Poulton-le-Fylde, 1996
D331VVV	Quest J	Jonckheere Piccolo P35	C33FT	1987	Goldenstand, Park Royal, 1994
F998SBC	Toyota Coaster HB31R	Caetano Optimo	C21F	1989	Wilson, Carnwath, 1993
F100UNV	LAG G355Z	LAG Panoramic	C49FT	1989	AG Executive, Pilling, 1997
PIL5258	EOS E180Z	EOS 90	C51FT	1994	Stone, Rochdale, 1998

Previous regisrations:

A20JDA	B222OJU	FIL4988	A318XHE	PIL5258	L546EHD

Livery: White and blue

The provision of school services is the principal activity of Archway Travel where four Leyland Atlanteans form the double-deck fleet. Pictured crossing the new Shard bridge is ONF698R, a former Greater Manchester vehicle with Northern Counties bodywork. *Paul Wigan*

BATTERSBY SILVER GREY

Harrisons Coaches (Morecambe) Ltd, The Coach Station, Middlegate, Morecambe, Lancashire, LA3 3PE

Reg	Chassis	Body	Seating	Year	Previous operator
D137NUS	Mercedes-Benz L608D	Alexander AM	B21F	1986	Highwayman, Errol, 1996
F102VFV	Mercedes-Benz 609D	Reeve Burgess Beaver	BC23F	1988	
F220RSE	Mercedes-Benz 407D	Devon Conversions	M15	1989	Middlehurst, Lancaster, 1994
G744WEE	Mercedes-Benz 811D	Coachcraft	BC26F	1989	Holmes, Clay Cross, 1993
HBZ4680	Dennis Javelin 8.5SDA1903	Plaxton Paramount 3200 III	C35F	1989	Luckett, Fareham, 1997
1359UP	Dennis Javelin 8.5SDA1915	Plaxton Paramount 3200 III	C35F	1989	Taylor, Sutton Scotney, 1995
3267HX	Mercedes-Benz 811D	Whittaker Europa	BC23F	1989	
7845UG	Volvo B10M-60	Plaxton Paramount 3500 III	C57F	1989	Wallace Arnold, 1992
7144FN	Volvo B10M-60	Plaxton Paramount 3500 III	C49F	1990	Wallace Arnold, 1993
7622UK	Volvo B10M-60	Plaxton Paramount 3500 III	C49F	1990	
8850WU	Dennis Javelin 8.5SDA1926	Plaxton Paramount 3200 III	C37F	1990	English, Orpington, 1995
J505DBE	Mercedes-Benz 709D	Reeve Burgess Beaver	BC24F	1991	Pennine Way, Preston, 1994
3182NF	Volvo B10M-60	Jonckheere Deauville P599	C49F	1993	Park's of Hamilton, 1994
L741NFS	Mercedes-Benz 609D	Onyx	BC24F	1994	Russell, Strathaven, 1997
7121RU	Volvo B10M-60	Plaxton Première 350	C49FT	1995	
7017UN	Volvo B10M-62	Plaxton Première 350	C49FT	1995	
5108VX	Volvo B10M-62	Plaxton Première 320	C53FT	1996	
4360WF	Volvo B10M-62	Plaxton Première 350	C53FT	1996	
P894TCK	Volvo B10M-62	Plaxton Première 350	C53FT	1996	
P895EEC	Volvo B10M-62	Plaxton Première 350	C53FT	1996	
P896EEC	Volvo B10M-62	Plaxton Première 350	C49FT	1997	
P897EEC	Volvo B10M-62	Plaxton Première 350	C49FT	1997	
R901WEC	Volvo B10M-62	Plaxton Première 350	C49FT	1998	
R902WEC	Volvo B10M-62	Plaxton Première 350	C49FT	1998	
S903LHG	Volvo B10M-62	Plaxton Première 350	C49FT	1998	
S904LHG	Volvo B10M-62	Plaxton Première 350	C49FT	1998	
S905LHG	Volvo B10M-62	Plaxton Première 350	C49FT	1999	

Previous registrations:

1359UP	G210UAS, G890TSE	5108VX	N892AEO	7622UK	G852MFV
3182NF	K916RGE	7017UN	N890NNR	7845UG	F435DUG
3267HX	G840KET	7121RU	M664GJF	8850WU	H131FLD
4360WF	N891AEO	7144FN	G551LWU	HBZ4680	F551CTX, XSV270, F766NSH

Depot: White Lund Industrial Estate, Morecambe; **Livery:** Two tone blue and cream

Battersby Silver Grey are based at Morecambe from where a wide range of tours and excursions are provided. The coaches can be found at many of the tourist venues, including Spalding where P896EEC was pictured when arriving for the Spring Bulb Festival. *Colin Lloyd*

BLACKBURN

Blackburn Borough Transport Ltd, Intack Garage, Whitebirk Road, Blackburn BB1 3JD

7-22					Leyland Atlantean AN68C/1R		East Lancashire		B43/31F	1982	
7	OCW7X	11	OCW11X	14	OCW14X	17	SBV17X	20	VBV20Y		
8	OCW8X	12	OCW12X	15	OCW15X	18	VBV18Y	21	VBV21Y		
9	OCW9X	13	OCW13X	16	SBV16X	19	VBV19Y	22	VBV22Y		
10	OCW10X										

23-29					Leyland Atlantean AN68D/1R		East Lancashire		B43/31F	1983	
23	A23JBV	25	FCK25Y	27	FCK27Y	28	A28JBV	29	A29 JBV		
24	FCK24Y	26	A26JBV								

43	ABV43B	Leyland PD2A/24	East Lancashire	B35/28R	1964
139	WRN139V	Leyland Atlantean AN68A/1R	East Lancashire	B43/31F	1980

143-147					Leyland Atlantean AN68C/1R		East Lancashire		B43/31F	1981	
143	DBV143W	144	DBV144W	145	DBV145W	146	DBV146W	147	DBV147W		

201-205					Volvo B10M-55		East Lancashire EL2000		BC51F	1991	
201	J421JBV	202	J422JBV	203	J423JBV	204	J424JBV	205	J425JBV		

206-210					Volvo B10BLE		Wright Renown		N44F	1999	
206	V206EBV	207	V207EBV	208	V208EBV	209	V209EBV	210	V210EBV		

321	F984HGE	Volvo B10M-60	Plaxton Paramount 3500 III	C49FT	1988	Park's of Hamilton, 1991
322	MIB920	Volvo B10M-61	Caetano Algarve	C49FT	1987	The Kings Ferry, Gillingham, 1991
323	G996RKN	Volvo B10M-60	Caetano Algarve	C49FT	1990	The Kings Ferry, Gillingham, 1991
324	LIJ749	Volvo B10M-61	Caetano Algarve	C49FT	1988	The Kings Ferry, Gillingham, 1992
325	G999RKN	Volvo B10M-60	Caetano Algarve	C49FT	1990	The Kings Ferry, Gillingham, 1992
326	H174EJU	Volvo B10M-60	Plaxton Paramount 3500 III	C51F	1991	Ambassador Travel, 1994
327	H724VWU	Volvo B10M-60	Plaxton Paramount 3500 III	C49F	1991	Dodsworth, Boroughbridge, 1995
328	L345ERU	Volvo B10M-62	Plaxton Première 320	C49FT	1995	Excelsior, Bournemouth, 1996
329	M351MRU	Volvo B10M-62	Plaxton Première 320	C49FT	1995	Excelsior, Bournemouth, 1996
330	N224THO	Volvo B10M-62	Plaxton Première 320	C49FT	1996	Excelsior, Bournemouth, 1998
331	P526BLJ	Volvo B10M-62	Plaxton Première 320	C49F	1997	Excelsior, Bournemouth, 1999
410	PUS158W	Leyland Leopard PSU3F/4R	Alexander AYS	B53F	1981	Kelvin Scottish, 1987
411	TSU639W	Leyland Leopard PSU3G/4R	Alexander AYS	B53F	1981	Kelvin Scottish, 1987
412	TSU640W	Leyland Leopard PSU3G/4R	Alexander AYS	B53F	1981	Kelvin Scottish, 1987
413	TSU641W	Leyland Leopard PSU3G/4R	Alexander AYS	B53F	1981	Kelvin Scottish, 1988
414	WPH134Y	Leyland Tiger TRCTL11/2R	Eastern Coach Works B51	B51F	1982	Kentish Bus, 1988
415	WPH137Y	Leyland Tiger TRCTL11/2R	Eastern Coach Works B51	B51F	1982	Kentish Bus, 1988
416	WPH138Y	Leyland Tiger TRCTL11/2R	Eastern Coach Works B51	B51F	1982	Kentish Bus, 1988
417	WPH141Y	Leyland Tiger TRCTL11/2R	Eastern Coach Works B51	B51F	1982	Kentish Bus, 1988
423	BVP807V	Leyland National 2 NL116L11/1R East Lancs Greenway (1993)		B49F	1980	North Western, 1992
424	AFM5W	Leyland National 2 NL116AL11/2R East Lancs Greenway (1993)		B49F	1981	North Western, 1992
425	PJT267R	Leyland National 11351A/2R	East Lancs Greenway (1994)	B49F	1976	Solent Blue Line, 1994
426	TCW868T	Leyland National 11351A/2R	East Lancs Greenway (1994)	B49F	1979	North Devon, 1994
427	TJN505R	Leyland National 11351A/1R[V]	East Lancs Greenway (1995)	B49F	1977	Eastern National, 1995
428	TOF694S	Leyland National 11351A/1R[V]	East Lancs Greenway (1995)	B49F	1978	Midland, Cannock, 1995
429	YEV317S	Leyland National 11351A/1R[V]	East Lancs Greenway (1995)	B49F	1978	Thamesway, 1995
430	YEV324S	Leyland National 11351A/1R[V]	East Lancs Greenway (1995)	B49F	1978	Thamesway, 1995
431	EXI2455	Leyland National 1151/1R/2802[V]East Lancs Greenway (1995)		B49F	1973	Express Motors, Bontnewydd, 1997
432	LUF549	Leyland National 1151/2R/0401[V]East Lancs Greenway (1995)		B49F	1973	Black Prince, Morley, 1998

Opposite, top: **Blackburn operate a coaching unit using the Coachlines name as well as providing transport services in the towns of Blackburn and Darwen. The coaches were first purchased to introduce limited stop services from the town, including connections into Manchester. Seen outside Preston rail station is 321, F984HGE.** *Paul Wigan*

Opposite, bottom: **During East Lancashire's Greenway programme Blackburn played an important role in preparing the vehicle's mechanical units ready for the bodybuilder. Consequently this operator now has nineteen, though some are expected to be replaced when the new Volvo B10B low floor buses are delivered towards the end of 1999. Seen leaving the bus station near Blackburn Cathedral is 429, YEV317S.** *Paul Wigan*

433	213ONU	Leyland National 11351A/1R[V]	East Lancs Greenway (1995)	B49F	1978	Black Prince, Morley, 1998
525	BFV861R	Leyland National 10351A/2R	East Lancs Greenway (1993)	B41F	1977	London Buses, 1992
526	BYW361V	Leyland National 10351A/2R	East Lancs Greenway (1993)	B41F	1979	Evag-Cannon, Bolton, 1992
527	LRN552N	Leyland National 10351/2R	East Lancs Greenway (1993)	B41F	1975	Isle of Man Road Services, 1992
528	JDT432N	Leyland National 10351/2R	East Lancs Greenway (1993)	B41F	1975	Isle of Man Road Services, 1992
529	JWG191P	Leyland National 10351/2R	East Lancs Greenway (1993)	B41F	1975	Isle of Man Road Services, 1992
530	HPF313N	Leyland National 10351/1R/SC	East Lancs Greenway (1993)	B41F	1975	Birmingham Omnibus, 1992
531	AYR324T	Leyland National 10351A/2R	East Lancs Greenway (1994)	B41F	1979	CMT Buses, Aintree, 1994
532	JJG907P	Leyland National 10351/1R	East Lancs Greenway (1994)	B41F	1975	Busylink, Hemel Hempstead, 1994
533	M533RCW	Volvo B6-9.9m	East Lancashire	B41F	1994	
534	M534RCW	Volvo B6-9.9m	East Lancashire	B41F	1994	
535	M535RCW	Volvo B6-9.9m	East Lancashire	B41F	1994	
536	M536RCW	Volvo B6-9.9m	East Lancashire	B41F	1994	
604	J967CGK	Optare MetroRider MR03	Optare	B26F	1991	London Central, 1998
605	J969CGK	Optare MetroRider MR03	Optare	B26F	1991	London Central, 1998
606	J704CGK	Optare MetroRider MR03	Optare	B26F	1991	London Central, 1998

610-615

| | | Optare MetroRider MR03 | Optare | B29F | 1992 | London Central, 1998 |

| 610 | J710CGK | 612 | J708CGK | 613 | J703CGK | 614 | J694CGK | 615 | K223MGT |
| 611 | J701CGK | | | | | | | | |

617-626

| | | MCW MetroRider MF159/3 | MCW | B33F* | 1988 | *625/6 are MF159/4 and BC33F |

| 617 | F617UBV | 619 | F619UBV | 621 | F621UBV | 623 | F623UBV | 625 | F625UBV |
| 618 | F618UBV | 620 | F620UBV | 622 | F622UBV | 624 | F624UBV | 626 | F626UBV |

627	M627WBV	Optare MetroRider MR15	Optare	B31F	1995
628	M628WBV	Optare MetroRider MR15	Optare	B31F	1995
629	M629WBV	Optare MetroRider MR15	Optare	B31F	1995
630	M630WFR	Optare MetroRider MR15	Optare	B31F	1995

631-644

| | | Optare MetroRider MR17 | Optare | B29F | 1995-98 |

631	M631WFR	634	N634LFR	637	P637ARN	640	P640ARN	643	R643OBV
632	M632WFR	635	N635LFR	638	P638ARN	641	R641OBV	644	R644OBV
633	N633LFR	636	N636LFR	639	P639ARN	642	R642OBV		

Previous Registrations:

213ONU	SKG924S	LIJ749	F870TNH	M351MRU	A14EXC
BFV861R	OJD880R	LRN552N	JDT437N, 3176MAN	N224THO	A13EXC
EXI2455	BCD801L	LUF549	PTF743L	P526BLJ	P526BLJ, A15XEL
JDT432N	JDT432N, 4647MAN	L345ERU	XEL31	TCW868T	AFJ757T
JWG191P	JWG191P, 4648MAN	MIB920	E841EUT		

Livery: Ivory and green

Blackburn was one of the early users of the MCW MetroRider, and its interest in the type has continued through to the improved Optare product. Nine second-hand vehicles from London Central were added to the fleet in1998 and one of these,613, J703CGK, is shown here.
Paul Wigan

BLACKPOOL

Blackpool Buses - Blackpool & Fleetwood Tramway - HandyBus

Blackpool Transport Services Ltd, Rigby Road, Blackpool, Lancashire FY1 5DD

101-130 DAF SB220LC550 Optare Delta BC46F* 1990-93 *131-3 are BC48F

101	G101NBV	108	G108NBV	115	H115YHG	122	H122CHG	128 K128UFV
102	G102NBV	109	H109YHG	116	H116YHG	123	J123GRN	129 K129UFV
103	G103NBV	110	H110YHG	117	H117YHG	124	J124GRN	130 K130UFV
104	G104NBV	112	H112YHG	118	H118CHG	125	J125GRN	131 H1FBT
105	G105NBV	113	H113YHG	119	H119CHG	126	J126GRN	132 H2FBT
106	G106NBV	114	H114YHG	120	H120CHG	127	K127UFV	133 H3FBT
107	G107NBV							

134	TKU462K	Leyland AT68M/2RF	Northern Counties Paladin (1992) BC42F	1971	Kingston-upon-Hull, 1987
135	TKU465K	Leyland AT68M/2RFT	Northern Counties Paladin (1992) BC42F	1971	Kingston-upon-Hull, 1987
136	TKU466K	Leyland AT68M/2RFT	Northern Counties Paladin (1992) BC42F	1971	Kingston-upon-Hull, 1987
137	TKU469K	Leyland AT68M/2RFT	Northern Counties Paladin (1992) BC42F	1971	Kingston-upon-Hull, 1987

210-218 Optare L1070 Optare Excel N40F 1999

210	T210HCW	212	T212HCW	214	T214HCW	216	T216HCW	218 T218HCW
211	T211HCW	213	T213HCW	215	T215HCW	217	T217HCW	

322-340 Leyland Atlantean AN68A/2R East Lancashire B50/36F 1979-80

322	URN322V	326	URN326V	330	URN330V	334	AHG334V	338 AHG338V
323	URN323V	327	URN327V	331	AHG331V	336	AHG336V	339 AHG339V
324	URN324V	328	URN328V	332	AHG332V	337	AHG337V	340 AHG340V
325	URN325V	329	URN329V	333	AHG333V			

341-350 Leyland Atlantean AN68C/2R East Lancashire B50/36F 1981

341	GHG341W	344	GHG344W	346	GHG346W	348	GHG348W	350 GHG350W
343	GHG343W	345	GHG345W	347	GHG347W	349	GHG349W	

Blackpool were one of the first customers for the Optare Excel taking twelve in 1996. These are being replaced by a further dozen to the latest specification as we go to press. Representing the first batch which carried *HandyBus* livery is 203, N203LCK.
Gerry Mead

351-364

		Leyland Atlantean AN68D/2R	East Lancashire				B49/36F*	1982-84	*363/4 are BC45/29F		
351	UHG351Y	354	UHG354Y	357	A357HHG	360	A360HHG	363	B363UBV		
352	UHG352Y	355	A355HHG	358	A358HHG	361	A361HHG	364	B364UBV		
353	UHG353Y	356	A356HHG	359	A359HHG	362	A362HHG				

365	UWW5X	Leyland Olympian ONLXB/1R	Roe	B47/29F	1982	West Yorkshire PTE, 1986
366	UWW11X	Leyland Olympian ONLXB/1R	Roe	B47/29F	1982	West Yorkshire PTE, 1986
367	UWW15X	Leyland Olympian ONLXB/1R	Roe	B47/29F	1982	West Yorkshire PTE, 1986

368-373

		Leyland Olympian ONCL10/1RZ	East Lancashire		B45/31F	1989				
368	F368AFR	370	F370AFR	371	F371AFR	372	F372AFR	373	F373AFR	
369	F369AFR									

374-379

		Volvo Olympian YN2RC16Z4	Northern Counties Palatine 2	B43/29F	1994					
374	M374SCK	376	M376SCK	377	M377SCK	378	M378SCK	379	M379SCK	
375	M375SCK									

401-410

		Leyland Olympian ONLXB/1R	Eastern Coach Works		B43/32F*	1983-84	Trent, 1996 *407-10 are B45/30F			
401	XAU701Y	403	XAU703Y	405	XAU705Y	407	A707DAU	409	A709DAU	
402	XAU702Y	404	XAU704Y	406	XAU706Y	408	A708DAU	410	A710DAU	

441	HIL5341	Leyland Atlantean AN68C/2R	Northern Counties	BC43/33F	1981	
442	HIL5342	Leyland Atlantean AN68C/2R	Northern Counties	BC43/33F	1982	
443	HIL5943	Leyland Atlantean AN68D/2RF	Northern Counties Palatine (1992)	BC43/33F	1983	
444	NJI5504	Leyland Atlantean AN68D/2R	Northern Counties	BC43/33F	1983	
445	NJI5505	Leyland Atlantean AN68D/2R	Northern Counties	BC43/33F	1984	
453	WRH294J	Leyland Atlantean PDR1A/1	Roe	O43/28F	1970	Kingston-upon-Hull, 1987
454	ARH309K	Leyland Atlantean PDR1A/1	Roe	O43/29F	1971	Kingston-upon-Hull, 1987
455	ARH304K	Leyland Atlantean PDR1A/1	Roe	B43/29F	1971	Kingston-upon-Hull, 1987
465	ONF660R	Leyland Atlantean AN68A/1R	Northern Counties	B43/32F	1976	GM Buses, 1989
466	ONF669R	Leyland Atlantean AN68A/1R	Northern Counties	B43/32F	1976	GM Buses, 1989
467	ONF673R	Leyland Atlantean AN68A/1R	Northern Counties	B43/32F	1976	GM Buses, 1989
468	SRJ756R	Leyland Atlantean AN68A/1R	Northern Counties	B43/32F	1977	GM Buses, 1989
469	SRJ757R	Leyland Atlantean AN68A/1R	Northern Counties	B43/32F	1977	GM Buses, 1989
470	TSD571S	Leyland Atlantean AN68A/1R	Northern Counties	B44/34F	1978	Clyde Coast, Ardrossan, 1990
471	OJI4371	Leyland Atlantean AN68A/1R	Northern Counties (1990)	B43/31F	1977	
472	OJI4372	Leyland Atlantean AN68M/1RF	Northern Counties (1990)	B43/31F	1977	
473	OJI4373	Leyland Atlantean AN68A/1R	Northern Counties (1990)	B43/31F	1977	
474	OJI4374	Leyland Atlantean AN68A/1R	Northern Counties (1990)	B43/31F	1977	
475	SIB8405	Leyland Atlantean AN68M/1RF	Northern Counties (1990)	B43 /31F	1976	
478	HRN98N	Leyland Atlantean AN68/1R	NCME/Willowbrook	B43/31F	1975	
479	HRN99N	Leyland Atlantean AN68/1R	NCME/Willowbrook	B43/31F	1975	
480	HRN100N	Leyland Atlantean AN68/1R	NCME/Willowbrook	B43/31F	1975	
481	HRN101N	Leyland Atlantean AN68/1R	NCME/Willowbrook	B43/31F	1975	
482	HRN102N	Leyland Atlantean AN68/1R	NCME/Willowbrook	B43/31F	1975	
483	HRN103N	Leyland Atlantean AN68/1R	NCME/Willowbrook	B43/31F	1975	
487	MIW8187	Leyland Atlantean AN68/1R	Roe	B43/29F	1973	Kingston-upon-Hull, 1992
489	RIB4089	Leyland Atlantean AN68/1R	Roe	B43/29F	1972	Kingston-upon-Hull, 1988
492	NIW6492	Leyland Atlantean AN68/1R	Roe	B43/29F	1972	Kingston-upon-Hull, 1992
495	RHG95T	Leyland Atlantean AN68A/1R	Northern Counties	B43/31F	1979	
496	XHG96V	Leyland Atlantean AN68A/1R	Northern Counties	B43/31F	1980	

501-518

		Optare MetroRider MR37	Optare		B25F	1996-98				
501	P501UFR	505	S505LHG	509	S509LHG	513	S513LHG	516	S516LHG	
502	P502UFR	506	S506LHG	510	S510LHG	514	S514LHG	517	S517LHG	
503	P503UFR	507	S507LHG	511	S511LHG	515	S515LHG	518	S518LHG	
504	P504UFR	508	S508LHG	512	S512LHG					

Opposite: **Blackpool is famous for its trams, fresh air and fun with an illuminations period from August bank holiday which significantly helps to extend the holiday season. Two of the trams are shown here. The upper picture is of Twin Car 671 which can most often be found running the Pleasure Beach - Cleveleys service. When new the trailer trams were lettered for the Coastal Tour running the whole length of the system from Fleetwood Ferry to Starr Gate. The lower picture shows open boat 605 at Manchester Square. These vehicles retain the trolley-poles to avoid carbon from a pantograph dropping onto passengers. In recent times the boats have been seen more in Fleetwood, particularly on market days when there is much traffic for this shoppers bonanza.** *Cliff Beeton/Paul Wigan*

Number 510 in the Blackpool fleet is S510LHG, an Optare MetroRider. Blackpool's minibus services operate as *HandyBus* and provide connections for the communities in the area. The vehicle is seen on route 12A as it emerges onto the Promenade at Manchester Square. *Paul Wigan*

559-582

559-582			Volkswagen LT55		Optare City Pacer		B21F	1987-88		
559	E559GFR	570	E570OCW	574	F574RCW	577	F577RCW	580	F580WCW
567	E567GFR	571	F571RCW	575	F575RCW	578	F578RCW	581	F581WCW
568	E568GFR	572	F572RCW	576	F576RCW	579	F579WCW	582	F582WCW
569	E569OCW	573	F573RCW						

583	F934AWW	Volkswagen LT55	Optare City Pacer	BC21F	1988	Optare demonstrator, 1989
584	M924TYG	Optare MetroRider MR37	Optare	B25F	1995	Optare demonstrator, 1995

585-596

585-596			Optare MetroRider MR37		Optare		B25F	1995-96		
585	N585GRN	588	N588GRN	591	N591GRN	593	N593LFV	595	N595LFV
586	N586GRN	589	N589GRN	592	N592GRN	594	N594LFV	596	N596LFV
587	N587GRN	590	N590GRN						

Trams

600-607

600-607			English Electric M4d		English Electric		OST56C*	1934-35	*602 is OST52C	
600		602		604		605		606		607

619		English Electric M4d		Blackpool Corporation (1987)	ST52D	1973	

621-637

621-637			EMB M4d		Brush		ST48C	1937					
621		623		626		630		631		632	633	634	636	637
622		625		627										

641-647

641-647			Primrose/Brush M4d		East Lancashire		ST52D	1984-88	641 is ST55D	
641		642		643		644		645		646	647

648		Maley & Taunton/Brush M4d	East Lancashire	ST53D	1985
660	.	Maley & Taunton M4d	Roberts	ST56C	1953

671-677

		Maley/English			
		English Electric, 1935 M4s	English Electric	ST53C	1960

671	672	673	674	675	676	677

678	English Electric, 1935 M4d	English Electric	ST48C	1960
679	English Electric, 1935 M4d	English Electric	ST48C	1960
680	English Electric, 1935 M4d	English Electric	ST48C	1960

681-687

Maley & Taunton M4d	MCW	ST61C	1960

681	682	683	684	685	686	687

700-726

English Electric M4d	English Electric	DT54/40C*	1934/35	*706 is ODT54/40C

700	703	707	710	713	716	718	720	722	724
701	704	708	711	715	717	719	721	723	726
702	706	709	712						

732	Dick Kerr M4s	Blackpool Corporation	48-seat	1960	*Moon Rocket*
733	English Electric M4d	Blackpool Corporation	35-seat	1962	*Wild West Loco*
734	Dick Kerr B4s	Blackpool Corporation	60-seat	1962	*Wild West coach*
735	English Electric M4d	Blackpool Corporation	57/42	1963	*Hovercraft*
736	Dick Kerr M4d	Blackpool Corporation	71-seat	1965	*Frigate*
761	English Electric (1934) M4d	Blackpool/East Lancs	DT56/44F	1979	
762	English Electric (1934) M4d	Blackpool/East Lancs	DT56/34D	1982	

Auxilliary vehicle:

907	HFR507E	Leyland Titan PD3A/1	MCW	TV	1967

Previous Registrations:

HIL5341	HBV97W	NJI5504	A74LHG	OJI4373	EBV87S
HIL5342	PCW98X	NJI5505	B75URN	OJI4374	EBV88S
HIL5943	ACK99Y	OJI4371	EBV85S	RIB4089	DRH329L
MIW8187	NAT339M	OJI4372	EBV86S	SIB8405	OCK84P
NIW6492	DRH327L				

Livery: Cream and green (most full size buses and trams) ; black and yellow (Handybus) most minibuses

During 1996 ten Leyland Olympians were acquired from Trent. One of these is 407, A707DAU, seen on promenade service 1 which serves the Pontins camp at its southern terminus.
Cliff Beeton

BLUE BUS

Blue Bus & Coach Services Ltd, Unit 4a Horwich Business Park, Chorley New Road, Horwich, Bolton BL6 5UE

1	K1BLU	Dennis Dart 9.8SDL3017	East Lancashire EL2000	B40F	1993	
2	M2BLU	Dennis Dart 9.8SDL3043	East Lancashire EL2000	B40F	1994	
3	N3BLU	Dennis Dart 9.8SDL3054	Plaxton Pointer	B40F	1995	
4	N4BLU	Dennis Dart 9.8SDL3054	Alexander Dash	B40F	1995	
5	N5BLU	Dennis Dart 9.8SDL3054	Alexander Dash	B40F	1996	
6	R6BLU	Dennis Dart SLF	Plaxton Pointer 2	N36F	1998	
7	R7BLU	Dennis Dart SLF	Plaxton Pointer 2	N36F	1998	
8	R8BLU	Dennis Dart SLF	Plaxton Pointer 2	N36F	1998	
9	S9BLU	Dennis Dart SLF	Plaxton Pointer 2	N36F	1998	
10	T10BLU	Dennis Dart SLF	Plaxton Pointer MPD	N28F	1999	
11	T11BLU	Dennis Dart SLF	Plaxton Pointer MPD	N28F	1999	
18w	ULS318T	Leyland Leopard PSU3E/4R	Alexander AYS	B53F	1979	Rossendale, 1993
19w	ULS329T	Leyland Leopard PSU3E/4R	Alexander AYS	B53F	1979	OK Travel, 1994
20	CSF160W	Leyland Leopard PSU3G/4R	Alexander AYS	B53F	1981	Fife Scottish, 1998
21	WFS141W	Leyland Leopard PSU3F/4R	Alexander AYS	B53F	1980	Fife Scottish, 1998
29w	GMS299S	Leyland Leopard PSU3E/4R	Alexander AYS	B53F	1978	Moffat & Williamson, Gauldry, 1994
39w	YCS93T	Leyland Leopard PSU3E/4R	Alexander AY	B53F	1978	Clydeside, 1996
41	V41DJA	Volvo Olympian	East Lancashire Pyoneer	B47/30F	1999	
42	T42PVM	Volvo Olympian	East Lancashire Pyoneer	B47/30F	1999	
43	S43BLU	Volvo Olympian	East Lancashire Pyoneer	B47/30F	1998	
44	R44BLU	Volvo Olympian	East Lancashire Pyoneer	BC45/30F	1998	
45	S45BLU	Volvo Olympian	East Lancashire Pyoneer	B47/30F	1998	
46	M646RCP	DAF DB250RS505	Northern Counties Palatine II	B47/30F	1995	Metrobus, Orpington, 1996
47	M647RCP	DAF DB250RS505	Northern Counties Palatine II	B47/30F	1995	Capital Citybus, 1996
50	PIB5144	Leyland PSU3E/4R (TL11)	Willowbrook Warrior (1991)	B48F	1978	Brighton & Hove, 1997

Seen in Wigan is Blue Bus 44, R44BLU, one of four East Lancashire Pyoneer-bodied Volvo Olympians that joined the Blue Bus fleet in the last couple of years. As more low-floor buses are added to the fleet, the days of the Leopards are now numbered. Two DAF SB220 with Hungarian-built Ikarus bodywork are due in December 1999. *Tony Wilson*

Blue Bus' low-floor vehicles are branded as Blue Buggy Bus as shown on Dennis Dart 7, R7BLU which was pictured while operating the Hall i'th' Wood route 527. This service operates north towards Blackburn, a road which sees operations by several of the operators that work in Bolton. *Richard Godfrey*

51	LDZ2951	Leyland Leopard PSU3E/4R [D]	East Lancashire EL2000 ('92)	B51F	1980	Trent, 1992
52	HIL9152	Leyland Leopard PSU3F/4R [D]	East Lancashire EL2000 ('92)	B51F	1982	Trent, 1992
53	WIB4053	Leyland Leopard PSU3F/4R [D]	East Lancashire EL2000 ('94)	B51F	1982	National Welsh, 1993
54	WIB4054	Leyland Leopard PSU3F/4R [D]	East Lancashire EL2000 ('95)	B51F	1982	United, 1995
56	E156XHS	Volvo B10M-56	Plaxton Derwent II	B54F	1988	Henderson, Hamilton, 1999
57	B957LHN	Leyland Tiger TRCTL11/2R	Duple Dominant	B55F	1984	United Bus (Tees), 1998
61	RJI2161	Volvo B58-56	East Lancashire EL2000 ('95)	BC49F	1980	Pride of the Road, 1994
62	F902JBB	Leyland Tiger TRBTL11/2RP	Duple 300	B55F	1989	Go-Gateshead, 1999
63	H163DJU	Dennis Javelin 11SDA1914	Duple 300	B55F	1991	Go-Gateshead, 1999
64	A664KUM	Leyland Tiger TRBTL11/2R	Duple Dominant	BC47F	1983	South Lancs, St Helens, 1996
66	A666KUM	Leyland Tiger TRBTL11/2R	Duple Dominant	BC47F	1983	South Lancs, St Helens, 1996
67	A667KUM	Leyland Tiger TRBTL11/2R	Duple Dominant	BC47F	1983	South Lancs, St Helens, 1996
68	B43UCK	Leyland Tiger TRBTL11/2RH	Duple Dominant	BC47F	1984	South Lancs, St Helens, 1997
71	LBZ4071	Leyland Tiger TRCTL11/2R(V)	East Lancashire EL2000 ('94)	B51F	1982	Burman, Dordon, 1994
72	WJI9072	Leyland Tiger TRBTL11/2R	East Lancashire EL2000 ('98)	B51F	1983	Fife Scottish, 1998
73	WJI9073	Leyland Tiger TRBTL11/2RP	East Lancashire	B47F	1983	Red & White (Rhondda), 1994
74	WJI9074	Leyland Tiger TRBTL11/2R	East Lancashire EL2000 ('98)	B51F	1983	Red & White (Parfitts), 1997
75	B25ADW	Leyland Tiger TRBTL11/2RP	East Lancashire	B47F	1984	Red & White (Rhondda), 1995
76	C76UHN	Leyland Tiger TRBTL11/2RP	Duple Dominant	B55F	1985	United Bus (Tees), 1998
94	N94BNF	Mercedes-Benz 709D	Plaxton Beaver	B25F	1996	
95	N95BNF	Mercedes-Benz 709D	Plaxton Beaver	B25F	1996	
100	K100BLU	DAF SB3000DKVF601	Van Hool Alizée HE	C55F	1993	
101	F701ENE	Leyland Tiger TRCL10/3ARZA	Plaxton Paramount 3200 III	C53F	1989	Shearings, 1992
200	N200BLU	DAF DE33WSSB3000	Van Hool Alizée HE	C53F	1996	
300	R300BLU	DAF DE33WSSB3000	Plaxton Première 320	C53F	1998	

Previous registrations:

HIL9152	SCH150X	WIB4053	KWO563X
K100BLU	K109TCP	WIB4054	LPY460W
LBZ4071	ESU157X, 403EXH, RDV903, HGD802X	WJI9072	MNS6Y
LDZ2951	KVO143W	WJI9073	A73VTX
PIB5144	UTD203T	WJI9074	EWR 657Y
RJI2161	PYD984V	YCS93T	YCS93T, WJI9074

BLUEBIRD

MTG, TA & M Dunstan, Alexander House, Greengate, Middleton, Rochdale, M24 1RU

1	R1BLU	Dennis Dart SLF	Wright Crusader	N32F	1997	
2	T2BLU	Dennis Dart SLF	Wright Crusader	N39F	1999	
3	V3BLU	Scania N113	East Lancashire	B45/33F	1999	
4	L4BLU	Iveco TurboDaily 59.12	Marshall C31	B27F	1994	
5	M5BLU	Iveco TurboDaily 59.12	Marshall C31	B19F	1995	
6	M6BLU	Iveco TurboDaily 59.12	Marshall C31	B19F	1995	
7	N7BLU	Iveco TurboDaily 59.12	UVG Citistar	B27F	1995	
8	M8BLU	Iveco TurboDaily 59.12	Marshall C31	B19F	1995	
9	M9BLU	Iveco TurboDaily 59.12	Marshall C31	B19F	1995	
10	M10BLU	Iveco TurboDaily 59.12	Marshall C31	B19F	1995	
11	F616UBV	MCW MetroRider	MCW	B31F	19	
12	M12BLU	Iveco TurboDaily 59.12	Marshall C31	B19F	1995	
13	N13BLU	Iveco TurboDaily 59.12	Mellor	B27F	1995	
14	N14BLU	Iveco TurboDaily 59.12	Mellor	B27F	1995	
15	R15BLU	Iveco TurboDaily 59.12	Marshall C31	B26F	1998	
16	R16BLU	Iveco TurboDaily 59.12	Marshall C31	B26F	1998	
17	N17BLU	Iveco TurboDaily 59.12	UVG Citistar	B27F	1995	
18	R18BLU	Mercedes-Benz Vario O810	UVG Citistar	B27F	1998	
19	R19BLU	Mercedes-Benz Vario O810	UVG Citistar	B27F	1998	
20	P20BLU	Dennis Dart SLF	Wright Crusader	N32F	1997	
21	V21BLU	Mercedes-Benz Vario O810	Marshall	B31F	1999	
22	V22BLU	Mercedes-Benz Vario O810	Marshall	B31F	1999	
23	G813RNC	Leyland Tiger TR2R62C21Z5	Plaxton Paramount 3200 III	C53F	1990	Blackpool, 1999
30	P30BLU	Dennis Dart SLF	Wright Crusader	N32F	1997	
40	P40BLU	Dennis Dart SLF	Wright Crusader	N32F	1997	

Bluebird is based in the Rochdale-suburb of Middleton, a town which transferred its allegiance under the local government reforms. However, the principal services still run from Middleton into Manchester, and S6BLU is seen outside the Arndale shopping centre. Eight Wright Crusader buses are now operated, all of which carry 'BLU' index marks. *Tony Wilson*

Bluebird acquired two Leyland Leopards from Burnley & Pendle in 1993 and these have now been rebodied by East Lancashire with their EL2000 body style. Cannon Street is the location for this picture of 70, MAZ4970, one of the pair. Several of the operators in Manchester have become quality partners with the PTE, and this is reflected in the vehicle's lettering. *Tony Wilson*

50	P50BLU	Dennis Dart SLF	Wright Crusader	N32F	1997	
52	S2BLU	Mercedes-Benz Vario O814	Plaxton Beaver 2	B27F	1998	
53	S3BLU	Mercedes-Benz Vario O814	Plaxton Beaver 2	B27F	1998	
54	S4BLU	Mercedes-Benz Vario O814	Plaxton Beaver 2	B27F	1998	
55	S5BLU	Dennis Dart SLF	Wright Crusader	N39F	1999	
56	S6BLU	Dennis Dart SLF	Wright Crusader	N39F	1999	
69	MAZ4969	Leyland Leopard PSU4E/4R	East Lancashire EL2000 (1996)	B45F	1980	Burnley & Pendle, 1993
70	MAZ4970	Leyland Leopard PSU4E/4R	East Lancashire EL2000 (1996)	B45F	1980	Burnley & Pendle, 1993

76-83			MCW Metrobus DR102/52	Alexander RL	B45/33F	1986	Midland (Stevensons) 1998
76	D676MHS	78	D678MHS	80	D680MHS	82	D682MHS	83	D683MHS

Special event vehicle

	TXJ540K	Leyland Leopard PSU3B/4R	Duple Viceroy	C49F	1972	Catholic CRS,East Didsbury, 1998

Ancilliary vehicles

TB1	HCS807N	Leyland Leopard PSU3/3R	Alexander AYS	TV	1975	Plymouth Citybus, 1998
TB2	OSJ610R	Leyland Leopard PSU3C/4R	Alexander AY	TV	1976	Plymouth Citybus, 1998

Previous registrations:

MAZ4969	YHG15V		
		MAZ4970	YHG16V, LBU607V

Named vehicles: 4 *Louise,* 5 *Jamie,* 6 *Janice,* 7 *Moira,* 8 *Pauline,* 9 *Fiona,* 10 *Karen,* 12 *Joan,* 13 *Katie,* 14 *Amy,* 15 *Barbara,* 16 *Jane,* 17 *Lucy,* 18 *Emma,* 19 *Stephanie,* 52 *Junie,* 53 *Caroline,* 54 *Connie,* 69 *Valarie,* 70, *Sarah.*

Livery: Blue and ivory

BORDER

Border Buses - Viscount Central

Border Buses, Bancroft Road, Burnley, BB10 2AZ

A member of the Status Bus & Coach Group

Border Buses

02	D102VRP	Mercedes-Benz L608D	Robin Hood	B20F	1986.	MK Metro, 1999
08	D108VRP	Mercedes-Benz L608D	Robin Hood	B20F	1986	MK Metro, 1999
77	D177VRP	Mercedes-Benz L608D	Dormobile Routemaker (1990)	B25F	1986	Milton Keynes, 1997
95	G114PGT	Mercedes-Benz 811D	Alexander Sprint	B28F	1989	London General, 1999
98	G98NBD	Mercedes-Benz 709D	Dormobile Routemaker	B29F	1989/90	Milton Keynes, 1997
99	G99NBD	Mercedes-Benz 709D	Dormobile Routemaker	B29F	1989/90	Milton Keynes, 1997
165	F865LCU	MCW MetroRider MF158/15	MCW	B31F	1988	Kentish Bus, 1998
175	G575PRM	Mercedes-Benz 709D	Alexander AM	B23F	1990	Stagecoach Ribble, 1998
176	G576PRM	Mercedes-Benz 709D	Alexander AM	B23F	1990	Stagecoach Ribble, 1998
192	E92LHG	Mercedes-Benz 709D	Alexander AM	B25F	1988	Stagecoach Ribble, 1998
194	E94LHG	Mercedes-Benz 709D	Alexander AM	B25F	1988	Stagecoach Ribble, 1998
207	BOK7V	MCW Metrobus DR102/12	MCW	B43/30F	1979	Travel West Midlands, 1999
213	CAU113T	Leyland Fleetline FE30ALR	Northern Counties	B44/31F	1979	City of Nottingham, 1994
221	ABN721T	Leyland Atlantean AN68A/1R	East Lancashire	B43/32F	1979	Rossendale, 1995
226	GOG226W	MCW Metrobus DR104/8	MCW	B43/30F	1981	Travel West Midlands, 1999
231	GOG231W	MCW Metrobus DR104/8	MCW	B43/30F	1981	Travel West Midlands, 1999
236	GOG236W	MCW Metrobus DR104/8	MCW	B43/30F	1981	Travel West Midlands, 1999
241	GOG241W	MCW Metrobus DR104/8	MCW	B43/30F	1981	Travel West Midlands, 1999
244	SRJ744R	Leyland Atlantean AN68A/1R	Northern Counties	B43/32F	1977	Yorkshire Rider, 1993
250	C950HWF	MCW Metrobus DR102.50	MCW	BC42/28F	1985	First Mainline, 1998
252	C952LWJ	MCW Metrobus DR102/53	MCW	BC42/28F	1986	First Mainline, 1998
253	ORJ353W	Leyland Atlantean AN68A/1R	Northern Counties	B43/32F	1981	G M Buses North, 1996
254	C954LWJ	MCW Metrobus DR102/53	MCW	BC42/28F	1986	First Mainline, 1998
257	FVR257V	Leyland Atlantean AN68A/1R	Northern Counties	B43/32F	1981	G M Buses North, 1996
260	DEM760Y	MCW Metrobus DR102/29	Alexander RH	B45/33F	1974	Classic Buses, Anfield Plain, 1999
261	NRG161M	Leyland Atlantean AN68/1R	Alexander AL	B45/36F	1974	Blue Bus, Horwich, 1993
265	NRG165M	Leyland Atlantean AN68/1R	Alexander AL	B45/36F	1974	Blue Bus, Horwich, 1993
267	NRG167M	Leyland Atlantean AN68/1R	Alexander AL	B45/36F	1974	Blue Bus, Horwich, 1993
275	GOG275W	MCW Metrobus DR104/8	MCW	B43/30F	1981	Travel West Midlands, 1999
285	KSU857P	Leyland Atlantean AN68/1R	Alexander AL	B45/31F	1976	Rossendale, 1993
288	XPG188T	Leyland Atlantean AN68A/1R	Roe	B43/30F	1979	London & Country, 1996

Viscount Central Coaches

301	N526PYS	Volvo B10M-61	Van Hool Alizèe	C49F	1996	
305	HXI311	Volvo B10M-61	Jonckheere Jubilee P50	C49FT	1988	Burnley & Pendle, 1997
307	XSU907	Volvo C10M-70	Ramseier & Jenzer	C49FT	1985	Burnley & Pendle, 1997
308	XSU908	Volvo C10M-70	Ramseier & Jenzer	C49FT	1985	Burnley & Pendle, 1997
309	XSU909	Volvo B10M-61	Jonckheere Jubilee P50	C51FT	1986	Burnley & Pendle, 1997
310	T10VCC	Volvo B10M-62	Plaxton Première 350	C49F	1999	
311	T11VCC	Volvo B10M-62	Plaxton Première 350	C49F	1999	
312	T12VCC	Dennis Javelin	Plaxton Première 350	C49F	1999	
313	T13VCC	Dennis Javelin	Plaxton Première 350	C49F	1999	
315	M907OVR	Dennis Javelin GX	Neoplan Transliner	C49F	1995	Timeline, 1998

The Border fleet has been transformed in recent months and is now part of the Status Bus & Coach Group which includes MK Metro as well as Classic Coaches and Moor-Dale in northeast England. Representing the fleet is Dennis Dart 94, H94MOB. With its Carlyle Dartline body it was one of a batch delivered to London Buses later moving to Metroline when the London Buses fleet was divided. As we go to press, the fleet has been re-numbered into the MK Metro series, and buses will become yellow and blue on repaint. *Bill Potter*

Border Buses

401	H101MOB	Dennis Dart 8.5SDL3003	Carlyle Dartline	B28F	1990	Metroline, 1997
405	H105MOB	Dennis Dart 8.5SDL3003	Carlyle Dartline	B28F	1990	Metroline, 1997
406	H106MOB	Dennis Dart 8.5SDL3003	Carlyle Dartline	B28F	1990	Metroline, 1997
413	A213SAE	Leyland Tiger TRCTL11/3R	Plaxton Paramount 3200	C51F	1983	Harrogate & District, 1998
437	H137MOB	Dennis Dart 8.5SDL3003	Carlyle Dartline	B28F	1990	Metroline, 1997
454	GSU554	Leyland Tiger TRCTL11/3R	Duple Laser	C53F	1983	Burnley & Pendle, 1997
455	XSU905	Leyland Tiger TRCTL11/3R	Duple Laser	C55F	1983	Burnley & Pendle, 1997
458	H858NOC	Dennis Dart 8.5SDL3003	Carlyle Dartline	B37F	1991	MK Metro, 1999
473	WEX827X	Leyland Leopard PSU3G/4R	Eastern Coach Works B51	BC53F	1982	Rossendale, 1994
474	XPW876X	Leyland Leopard PSU3G/4R	Eastern Coach Works B51	BC53F	1982	Rossendale, 1994
488	AAX488A	Leyland Tiger TRCTL11/3R	Plaxton Paramount 3200	C51F	1983	Stagecoach Red & White, 1998
494	H94MOB	Dennis Dart 8.5SDL3003	Carlyle Dartline	B28F	1990	Metroline, 1997
498	H98MOB	Dennis Dart 8.5SDL3003	Carlyle Dartline	B28F	1990	Metroline, 1997
529	MNC529W	Leyland Atlantean AN68A/1R	Northern Counties	B43/32F	1980	Hall, Kennoway, 1998

Previous registrations:

AAX488A	SDW918Y	LIB1184	NDW148X	XSU905	ANA53Y, XFK305
GSU552	D202VBV	NXI414	B708EOF, HHG25	XSU907	C641KDS
GSU553	D203VBV	RJI8720	F763ENE	XSU908	C661KDS
GSU554	ANA52Y	WEX827X	WEX827X, PJI9173	XSU909	D111BNV
HXI311	E508KNV	XPW876X	XPW876X, PJI9174	XSU910	E507KNV
LIB1183	NDW149X				

Livery: Yellow and blue; red and white (Viscount)

Depots: Bancroft Road, Burnley and Dean Mill, Plumbe Street, Burnley

BROWNRIGG'S

S H Brownrigg Ltd, 53 Main Street, Egremont, Cumbria, CA22 2DB

Reg	Chassis	Body	Seating	Year	Previous owner
SIW2805	Volvo B58-61	Plaxton Supreme IV	C55F	1979	Stephenson, Maryport, 1998
JND264V	Leyland Leopard PSU5C/4R	Duple Dominant II	C53F	1980	Ribble, 1991
GRM623V	Leyland Leopard PSU3E/4R	Duple Dominant II Express	C49F	1980	Cumberland, 1992
LVS424V	Leyland Leopard PSU5C/4R	Duple Dominant II	C53F	1980	Stephenson, Maryport, 1996
PWK7W	Leyland Leopard PSU3F/5R	Duple Dominant II	C53F	1981	Robinsons, Great Harwood, 1986
RHL174X	Leyland Tiger TRCTL11/3R	Duple Dominant IV	C49FT	1982	East Midland, 1996
PJI4317	Leyland Tiger TRCTL11/2R	Duple Dominant IV	C47F	1983	Grimsby Cleethorpes, 1996
YPD129Y	Leyland Tiger TRCTL11/2R	Duple Dominant IV Express	C53F	1983	East Midland, 1996
YPD133Y	Leyland Tiger TRCTL11/2R	Duple Dominant IV Express	C53F	1983	East Midland, 1996
563UM	Leyland Royal Tiger RTC	Leyland Doyen	C49FT	1986	East Midland, 1995
C336SFL	Ford Transit 190	Carlyle	BC16F	1986	Stagecoach Cambus, 1999
E755VJO	MCW Metrorider MF150/26	MCW	B25F	1987	City of Oxford, 1998
E754CHH	MCW Metrorider MF150/29	MCW	C25F	1988	
E45HFE	MCW Metrorider MF150/94	MCW	B23F	1988	East Midland, 1996
E46HFE	MCW Metrorider MF150/94	MCW	B23F	1988	East Midland, 1996
E56HFE	MCW Metrorider MF150/94	MCW	BC23F	1988	East Midland, 1998
E57HFE	MCW Metrorider MF150/94	MCW	BC23F	1988	East Midland, 1998
ESU913	Scania K92CRB	Van Hool Alizée H	C53F	1988	G M South, 1998
ESU920	Scania K92CRB	Van Hool Alizée H	C53F	1988	G M South, 1998
TAZ5004	Scania K113CRB	Plaxton Paramount 3500 III	C48FT	1988	G M South, 1998
RAZ7353	Scania K113CRB	Plaxton Paramount 3500 III	C49FT	1988	G M South, 1998
NIL8663	Volvo B10M-61	Plaxton Paramount 3500 III	C49FT	1988	Moxon, Oldcoats, 1997
NIL6108	Volvo B10MT	Van Hool Alizée H	C49FT	1989	Dover, Hetton, 1997
H149SAO	Ford Transit VE6	Ford	M8	1991	Lakeland Self Drive, 1995
H649UWR	Volvo B10M-60	Plaxton Paramount 3500 III	C49FT	1991	Stagecoach Cambus, 1999
H652UWR	Volvo B10M-60	Plaxton Paramount 3500 III	C48FT	1991	Stagecoach Cambus, 1999
H653UWR	Volvo B10M-60	Plaxton Paramount 3500 III	C48FT	1991	Stagecoach Cambus, 1999
L547KRE	Ford Transit VE6	Ford	M8	1994	United Rentals, 1998
L506MAO	Ford Transit VE6	Ford	M8	1994	United Rentals, 1998
L510MAO	Ford Transit VE6	Ford	M8	1994	United Rentals, 1998
M204VWF	Mercedes-Benz 814D	Plaxton Beaver	BC33F	1994	Armstrong, Inverkeithing, 1997
N976LWR	Mercedes-Benz 814D	Mellor Solo	BC33F	1996	Cropper, Kirkstall, 1998

Previous registrations:

563 UM	C792LWA	PJI 4317	UHE38Y
ESU913	F951NER	RAZ 7353	F948NER
ESU920	F950NER	RHL174X	OHE276X, 563UM
NIL6108	G200XAC, HS8882	SIW2805	GGD662T, ESU933, KGE46T
NIL8663	E588VTH, GIL4271, E850AHL	TAZ5004	F947 NER

Brownriggs coach fleet includes Van Hool-bodied Volvo B10M NIL6108. This tri-axle version of the B10M uses a trailing axle, which is that shown in the picture with chrome wheel guards. The vehicle is in an attractive silver and purple livery.
Bill Potter

BU-VAL

M Bull, Unit 5 Paragon Industrial Estate, Smithybridge, Littleborough, OL15 8QF

E181CNE	Iveco Daily 49.10	Northern Counties	B22F	1988	G M Buses, 1989
E186CNE	Iveco Daily 49.10	Northern Counties	B22F	1988	G M Buses, 1989
E238UWR	MCW MetroRider MF150/80	MCW	B23F	1988	Yorkshire Rider, 1995
E245UWR	MCW MetroRider MF150/80	MCW	B23F	1988	Yorkshire Rider, 1995
E254UWR	MCW MetroRider MF150/80	MCW	B23F	1988	Yorkshire Rider, 1995
F226FNE	Iveco Daily 49.10	Northern Counties	B24F	1988	
F241FNE	Iveco Daily 49.10	Northern Counties	B22F	1988	
F243FNE	Iveco Daily 49.10	Northern Counties	B22F	1988	
G449LKW	Iveco Daily 49.10	Reeve Burgess Beaver	B25F	1989	Citibus, Middleton, 1996
G275MWU	Iveco Daily 49.10	Reeve Burgess Beaver	B25F	1990	Citibus, Middleton, 1996
G276MWU	Iveco Daily 49.10	Reeve Burgess Beaver	B25F	1990	Citibus, Middleton, 1996
H918XUA	Iveco Daily 49.10	Reeve Burgess Beaver	B25F	1990	Citibus, Middleton, 1996
K529EFL	Iveco Daily 49.10	Marshall C29	B23F	1993	Stagecoach Midlland Red, 1999
L803FBA	Iveco TurboDaily 59.12	Mellor	B27F	1994	
L804FBA	Iveco TurboDaily 59.12	Mellor	B27F	1994	
R801WJA	Iveco TurboDaily 59.12	Mellor Solo	B27F	1997	
R805WJA	Iveco TurboDaily 59.12	Mellor Solo	B27F	1997	
S933SVM	Iveco TurboDaily 59.12	Mellor Solo	B27F	1997	
S934SVM	Iveco TurboDaily 59.12	Mellor Solo	B27F	1997	

Previous registrations:
H918XUA   H281SWW, H12SDW

Livery: Red, white and black

Bu-val is a minibus operator whose main area of operation is Rochdale, a town that has seen many operators arrive after the Greater Manchester depot closed. The Bu-val fleet comprises mostly Iveco products, and its F241FNE is an Iveco Daily with coachwork conversion by Northern Counties. *Bill Potter*

R BULLOCK

R Bullock & Co (Transport) Ltd, Commercial Garage, Stockport Road, Cheadle, Greater Manchester, SK8 2AG

JIL8204	Leyland Leopard PSU5/4R	Plaxton Panorama Elite III	C57F	1975	
NDE916R	Bristol LH6L	Eastern Coach Works	B45F	1977	Vickers, Worksop, 1999
JIL8214	Leyland National 11351A/1R		B49F	1978	PMT, 1996
JIL8215	Leyland National 11351A/1R		B49F	1978	BNFL, Salwick, 1996
JIL8209	MCW Metrobus DR102/1	MCW	B45/31F	1978	Tees & District, 1996
JIL8205	AEC Reliance 6U2R	Duple Dominant II Express	C53F	1979	Bibby, Ingleton, 1994
BYW379V	Leyland National 10351A/2R (Volvo)		B44F	1979	Arriva North West, 1999
BUI1675	Leyland Leopard PSU3F/4R	East Lancashire (1993)	B51F	1981	Go-Ahead Northern, 1990
JIL8206	MCW Metrobus DR104/11	MCW	B47/33F	1983	Mainline, 1998
JIL8211	MCW Metrobus DR104/11	MCW	B47/33F	1983	Mainline, 1997
JIL8212	MCW Metrobus DR104/11	MCW	B47/33F	1983	Mainline, 1997
A280ROW	Leyland Olympian ONLXB/1R	East Lancashire	B45/31F	1983	Stephenson, Rochford, 1998
BUI1610	Dennis Dorchester SDA805	Plaxton Paramount 3200	C57F	1984	
JIL8216	Leyland National 2 NL116HLXCT/1R		B52F	1984	Victoria Travel, Haydock, 1994
JIL8217	Leyland National 2 NL116HLXCT/1R		BC47F	1984	Victoria Travel, Haydock, 1994
JIL8208	MCW Metrobus DR104/11	MCW	B47/33F	1984	Mainline, 1997
B930CDT	MCW Metrobus DR104/11	MCW	B47/33F	1984	Mainline, 1998
BUI1133	Dennis Dorchester SDA805	Plaxton Paramount 3200	C57F	1985	
B944FET	MCW Metrobus DR102/50	MCW	BC42/28F	1985	Mainline, 1998
B946FET	MCW Metrobus DR102/50	MCW	BC42/28F	1985	Mainline, 1998
C718NCD	Dennis Dominator DDA1005	East Lancashire	B43/32F	1985	Brighton, 1996
C719NCD	Dennis Dominator DDA1005	East Lancashire	B43/32F	1985	Brighton, 1996

Princess Street in Manchester passes the side of the Town Hall and is the location of this view of M788NBA from the R Bullock fleet. The Volvo Olympian carries East Lancashire bodywork to a design with similar features as that built by Alexander. Route 42 is travelling the well known Wilmslow Road corridor where one can see some fifty buses an hour, and even more at peak periods. *Tony Wilson*

R Bullock has expanded its area of operation to include routes in Stockport. Pictured in Mersey Square after a circuit of Brinnington route 325 is Metrobus B930CDT which latterly operated with Mainline in Sheffield. The older double-deck fleet is predominantly based on Metrobuses and Dennis Dominators.
Bill Potter

C720NCD	Dennis Dominator DDA1005	East Lancashire	BC43/28F	1985	Brighton, 1996
C721NCD	Dennis Dominator DDA1005	East Lancashire	BC43/28F	1985	Brighton, 1996
BUI1484	Leyland Tiger TRCLXCT/3RZ	Plaxton P'mount 3500 III (1993)	C51FT	1986	
C281BBP	Dennis Dominator DDA1008	East Lancashire	B45/31F	1986	Southampton Citybus, 1991
C282BBP	Dennis Dominator DDA1008	East Lancashire	B45/31F	1986	Southampton Citybus, 1991
C283BBP	Dennis Dominator DDA1008	East Lancashire	B45/31F	1986	Southampton Citybus, 1991
C284BBP	Dennis Dominator DDA1008	East Lancashire	B45/31F	1986	Southampton Citybus, 1991
C285BBP	Leyland Olympian ONLXB/1R	East Lancashire	BC43/27F	1986	Southampton Citybus, 1992
C959LWJ	MCW Metrobus DR102/53	MCW	BC42/28F	1986	Mainline, 1998
BUI1424	Scania N112DRB	Van Hool Alizée L	BC49F	1987	Speedlink, 1996
F452FDB	Leyland Tiger TRBTL11/2RP	Duple 300	B55F	1989	
F682SRN	Leyland Tiger TRCL10/3RZA	Plaxton Paramount 3500 III	C51FT	1989	D Coaches, Morriston, 1994
G423SNF	Leyland Tiger TRBTL11/2RP	Duple 300	B55F	1990	
G918DVX	Ford Transit 190	Dormobile	B16F	1990	Marton Community Bus, 1998
J200BUL	Leyland Tiger TRCL10/3ARZA	Plaxton Paramount 3200 III	C57F	1991	
J400BUL	Volvo B10M-60	Plaxton Paramount 3500 III	C53F	1992	
K600BUL	Volvo B10M-60	Plaxton Paramount 3200 III	C53F	1993	
L10BUL	Leyland Olympian ON2R50C13Z4	East Lancashire	B45/31F	1993	
L20BUL	Leyland Olympian ON2R50C13Z4	East Lancashire	B45/31F	1993	
L800BUL	Volvo B10M-60	Van Hool Alizée HE	C51FT	1994	
L8SLT	Dennis Javelin	Berkhof Excellence 1000	C51F	1994	
L42DBC	Toyota Coaster HZB50R	Caetano Optimo	C18F	1994	Hertz, Heathrow, 1998
M786NBA	Dennis Javelin 12SDA2131	Berkhof Excellence 1000	C51FT	1995	
M788NBA	Volvo Olympian YN2RV18Z4	East Lancashire	B45/30F	1995	
M789NBA	Volvo Olympian YN2RV18Z4	East Lancashire	B45/30F	1995	
M790NBA	Volvo Olympian YN2RC16Z5	East Lancashire	B45/31F	1994	
N620XBU	Volvo B10M-62	Caetano Algarve II	C53FT	1995	
N621XBU	Volvo B10M-62	Caetano Algarve II	C53F	1996	
N630XBU	Scania L113CRL	Wright Axcess-ultralow	N43F	1996	
N631XBU	Scania L113CRL	Wright Axcess-ultralow	N42F	1996	
N632XBU	Scania L113CRL	Wright Axcess-ultralow	N42F	1996	
N633XBU	Scania L113CRL	Wright Axcess-ultralow	N42F	1996	
N634XBU	Scania L113CRL	Wright Axcess-ultralow	N42F	1996	
P480HBA	Volvo B10M-62	Van Hool Alizée HE	C51FT	1996	

Four Northern Counties Palatine II bodied Volvo Olympians joined the fleet of R Bullock at the start of 1999 and are most frequently found on route 42 between Manchester and Stockport. Pictured arriving in Manchester is S958URJ in the latest livery variant. *Tony Wilson*

P481HBA	Volvo B10M-62	Caetano Algarve II	C49FT	1997
P482HBA	Volvo B10M-62	Caetano Algarve II	C53F	1997
P483HBA	Volvo Olympian YN2RV18Z4	Northern Counties Palatine	B47/30F	1996
P484HBA	Volvo Olympian YN2RV18Z4	Northern Counties Palatine	B47/30F	1996
P485HBA	Volvo Olympian YN2RV18Z4	Northern Counties Palatine	B47/30F	1996
P486HBA	Volvo Olympian YN2RV18Z4	Northern Counties Palatine	B47/30F	1996
R290CVM	DAF DE02RSDB250	Optare Spectra	B50/27F	1998
R291CVM	DAF DE02RSDB250	Optare Spectra	B50/27F	1998
R292CVM	Volvo B10M-62	Caetano Algarve II	C53FT	1998
R293CVM	Volvo B10M-62	Caetano Algarve II	C53FT	1998
S957URJ	Volvo Olympian	Northern Counties Palatine 2	B47/30F	1999
S958URJ	Volvo Olympian	Northern Counties Palatine 2	B47/30F	1999
S959URJ	Volvo Olympian	Northern Counties Palatine 2	B47/30F	1999
S960URJ	Volvo Olympian	Northern Counties Palatine 2	B47/30F	1999
T68FBN	Volvo B10M-62	Caetano Enigma	C53F	1999
T69FBN	Volvo B10M-62	Caetano Enigma	C49FT	1999

Previous registrations:

BUI1133	B593SNC	JIL8205	YPL88T, BIB7667, SWH271T	JIL8212	A120XWE
BUI1424	E213FLD	JIL8206	A118XWE	JIL8214	EMB358S
BUI1484	C33EVM	JIL8207	-	JIL8215	CFM348S
BUI1610	A530OBU	JIL8208	B925CDT	JIL8216	A301JFA
BUI1675	FNL687W	JIL8209	SDA832S	JIL8217	A303JFA
J400BUL	J729 KBC	JIL8211	A105XWE	K600BUL	K433ANE
JIL8204	HFM804N				

Livery: - Red and white

CUMBRIA CLASSIC COACHES

Hamer & Morris, Cumbia Classic Coaches, Bowker Head, Ravenstonedale,
Kirkby Stephen, Cumbria, CA17 4NL

WG2373	Leyland Lion LT5B	Burlingham (1947)	B35F	1934	preservation, 1998
TSK736	Commer Commander 17A	Scottish Aviation	C30F	1949	preservation, 1999
CRN80	Leyland Tiger PS1/1	East Lancashire	B34R	1949	preservation, 1999
CWG286	Leyland Tiger PS1	Alexander	C38F	1950	preservation, 1999

Previous Registration:

TSK736	CMS9

Livery: Each vehcle features an individual livery.

Cumbria Classic Coaches have featured on the Kendal Park and Ride service during the summer of 1999. Four vehicles are operated by the company with the two shown here both originating with the former Alexander group. The upper picture shows Burlingham-bodied Leyland Lion WG2373 carrying its original operators colours. The vehicle was heading for its home base in Ravenstonedale when encountered. The lower picture shows off the lines of Alexander-bodied CWG286 now in a green and cream livery. This vehicle also carries route boards for the service which is known as the Kendal Klipper.
Tony Wilson

THE COACHMASTERS

H Ramm, Royle Works, Royle Road, Rochdale, OL11 3ET

WLT697	Volvo B10M-61	Plaxton Paramount 3500 II	C46FT	1989	Stagecoach Western, 1999
C100HSJ	Scania N112DRB	East Lancashire	B47/33F	1986	Stagecoach Transit (Hull), 1999

	Dennis Dominator DDA1027	East Lancashire	B47/33F	1989	Stagecoach Transit (Hull), 1999
F152HAT	F154HAT	F155HAT	F156HAT		F157HAT
F153HAT					

	Scania N113DRB	East Lancashire	B51/37F*	1989-90	*809-16 are B47/37F
					Stagecoach Transit (Hull), 1999
G801JRH	G804JRH	H810WKH	H813WKH		H815WKH
G802JRH	G805JRH	H812WKH	H814WKH		H816WKH
G803JRH	H809WKH				

L266VUS	Scania K113CRB	Van Hool Alizée HE	C51FT	1994	Owen, Newhouse, 1998

Previous Registrations
WLT697   B197EGA

Livery: Yellow

The Coachmasters began services in Greater Manchester following the award of school contracts for many schools to the north of the county. Daytime services between Rochdale and Wigan are also operated using the fleet of double-deck buses latterly based at the Hull depot of Stagecoach Transit. Pictured here is Scania H816WKH operating route 652. *Andrew Jarosz*

DARWEN COACH SERVICES

D R Russell, 5 West View, Knowle Lane, Darwen, Lancashire, BB3 ONP

B931YCW	Mercedes-Benz L307D	Rovanne	M12	1985	private owner, 1986
C410VVN	Mercedes-Benz L608D	Reeve Burgess	B20F	1986	East Yorkshire, 1998
C419VVN	Mercedes-Benz L608D	Reeve Burgess	B20F	1986	East Yorkshire, 1998
D672SHH	Mercedes-Benz 609D	Ribble / Cumbria Commercials	B25F	1986	Ribble, 1997
D239NCS	Renault-Dodge S56	Alexander AM	B25F	1987	Blue Bus, Horwich, 1996
D682SEM	Renault-Dodge S56	Alexander AM	B23F	1987	MTL (Merseybus), 1997
D683SEM	Renault-Dodge S56	Alexander AM	B23F	1987	MTL (Merseybus), 1997
D685SEM	Renault-Dodge S56	Alexander AM	B23F	1987	MTL (Merseybus), 1997
D689SEM	Renault-Dodge S56	Alexander AM	B23F	1987	MTL (Heysham Travel), 1997
E177UWF	Renault-Dodge S56	Reeve Burgess Beaver	B25F	1987	Mainline, 1995
E144RAX	Freight Rover Sherpa	Carlyle	B20F	1987	Powercrafts, Blackburn, 1995
E402TBS	Renault-Dodge S56	Alexander AM	B25F	1988	Blue Bus, Huddersfield, 1996
E101EVM	Mercedes-Benz 811D	Reeve Burgess	BC21F	1988	East Yorkshire, 1998
E102EVM	Mercedes-Benz 811D	Reeve Burgess	BC21F	1988	East Yorkshire, 1998
F905YWY	Mercedes-Benz 811D	Optare StarRider	B26F	1988	Boomerang Bus, Tewkesbury, 1998
F915YWY	Mercedes-Benz 811D	Optare StarRider	B29F	1988	Boomerang Bus, Tewkesbury, 1998

Livery: Red and cream

A network of minibus routes based on Darwen is provided by Darwen Coach Services. The Renault-Dodge is the most prolific chassis make in the fleet, represented here by D685SEM which was new to Merseyside. A livery of red and cream is used, these being the colours of the former Darwen Corporation Transport.
Paul Wigan

DENNIS'S

R & M Cooper, 4 Charles Street, Dukinfield, Tameside, SK16 4SD

RAZ8627	Volvo B10M-60	Plaxton Expressliner	C53F	1989	Stagecoach South, 1997
RAZ8628	Volvo B10M-60	Plaxton Expressliner	C53F	1989	Easson, Southampton, 1997
L680GNA	Mercedes-Benz 709D	Plaxton Beaver	B27F	1994	
L681GNA	Mercedes-Benz 709D	Plaxton Beaver	B27F	1994	
L682GNA	Mercedes-Benz 709D	Plaxton Beaver	B27F	1994	
L683GNA	Mercedes-Benz 709D	Plaxton Beaver	B27F	1994	
L510JND	Mercedes-Benz 709D	Plaxton Beaver	B27F	1994	
M728MBU	Mercedes-Benz 709D	Plaxton Beaver	B27F	1994	
M729MBU	Mercedes-Benz 709D	Plaxton Beaver	B27F	1994	
M730MBU	Mercedes-Benz 709D	Plaxton Beaver	B27F	1994	
N320YNC	Mercedes-Benz 709D	Plaxton Beaver	B27F	1995	
N321YNC	Mercedes-Benz 709D	Plaxton Beaver	B27F	1995	
N322YNC	Mercedes-Benz 709D	Plaxton Beaver	B27F	1995	
N796CVU	Mercedes-Benz 814D	Plaxton Beaver	BC33F	1996	
VAZ2619	Mercedes-Benz Vario O814	Plaxton Beaver 2	BC33F	1996	
P547HVM	Dennis Dart SLF	Plaxton Pointer	N37F	1996	
P978LNB	Dennis Dart SLF	Plaxton Pointer	N37F	1996	
P979LNB	Dennis Dart SLF	Plaxton Pointer	N37F	1996	
P980LNB	Dennis Dart SLF	Plaxton Pointer	N37F	1996	
P112OJA	Dennis Dart SLF	Plaxton Pointer	N37F	1996	
P113OJA	Dennis Dart SLF	Plaxton Pointer	N37F	1996	
R572ABA	Dennis Dart SLF	Plaxton Pointer	N36F	1997	
R573ABA	Dennis Dart SLF	Plaxton Pointer	N36F	1997	
R574ABA	Dennis Dart SLF	Plaxton Pointer	N39F	1997	
R575ABA	Dennis Dart SLF	Plaxton Pointer	N39F	1997	
R103BDB	Dennis Dart SLF	Plaxton Pointer	N39F	1998	
T965PVR	Dennis Dart SLF	Plaxton Pointer 2	N39F	1999	

Previous registrations:

RAZ8627	G901PKK	RAZ8628	G554SSP	VAZ2619	P82KNF

Depot: Platt Street, Dukinfield

Livery: Red and grey

Dennis's fleet has expanded in recent times through the use of an increased number of Dennis Dart minibuses, including some of the earliest low-floor models. Pictured in Piccadilly Manchester, T965PVR is seen operating route 216 to Ashton.
Gerry Mead

EAST LANCASHIRE MOTOR SERVICES

J G Haydock, F West End Business Park, Blackburn Road, Oswaldtwistle, BB5 4WE

1	XJI1301	Volvo B10M-60	Plaxton Expressliner	C46FT	1989	Newline Coaches, Melling, 1998
2	XJI1302	Volvo B10M-61	Jonckheere Bermuda	C49FT	1981	Maypole, Patricroft, 1995
3	XJI1303	Volvo B10M-61	Duple Caribbean	C51F	1983	Carnell, Sutton Bridge, 1998
4	NIW6514	Volvo B10M-61	Van Hool Alizée H	C46FT	1981	Highland Country, 1998
5	NIW6515	Volvo B10M-61	Van Hool Alizée H	C49FT	1981	Haydock, Intack, 1997
6	WIB1366	Volvo B10M-61	Van Hool Alizée H	C46FT	1981	Brownrigg, Egremont, 1998
8	A728ANH	Volvo B10M-61	Plaxton Paramount 3200 Exp	C50FT	1983	Stagecoach United Counties, 1998
9	A729ANH	Volvo B10M-61	Plaxton Paramount 3200 Exp	C50FT	1983	Stagecoach United Counties, 1998
10	F100BPW	Volvo B10M-61	Plaxton Expressliner	C51FT	1989	Ambassador, Great Yarmouth, 1999
11	F101BPW	Volvo B10M-61	Plaxton Expressliner	C51FT	1989	Ambassador, Great Yarmouth, 1999
12	GIL3112	Volvo B10M-61	Berkhof Everest 370	C49FT	1983	M C, Melksham, 1998
14	WEC768Y	Volvo B10M-61	Plaxton Paramount 3500	C51F	1983	Moore, Greenisland, 1999
15	A129MFL	Dennis Dorchester	Duple Carribean	C51FT	1983	Lee-Roy Travel, Epping, 1999
58	F638HVU	Renault-Dodge S56	Alexander	B22F	1988	JPTravel, Middleton, 1999
59	D759YCW	Renault-Dodge S56	Northern Counties	B22F	1987	Preston Bus, 1999

Previous registrations:

A728ANH	A798TGG, 7878SC, A320ANH, 647DYE	WIB1366	TGD766W, VLF578	
A729ANH	A800TGG, 4009SC, A332ANH, WLT508	WEC768Y	UPY33, RFV41	
GIL3112	A135GTA	XJI1301	G563VHY	
NIW6514	TGD767W, TRM144, MBS271W, JAZ9851, MBS271W	XJI1302	WNV822W, 1656RU, SVM171W, PJI2668, SVM171W	
NIW6515	STT604X, 942AYA, 170BHR	XJI1303	THL295Y	

East Lancashire Motor Services operate seasonal express services to the Fylde coast. Seen on lay-over at Fleetwood while working route X81 from Accrington is Jonckheere Bermuda SVM171W, numbered 2 in the fleet. Since this 1998 view was taken the vehicle has been re-registered XJI1302. *Brian Ridgway*

FINGLANDS

Finglands Coachways Ltd, 261 Wilmslow Road, Rusholme, Manchester M14 5LJ

Part of East Yorkshire Group

234	SIB6614	Leyland Leopard PSU3F/4R	East Lancashire EL2000 (1992)	BC49F	1981	East Yorkshire, 1995
235	SIB6615	Leyland Leopard PSU5B/4R	East Lancashire EL2000 (1992)	BC51F	1977	East Yorkshire, 1995
237	HIL7747	Leyland Leopard PSU5C/4R	Plaxton Derwent II (1992)	B57F	1979	Allander, Milngavie, 1995
301	F301JNC	Leyland Tiger TRBTL11/2RP	Duple 300	BC55F	1989	
302	F302JNC	Leyland Tiger TRBTL11/2RP	Duple 300	BC55F	1989	
359	HIL7746	Volvo B10M-61	Plaxton Paramount 3500 III	C53F	1989	
360	10RU	Mercedes-Benz 0303-15R	Mercedes Benz	C49FT	1990	
361	SIA6180	Mercedes-Benz 0303-15R	Mercedes Benz	C53F	1990	
362	647JOE	Leyland Tiger TRCL10/3ARZM	Plaxton Paramount 3500 III	C49FT	1992	
363	KAZ1363	Volvo B10M-61	Plaxton Paramount 3500 III	C53FT	1991	Park's of Hamilton, 1993
364	RYV77	Volvo B10M-61	Berkhof Excellence 1000LD	C49FT	1995	
365	N365BNF	Volvo B10M-62	Plaxton Première 320	C53F	1996	
366	HIL7745	Volvo B10M-62	Plaxton Première 320	C53F	1995	Excelsior, Bournemouth, 1997
367	R367WNC	Volvo B10M-62	Van Hool Alizée	C33FT	1997	
368	P533CLJ	Volvo B10M-62	Plaxton Première 320	C53F	1997	Excelsior, Bournemouth, 1998
369	S369SND	Toyota Coaster BB50R	Caetano Optimo IV	C21F	1998	
370	T370JVR	Volvo B10M-6200	Plaxton Première 350	C49FT	1999	
1422	M422RRN	Volvo B10M-55	Alexander PS	BC48F	1994	Stagecoach Manchester, 1995
1423	M423RRN	Volvo B10M-55	Alexander PS	BC48F	1994	Stagecoach Manchester, 1995
1424	M424RRN	Volvo B10M-55	Alexander PS	BC48F	1994	Stagecoach Manchester, 1995
1425	M425RRN	Volvo B10M-55	Alexander PS	BC48F	1994	Stagecoach Manchester, 1995
1426	M426RRN	Volvo B10M-55	Alexander PS	BC48F	1994	Stagecoach Manchester, 1995
1427	M427RRN	Volvo B10M-55	Alexander PS	BC48F	1994	Stagecoach Manchester, 1995

Finglands is the Manchester based operation of East Yorkshire Motor Services with its base located in the Rusholm district of Manchester. Two of the fleet are shown in colour opposite. The upper picture shows Alexander PS-bodied Volvo 1427, M427RRN, while the lower picture shows 1740, N740VBA, a Volvo Olympian with Alexander Royale bodywork, seen working on route 42. Below is 1758, JTY404X, seen in Chorlton Street, the first Eastern Coach Works-bodied Leyland Olympian for the fleet. It has been followed by four more from Trent. New buses due for delivery are two integral Mercedes-Benz O405N buses.
Cliff Beeton/Gerry Mead/Paul Wigan

1428	V428DND	Mercedes-Benz O405	Mercedes-Benz	N--F	1999	
1429	V429DND	Mercedes-Benz O405	Mercedes-Benz	N--F	1999	
1710	F242MBA	Volvo Citybus B10M-50	Alexander RV	BC47/35F	1989	
1713	G613OTV	Leyland Olympian ONLXB/1R	Eastern Coach Works	B45/32F	1982	Trent, 1999
1716	G616OTV	Leyland Olympian ONLXB/1R	Eastern Coach Works	B45/32F	1982	Trent, 1999
1717	G617OTV	Leyland Olympian ONLXB/1R	Eastern Coach Works	B45/32F	1982	Trent, 1999
1718	G618OTV	Leyland Olympian ONLXB/1R	Eastern Coach Works	B45/32F	1982	Trent, 1999
1726	E473SON	MCW Metrobus DR102/63	MCW	B45/30F	1987	Metroline, 1992
1727	E474SON	MCW Metrobus DR102/63	MCW	B45/30F	1987	Metroline, 1992
1728	E476SON	MCW Metrobus DR102/63	MCW	B45/30F	1988	Metroline, 1992
1729	E477SON	MCW Metrobus DR102/63	MCW	B45/30F	1988	Metroline, 1992
1730	E480UOF	MCW Metrobus DR102/63	MCW	B45/30F	1988	Metroline, 1992
1739	M832HVC	Volvo Olympian YN2RV18Z4	Alexander Royale	B45/29F	1994	Volvo demonstrator, 1995
1740	N740VBA	Volvo Olympian YN2RV18Z4	Alexander Royale	B45/29F	1995	
1741	N741VBA	Volvo Olympian YN2RV18Z4	Alexander Royale	B45/29F	1995	
1742	N742VBA	Volvo Olympian YN2RV18Z4	Alexander Royale	B45/29F	1995	
1743	N743VBA	Volvo Olympian YN2RV18Z4	Alexander Royale	B45/29F	1995	
1744	N744ANE	Volvo Olympian YN2RV18Z4	Northern Counties Palatine II	B47/30F	1996	
1745	N745ANE	Volvo Olympian YN2RV18Z4	Northern Counties Palatine II	B47/30F	1996	
1746	N746ANE	Volvo Olympian YN2RV18Z4	Northern Counties Palatine II	B47/30F	1996	
1747	N47ANE	Volvo Olympian YN2RV18Z4	Northern Counties Palatine II	B47/30F	1996	
1748	N748ANE	Volvo Olympian YN2RV18Z4	Northern Counties Palatine II	B47/30F	1996	
1749	ANA538Y	Leyland Atlantean AN68D/1R	Northern Counties	B43/32F	1982	GM South, 1997
1750	ANA543Y	Leyland Atlantean AN68D/1R	Northern Counties	B43/32F	1982	GM South, 1997
1751	ANA564Y	Leyland Atlantean AN68D/1R	Northern Counties	B43/32F	1982	GM South, 1997
1753	ANA637Y	Leyland Atlantean AN68D/1R	Northern Counties	B43/32F	1983	GM South, 1997
1754	A710LNC	Leyland Atlantean AN68D/1R	Northern Counties	B43/32F	1984	GM South, 1997
1755	ANA639Y	Leyland Atlantean AN68D/1R	Northern Counties	B43/32F	1983	Stagecoach Manchester, 1998
1756	A671HNB	Leyland Atlantean AN68D/1R	Northern Counties	B43/32F	1983	Stagecoach Manchester, 1998
1758	JTY404X	Leyland Olympian ONLXB/1R	Eastern Coach Works	B45/32F	1982	Go Ahead, 1998
1760	KPJ286W	Leyland Atlantean AN68B/1R	Roe	B43/30F	1979	London & Country, 1998

Previous Registrations:

10RU	from new	HIL7747	SBS6791, Q652WWJ, KGE74T	SIA6180	from new
647JOE	from new	KAZ1363	H907AHS	SIB6614	XAG206X
HIL7745	A12XEL, M516NCG	P533CLJ	A15XEL	SIB6615	UGR501R
HIL7746	F300JNC	RYV77	M364SNB		

Livery: White, brown, orange and beige

Finglands coach fleet includes two Mercedes-Benz O303 integral coaches with 361, SIA6180, pictured while on an Omnibus Society Tour. Finglands has traditionally included many high-quality coaches for excursions and tours programmes, the latest arrival being a Plaxton-bodied Volvo.
Paul Wigan

FIRST MANCHESTER

Manchester - Pioneer

First Manchester Ltd; First Pioneer Bus Ltd,
Wallshaw Street, Oldham, OL1 3TR

101-115   Scania L94UB   Wright Axcess Floline   N40F   1998

101	S101TNB	104	S104TNB	107	S107TNB	110	S110TNB	113	S113TNB
102	S102TNB	105	S105TNB	108	S108TNB	111	S651RNA	114	S114TNB
103	S103TNB	106	S106TNB	109	S109TNB	112	S112TNB	115	S115TNB

116-141   Scania L94UB   Wright Axcess Floline   N40F   1999

116	T916SSF	122	V122DND	127	V127DND	132	V132DND	137	V137DND
117	T917SSF	123	V330DBU	128	V128DND	133	V133DND	138	V138DND
118	T918SSF	124	V124DND	129	V129DND	134	V134DND	139	V139DND
119	T919SSF	125	V125DND	130	V130DND	135	V135DND	140	V140DND
121	V142DND	126	V126DND	131	V131DND	136	V136DND	141	V141DND

301-330   Mercedes-Benz Citaro   Mercedes-Benz   N--F   On order

301	V301DBU	307	V307DBU	313	V313DBU	319	V319DBU	325	V
302	V302DBU	308	V308DBU	314	V314DBU	320	V320DBU	326	V
303	V303DBU	309	V309DBU	315	V315DBU	321	V	327	V
304	V304DBU	310	V310DBU	316	V316DBU	322	V	328	V
305	V305DBU	311	V311DBU	317	V317DBU	323	V	329	V
306	V306DBU	312	V312DBU	318	V318DBU	324	V	330	V

401-414   Leyland Tiger TR2R62C16Z4   Alexander N   B55F   1989   Timeline, 1998

401	G57RND	406	G64RND	408	G66RND	410	G68RND	413	G71RND
402	G58RND	407	G65RND	409	G67RND	411	G69RND	414	G72RND
403	G60RND								

During 1998 Timeline's bus operations based in the Manchester area were acquired by First Manchester. Some of the vehicles involved in the purchase were Leyland Tigers with Alexander N-type bodywork. Seen in Didsbury in its new colours is 413, G71RND.
Cliff Beeton

Bury Interchange is the location for this view of Volvo B10L 565, N303WNF. The vehicle carries an Alexander Ultra body and was supplied to Timeline as part of a Greater Manchester PTE package. *Paul Wigan*

501-556

Volvo B10B-58   Wright Endurance   BC50F   1994-96

501	M501PNA	512	M512PNA	523	N523WVR	534	N534WVR	545	N545WVR
502	M502PNA	513	M513PNA	524	N524WVR	535	N535WVR	546	N546WVR
503	M503PNA	514	M514PNA	525	N525WVR	536	N536WVR	547	N547WVR
504	M504PNA	515	M515PNA	526	N526WVR	537	N537WVR	548	N548WVR
505	M505PNA	516	M516PNA	527	N527WVR	538	N538WVR	549	N549WVR
506	M506PNA	517	M517PNA	528	N528WVR	539	N539WVR	550	N550WVR
507	M507PNA	518	M518PNA	529	N529WVR	540	N540WVR	551	N551WVR
508	M508PNA	519	M519PNA	530	N530WVR	541	N541WVR	552	N552WVR
509	M509PNA	520	M520PNA	531	N531WVR	542	N542WVR	553	N553WVR
510	M510PNA	521	N521WVR	532	N532WVR	543	N543WVR	554	N554WVR
511	M511PNA	522	N522WVR	533	N533WVR	544	N544WVR	556	N556WVR

557-562

Volvo B10L   Wright Liberator   NC41F   1996

557	N557BNF	558	N558BNF	559	N559BNF	561	N561BNF	562	N562BNF

563-568

Volvo B10L   Alexander Ultra   N43F   1995-96   Timeline, 1998

563	N301WNF	565	N303WNF	566	N304WNF	567	N305WNF	568	N306WNF
564	N302WNF								

Opposite, top: As revealed in the 1999 FirstGroup Bus Handbook, First Manchester is one of the fleets that will receive the latest integral saloon from Mercedes-Benz, the Citaro. The vehicles detailed here are the 12-metre version. This model follows on from a delivery of Scania L94 buses that are all currently based at Oldham and work route 409 from Ashton to Rochdale. Seen returning south on the route, shortly after its entry into service, is 110, S110TBA. *Bill Potter*

Opposite, bottom: The articulated buses for First Manchester are all allocated to the Bury-Manchester service 135, with most of the type carrying route-branding. These Volvo B10MAs are to be followed by further articulated buses for the group, as the greater capacity within the low-floor area make the articulated vehicle more attractive to the tendering authorities. *Paul Wigan*

571-591 — Volvo B10BLE — Wright Renown — N42F — 1997-98

571	R571YNC	576	R576SBA	580	R580SBA	584	R584SBA	588	R588SBA
572	R572SBA	577	R577SBA	581	R581SBA	585	R585SBA	589	R589SBA
573	R573SBA	578	R578SBA	582	R582SBA	586	R586SBA	590	R590SBA
574	R574SBA	579	R579SBA	583	R583SBA	587	R587SBA	591	R591SBA
575	R575SBA						

608-618 — Dennis Dart 9.8SDL3054 — Northern Counties Paladin 2 — B39F — 1995

608	M608SBA	610	M610SBA	612	M612SBA	614	M614SBA	618	M618SBA
609	M609SBA	611	M611SBA	613	M613SBA	617	M617SBA		

621-655 — Volvo B10BLE — Wright Renown — N42F — 1998

621	R621CVR	628	R628CVR	635	R635CVR	642	R642CVR	649	R649CVR
622	R622CVR	629	R629CVR	636	R636CVR	643	R643CVR	650	R650CVR
623	R623CVR	630	R630CVR	637	R637CVR	644	R644CVR	651	R651CVR
624	R624CVR	631	R631CVR	638	R638CVR	645	R645CVR	652	S652RNA
625	R625CVR	632	R632CVR	639	R639CVR	646	R646CVR	653	S653RNA
626	R626CVR	633	R633CVR	640	R640CVR	647	R647CVR	654	S654RNA
627	R627CVR	634	R634CVR	641	R641CVR	648	R648CVR	655	S655RNA

656	S656RNA	Volvo B10BLE	Wright Renown	N41F	1998
657	S657RNA	Volvo B10BLE	Wright Renown	N41F	1998

669-673 — Volvo B10BLE — Wright Renown — N41F — 1998-99

669	S669SVU	670	S670SVU	671	S671SVU	672	S672SVU	673	S673SVU

701	J461OVU	Volvo B10M-50	Northern Counties Paladin	B49F	1991	
1043	N343CJA	Volvo B6-9.9m	Alexander Dash	B36F	1996	
1044	N344CJA	Volvo B6-9.9m	Alexander Dash	B36F	1996	
1047	N347CJA	Volvo B6-9.9m	Alexander Dash	B36F	1996	
1048	N348CJA	Volvo B6-9.9m	Alexander Dash	B36F	1996	
1049	M947OVC	Volvo B6-9.9m	Alexander Dash	B40F	1995	Volvo demonstrator, 1996
1050	M260KWK	Volvo B6-9.9m	Alexander Dash	B36F	1995	Volvo demonstrator, 1996

1051-1070 — Volvo B6-9.9m — Northern Counties Paladin 2 — B40F — 1994-95

1051	M251NVM	1055	M255NVM	1059	M259NVM	1063	M263SVU	1067	M267SVU
1052	M252NVM	1056	M256NVM	1060	M260NVM	1064	M264SVU	1068	M268SVU
1053	M253NVM	1057	M257NVM	1061	M261SVU	1065	M265SVU	1069	M269SVU
1054	M254NVM	1058	M258NVM	1062	M262SVU	1066	M266SVU	1070	M270SVU

1071	N71YNF	Volvo B6LE	Wright Crusader	N37F	1995

1072-1086 — Volvo B6LE — Wright Crusader — N38F* — 1996 — *1072/3/7 are N36F, 1081-6 are N35F

1072	N372CJA	1075	N375CJA	1078	N378CJA	1081	N381CJA	1084	N384CJA
1073	N373CJA	1076	N376CJA	1079	N379CJA	1082	N382CJA	1085	N385CRJ
1074	N374CJA	1077	N377CJA	1080	N380CJA	1083	N383CJA	1086	N386CRJ

1093-1098 — Volvo B6-9.9m — Alexander Dash — B38F — 1994-95 — Timeline, 1998

1093	N207WBA	1095	N209WBA	1096	N210WBA	1097	N211WBA	1098	N212WBA
1094	N208WBA								

1101-1106 — Dennis Dart 9.8SDL3054 — Northern Counties Paladin — B39F — 1995

1101	M101RRJ	1103	M103RRJ	1104	M104RRJ	1105	M105RRJ	1106	M106RRJ
1102	M102RRJ								

1119-1138 — Dennis Dart 9.8SDL3054 — Northern Counties Paladin — B39F — 1996

1119	N619CDB	1123	N623CDB	1127	N627CDB	1131	N631CDB	1135	N635CDB
1120	N620CDB	1124	N624CDB	1128	N628CDB	1132	N632CDB	1136	N636CDB
1121	N621CDB	1125	N625CDB	1129	N629CDB	1133	N633CDB	1137	N637CDB
1122	N622CDB	1126	N626CDB	1130	N630CDB	1134	N634CDB	1138	N638CDB

1139	N742GKH	Dennis Dart 9.8SDL3054	Plaxton Pointer	B40F	1996	Plaxton demonstrator, 1996

First Pioneer are now included within the First Manchester fleet. Although some of the buses still carry the purple and yellow livery, many are now in orange colours, including the B6s. Pictured heading out of Rochdale is Mercedes-Benz 1733, J35KLR. This vehicle has the longer 811 chassis and features a Plaxton Beaver body. *Bill Potter*

1140-1153

		Dennis Dart 9.8SDL3054		Plaxton Pointer		B40F	1996		
1140	N640CDB	1143	N643CDB	1146	N646CDB	1149	N649CDB	1152	N652CDB
1141	N641CDB	1144	N644CDB	1147	N647CDB	1150	N650CDB	1153	N653CDB
1142	N642CDB	1145	N645CDB	1148	N648CDB	1151	N651CDB		

1171	P871TAV	Dennis Dart	Marshall C37	B40F	1997	Pioneer, Rochdale, 1998
1172	P872TAV	Dennis Dart	Marshall C37	B40F	1997	Pioneer, Rochdale, 1998
1401	D501LNA	Leyland Lynx LX563.6LXCTZR1	Leyland	B48F	1986	
1402	D502LNA	Leyland Lynx LX112LXCTZR1	Leyland	B48F	1986	
1403	D503LNA	Leyland Lynx LX112LXCTZR1	Leyland	B48F	1986	
1404	D504LNA	Leyland Lynx LX112LXCTZR1	Leyland	B48F	1986	
1481	C481CBU	Volvo Citybus B10M-50	Northern Counties	B46/33F	1986	
1482	C482CBU	Volvo Citybus B10M-50	Northern Counties	B46/33F	1986	
1483	C483CBU	Volvo Citybus B10M-50	Northern Counties	B46/33F	1986	
1601	V41DTE	Optare Solo	Optare	N27F	1999	
1602	V42DTE	Optare Solo	Optare	N27F	1999	
1603	V43DTE	Optare Solo	Optare	N27F	1999	

The latest vehicles for Wigan's duties are eight Volvo B6BLE with Wright Crusader bodywork. Pictured in the town is 6706, T706PND. Vehicles are now allocated to companies as needs arise. Under this policy three Optare Solo buses are due to enter service shortly on the Centreline service that links the finance district with Piccadilly rail station and Victoria. *Cliff Beeton*

1703-1714

		Mercedes-Benz 811D	Plaxton Beaver	B28F	1992	Citibus, Middleton, 1995

1703	J603HMF	1706	J606HMF	1708	J608HMF	1709	J609HMF	1714	J614HMF
1704	J604HMF	1707	J607HMF						

1717	F597FAM	Mercedes-Benz 811D	Optare StarRider	BC31F	1988	MTL (Merseybus), 1995
1719	J619HMF	Mercedes-Benz 811D	Plaxton Beaver	B28F	1992	Citibus, Middleton, 1995
1721	M158LNC	Mercedes-Benz 811D	Alexander Sprint	B31F	1994	Timeline, 1998
1722	M159LNC	Mercedes-Benz 811D	Alexander Sprint	B31F	1994	Timeline, 1998
1723	M160LNC	Mercedes-Benz 811D	Alexander Sprint	B31F	1994	Timeline, 1998
1724	M161LNC	Mercedes-Benz 811D	Alexander Sprint	B31F	1994	Timeline, 1998
1731	J32KLR	Mercedes-Benz 811D	Plaxton Beaver	B33F	1991	Pioneer, Rochdale, 1998
1732	J34KLR	Mercedes-Benz 811D	Plaxton Beaver	B33F	1991	Pioneer, Rochdale, 1998
1733	J35KLR	Mercedes-Benz 811D	Plaxton Beaver	B33F	1991	Pioneer, Rochdale, 1998
1734	J36KLR	Mercedes-Benz 811D	Plaxton Beaver	B33F	1991	Pioneer, Rochdale, 1998

1801-1820

		Mercedes-Benz 709D	Plaxton Beaver	B23F*	1995	Yorkshire Rider, 1996-97
						*1801/3/6-10 are B20F

1801	M234VWU	1805	M239VWU	1809	M218VWU	1813	M224VWU	1817	M214VWU
1802	M236VWU	1806	M248VWU	1810	M247VWU	1814	M225VWU	1818	M213VWU
1803	M237VWU	1807	M249VWU	1811	M245VWU	1815	M209VWU	1819	M215VWU
1804	M238VWU	1808	M211VWU	1812	M223VWU	1816	M212VWU	1820	M226VWU

1821	M207VWU	Mercedes-Benz 709D	Plaxton Beaver	B21F	1995	Yorkshire Rider, 1997
1822	M244VWU	Mercedes-Benz 709D	Plaxton Beaver	B21F	1995	Yorkshire Rider, 1997

1831-1835

		Mercedes-Benz 811D	Alexander Sprint	B31F	1994	Timeline, 1998

1831	N173WNF	1832	N174WNF	1833	N175WNF	1834	N176WNF	1835	N177WNF

During the summer of 1999 the Manchester articulated buses were augmented with a pair from Leeds. Seen here is 2006, T506JNA. Wright Fusion bodywork on this batch includes air conditioning, double glazing etc. The type carry FirstGroup's Gold Service lettering. *Tony Wilson*

1841	H372OHK	Mercedes-Benz 709D	Reeve Burgess Beaver	B23F	1991	First Essex Buses (T), 1999
1842	H374OHK	Mercedes-Benz 709D	Reeve Burgess Beaver	B23F	1991	First Essex Buses (T), 1999
1843	H373OHK	Mercedes-Benz 709D	Reeve Burgess Beaver	B23F	1991	First Essex Buses (T), 1999

1901-1925   Renault S75   Wright TS303 Citybus   B28F   1990   First CentreWest (Beeline),1999

1901	HDZ5405	1906	HDZ5425	1911	HDZ5437	1916	HDZ5404	1921	HDZ5431
1902	HDZ5406	1907	HDZ5426	1912	HDZ5438	1917	HDZ5408	1922	HDZ5443
1903	HDZ5409	1908	HDZ5429	1913	HDZ5439	1918	HDZ5419	1923	HDZ5449
1904	HDZ5420	1909	HDZ5433	1914	HDZ5445	1919	HDZ5422	1924	HDZ5450
1905	HDZ5424	1910	HDZ5435	1915	HDZ5448	1920	HDZ5423	1925	HDZ5451

| 1998 | F140HNC | Renault-Dodge S56 | Northern Counties | B23F | 1988 | Pioneer, Rochdale, 1998 |

2001-2015   Volvo B10BLA   Wright Fusion   AN53F   1999

2001	S111FML	2004	S994UJA	2007	T507JNA	2010	T510JNA	2013	T513JNA
2002	S992UJA	2005	S995UJA	2008	T508JNA	2011	T511JNA	2014	T514JNA
2003	S993UJA	2006	T506JNA	2009	T509JNA	2012	T512JNA	2015	T515JNA

Leyland Olympian 3220, C220CBU is one of the 1986 intake of standard vehicles for GM Buses before the former PTE-owned organisation was split ready for sale. The vehicle is seen at Oldham Mumps, a short walk from its home depot. *Bill Potter*

3011-3015
Leyland Olympian ONTL11/1R Northern Counties B43/30F 1983

| 3011 | A576HDB | 3012 | A577HDB | 3013 | A578HDB | 3014 | A579HDB | 3015 | A580HDB |

3037-3238
Leyland Olympian ONLXB/1R* Northern Counties B43/30F* 1984-86 *3038 is ONLXB/1R (LG1200)
*3218/37 are B43/26F

3037	B37PJA	3073	B73PJA	3108	B108SJA	3152	B152XNA	3202	C202CBU
3038	B38PJA	3075	B75PJA	3109	B109SJA	3157	C157YBA	3203	C203CBU
3040	B40PJA	3076	B76PJA	3111	B111SJA	3159	C159YBA	3204	C204CBU
3041	B41PJA	3078	B78PJA	3112	B112SJA	3160	C160YBA	3206	C206CBU
3042	B42PJA	3079	B79PJA	3113	B113SJA	3161	C161YBA	3209	C209CBU
3043	B43PJA	3081	B81PJA	3115	B115SJA	3162	C162YBA	3211	C211CBU
3044	B44PJA	3083	B83PJA	3116	B116TVU	3163	C163YBA	3217	C217CBU
3045	B45PJA	3085	B85PJA	3120	B120TVU	3168	C168YBA	3218	C218CBU
3046	B46PJA	3090	B90SJA	3123	B123TVU	3171	C171YBA	3219	C219CBU
3047	B47PJA	3092	B92SJA	3127	B127WNB	3177	C177YBA	3220	C220CBU
3048	B48PJA	3093	B93SJA	3128	B128WNB	3180	C180YBA	3222	C222CBU
3050	B350PJA	3096	B96SJA	3129	B129WNB	3182	C182YBA	3223	C223CBU
3051	B351PJA	3097	B97SJA	3130	B130WNB	3183	C183YBA	3225	C225CBU
3052	B52PJA	3098	B98SJA	3131	B131WNB	3186	C186YBA	3227	C227ENE
3054	B54PJA	3099	B99SJA	3134	B134WNB	3187	C187YBA	3228	C228ENE
3059	B59PJA	3100	B100SJA	3136	B136WNB	3188	C188YBA	3229	C229ENE
3061	B61PJA	3101	B101SJA	3140	B140WNB	3189	C189YBA	3231	C231ENE
3062	B62PJA	3102	B102SJA	3141	B141WNB	3190	C190YBA	3232	C232ENE
3063	B63PJA	3103	B103SJA	3142	B142WNB	3192	C192YBA	3233	C233ENE
3064	B64PJA	3104	B104SJA	3144	B144WNB	3194	C194YBA	3235	C235ENE
3066	B66PJA	3105	B105SJA	3148	B148XNA	3200	C200YBA	3237	C237EVU
3068	B68PJA	3106	B106SJA	3151	B151XNA	3201	C201CBU	3238	C238EVU
3071	B71PJA	3107	B107SJA						

3239-3276   Leyland Olympian ONLXB/1R   Northern Counties   B43/26F   1986-87

3239	C239EVU	3246	C246FRJ	3253	C253FRJ	3262	D262JVR	3270	D270JVR
3240	C240EVU	3247	C247FRJ	3254	C254FRJ	3263	D263JVR	3271	D271JVR
3241	C241EVU	3248	C248FRJ	3256	D256JVR	3264	D264JVR	3273	D273JVR
3242	C242EVU	3249	C249FRJ	3257	D257JVR	3265	D265JVR	3274	D274JVR
3243	C243EVU	3250	C250FRJ	3258	D258JVR	3266	D266JVR	3275	D275JVR
3244	C244EVU	3251	C251FRJ	3259	D259JVR	3267	D267JVR	3276	D276JVR
3245	C245EVU	3252	C252FRJ	3261	D261JVR				

3278-3305   Leyland Olympian ONLXB/1RZ   Northern Counties   B43/30F   1988-89

3278	F278DRJ	3281	F281DRJ	3287	F287DRJ	3292	F292DRJ	3302	F302DRJ
3279	F279DRJ	3284	F284DRJ	3288	F288DRJ	3293	F293DRJ	3303	F303DRJ
3280	F280DRJ	3286	F286DRJ	3290	F290DRJ	3299	F299DRJ	3305	F305DRJ

3401-3410   Volvo Olympian   Alexander Royale RV   B43/29F   1998

3401	S654NUG	3403	S656NUG	3405	S658NUG	3407	S660NUG	3409	S662NUG
3402	S655NUG	3404	S657NUG	3406	S659NUG	3408	S661NUG	3410	S663NUG

4416-4446   Leyland Atlantean AN68A/1R   Northern Counties   B43/32F   1981

4416	SND416X	4438	SND438X	4442	SND442X	4444	SND444X	4446	SND446X
4419	SND419X	4441	SND441X						

4448-4524   Leyland Atlantean AN68B/1R*   Northern Counties   B43/32F   1981-82
*4448/56/86/91/7-99 are AN68A/1R

4448	SND448X	4464w	SND464X	4490	SND490X	4503	SND503X	4516w	SND516X
4456w	SND456X	4469	SND469X	4491	SND491X	4504w	SND504X	4517	SND517X
4458	SND458X	4471	SND471X	4497	SND497X	4507w	SND507X	4522	SND522X
4459w	SND459X	4474	SND474X	4498	SND498X	4508	SND508X	4523	SND523X
4460	SND460X	4475	SND475X	4499w	SND499X	4509w	SND509X	4524	SND524X
4461	SND461X	4486	SND486X	4502	SND502X				

4529-4599   Leyland Atlantean AN68D/1R   Northern Counties   B43/32F   1982

4529	SND529X	4542	ANA542Y	4558	ANA558Y	4573	ANA573Y	4588	ANA588Y
4531	ANA531Y	4547	ANA547Y	4561	ANA561Y	4575w	ANA575Y	4590	ANA590Y
4532	ANA532Y	4548	ANA548Y	4563	ANA563Y	4576	ANA576Y	4591	ANA591Y
4535	ANA535Y	4549	ANA549Y	4566	ANA566Y	4578	ANA578Y	4594	ANA594Y
4539	ANA539Y	4551	ANA551Y	4567	ANA567Y	4580	ANA580Y	4595	ANA595Y
4540	ANA540Y	4554	ANA554Y	4570	ANA570Y	4584	ANA584Y	4599	ANA599Y
4541	ANA541Y	4555	ANA555Y	4571	ANA571Y	4587	ANA587Y		

4603-4697   Leyland Atlantean AN68D/1R   Northern Counties   B43/32F   1982-84

4603	ANA603Y	4622	ANA622Y	4641	ANA641Y	4658	A658HNB	4677	A677HNB
4606	ANA606Y	4623	ANA623Y	4645	ANA645Y	4659w	A659HNB	4681w	A681HNB
4607	ANA607Y	4626	ANA626Y	4648	ANA648Y	4662	A662HNB	4682	A682HNB
4610	ANA610Y	4629	ANA629Y	4649	ANA649Y	4663	A663HNB	4686	A686HNB
4611	ANA611Y	4633	ANA633Y	4650	ANA650Y	4667	A667HNB	4689	A689HNB
4615	ANA615Y	4635	ANA635Y	4652	ANA652Y	4670	A670HNB	4691	A691HNB
4616	ANA616Y	4636	ANA636Y	4654	ANA654Y	4672	A672HNB	4692	A692HNB
4617	ANA617Y	4638	ANA638Y	4655	ANA655Y	4673	A673HNB	4697	A697HNB
4621	ANA621Y	4640	ANA640Y	4656	A656HNB	4676	A676HNB		

4701-4765   Leyland Atlantean AN68D/1R   Northern Counties   B43/32F*   1984
*4721 is B43/30F

4701	A701LNC	4717	A717LNC	4729	A729LNC	4739	A739NNA	4756	A756NNA
4703	A703LNC	4718	A718LNC	4732	A732LNC	4740	A740NNA	4758	A758NNA
4709	A709LNC	4720	A720LNC	4733w	A733LNC	4746	A746NNA	4760	A760NNA
4712	A712LNC	4721	A721LNC	4736	A736LNC	4753	A753NNA	4763	A763NNA
4713	A713LNC	4727	A727LNC	4738	A738NNA	4755	A755NNA	4765	A765NNA
4716	A716LNC	4728	A728LNC						

5013	GBU13V	MCW Metrobus DR102/10	MCW		B43/30F	1980	
5014w	GBU14V	MCW Metrobus DR102/10	MCW		B43/30F	1980	
5015	GBU15V	MCW Metrobus DR102/10	MCW		B43/30F	1980	

5032-5104   MCW Metrobus DR102/21   MCW   B43/30F   1981

5032	MRJ32W	5050	MRJ50W	5068w	MRJ68W	5085	ORJ85W	5101	SND101X
5033	MRJ33W	5056w	MRJ56W	5070	MRJ70W	5089w	ORJ89W	5102	SND102X
5034	MRJ34W	5058	MRJ58W	5082	ORJ82W	5096	ORJ96W	5103	SND103X
5035	MRJ35W	5060	MRJ60W	5084	ORJ84W	5097	ORJ97W	5104	SND104X
5039w	MRJ39W	5064	MRJ64W						

5112-5188   MCW Metrobus DR102/23   MCW   B43/30F   1981-83

5112	SND112X	5133	SND133X	5148	SND148X	5168	ANA168Y	5178	ANA178Y
5114	SND114X	5136	SND136X	5149	SND149X	5169	ANA169Y	5181	ANA181Y
5115	SND115X	5137w	SND137X	5150	SND150X	5171	ANA171Y	5183	ANA183Y
5122	SND122X	5138w	SND138X	5151	ANA151Y	5172	ANA172Y	5184	ANA184Y
5126	SND126X	5139	SND139X	5152	ANA152Y	5174	ANA174Y	5186	ANA186Y
5129	SND129X	5140	SND140X	5166	ANA166Y	5175w	ANA175Y	5187	ANA187Y
5130	SND130X	5147	SND147X	5167	ANA167Y	5176w	ANA176Y	5188	ANA188Y
5131	SND131X								

5201-5210   MCW Metrobus DR132/8   Northern Counties   BC43/29F*   1986   *Seating varies

| 5201 | C201FVU | 5203 | C203FVU | 5205 | C205FVU | 5207 | C207FVU | 5209 | C209FVU |
| 5202 | C202FVU | 5204 | C204FVU | 5206 | C206FVU | 5208 | C208FVU | 5210 | C210FVU |

5301-5320   MCW Metrobus DR102/51   Northern Counties   BC43/29F*   1986-87   *Seating varies

5301	D301JVR	5305	D305JVR	5309	D309JVR	5313	D313LNB	5317	D317LNB
5302	D302JVR	5306	D306JVR	5310	D310JVR	5314	D314LNB	5318	D318LNB
5303	D303JVR	5307	D307JVR	5311	D311LNB	5315	D315LNB	5319	D319LNB
5304	D304JVR	5308	D308JVR	5312	D312LNB	5316	D316LNB	5320	D320LNB

| 5532 | CUB532Y | MCW Metrobus DR101/32 | MCW | | B43/30F | 1983 | Yorkshire Rider, 1996 |

5541-5579   MCW Metrobus DR102/38   MCW   B43/30F   1984   Yorkshire Rider, 1996

5541	A541KUM	5553	A753LWY	5564	B564RWY	5569	B569RWY	5572	B572RWY
5546	A546KUM	5555	A755LWY	5565	B565RWY	5571	B571RWY	5579	B579RWY
5547	A547KUM	5562	B562RWY	5568	B568RWY				

6001-6025   Dennis Dart SLF   Plaxton Pointer   N41F   1996-97

6001	P301LND	6006	P306LND	6011	P311LND	6016	P316LND	6021	P321LND
6002	P302LND	6007	P307LND	6012	P312LND	6017	P317LND	6022	P322LND
6003	P303LND	6008	P308LND	6013	P313LND	6018	P318LND	6023	P323LND
6004	P304LND	6009	P309LND	6014	P314LND	6019	P319LND	6024	P324LND
6005	P305LND	6010	P310LND	6015	P315LND	6020	P320LND	6025	P325LND

6034-6080   Dennis Dart SLF   Plaxton Pointer 2   N37F   1997

6034	R234SBA	6044	R244SBA	6054	R254SBA	6063	R263SBA	6072	R272SBA
6035	R235SBA	6045	R245SBA	6055	R255SBA	6064	R264SBA	6073	R273SBA
6036	R236SBA	6046	R246SBA	6056	R256SBA	6065	R265SBA	6074	R274SBA
6037	R237SBA	6047	R247SBA	6057	R257SBA	6066	R266SBA	6075	R275SBA
6038	R238SBA	6048	R248SBA	6058	R258SBA	6067	R267SBA	6076	R276SBA
6039	R239SBA	6049	R249SBA	6059	R259SBA	6068	R268SBA	6077	R277SBA
6040	R240SBA	6050	R250SBA	6060	R260SBA	6069	R269SBA	6078	R278SBA
6041	R241SBA	6051	R251SBA	6061	R261SBA	6070	R270SBA	6079	R279SBA
6042	R242SBA	6052	R252SBA	6062	R262SBA	6071	R271SBA	6080	R280SBA
6043	R243SBA	6053	R253SBA						

G M Buses practiced a dual-source policy for their double-deck buses taking MCW Metrobuses as well as Atlantean/Olympian products from Leyland. The type has now disappeared from the southern part - now Stagecoach Manchester - while those with First Manchester in the northern part remain at Manchester and Oldham depots. Pictured here is 5129, SND129X, complete with OM depot code.
Bill Potter

The final thirty Metrobuses were bodied by Northern Counties to a variant of the GM Standard vehicle. Shown coming off duty in Rochdale is 5304, D304JVR. GM Buses closed depots at Altrincham, Rochdale and Tameside prior to deregulation and all three towns now host a variety of operators that compete with the successors of GM Buses.
Bill Potter

Just one Optare Excel from the Timeline fleet is based in Wigan, the remainder are based at Bolton. One of these, 6604, R216SBA, is seen in Manchester's Piccadilly while operating service 29 from Bolton. Bolton has now become the largest of the First Manchester depots. Indeed, less than nineteen percent of the fleet is actually based in Manchester. *Tony Wilson*

6091	S395HVV	Dennis Dart SLF	Plaxton Pointer 2	N39F	1998
6092	S396HVV	Dennis Dart SLF	Plaxton Pointer 2	N39F	1998
6093	S397HVV	Dennis Dart SLF	Plaxton Pointer 2	N39F	1998

6501-6530

Dennis Dart SLF · Wright Crusader · NC41F* · 1996-97 · *seating varies

6501	P501LND	6507	P507LND	6513	P513LND	6519	P519LND	6525	P525LND
6502	P502LND	6508	P508LND	6514	P514LND	6520	P520LND	6526	P526LND
6503	P503LND	6509	P509LND	6515	P515LND	6521	P521LND	6527	P527LND
6504	P504LND	6510	P510LND	6516	P516LND	6522	P522LND	6528	P528LND
6505	P505LND	6511	P511LND	6517	P517LND	6523	P523LND	6529	P529LND
6506	P506LND	6512	P512LND	6518	P518LND	6524	P524LND	6530	P530LND

6601-6610

Optare L1070 · Optare Excel · N37F · 1996-97 · Timeline, 1998

6601	P213HRJ	6603	R215SBA	6605	R217SBA	6607	R219SBA	6609	R221SBA
6602	R214SBA	6604	R216SBA	6606	R218SBA	6608	R220SBA	6610	R223SBA

6701-6708

Volvo B6BLE · Wright Crusader · N F · 1999

6701	T701PND	6703	T703PND	6705	T705PND	6707	T707PND	6708	T708PND
6702	T702PND	6704	T704PND	6706	T706PND				

7003-7010

Volvo Citybus B10M-50 · Northern Counties Palatine · B45/31F* · 1991-92 · *7009/10 are B45/26FL

7003	H703GVM	7005	H705GVM	7008	H708GVM	7009	J709ONF	7010	J710ONF

| 7077 | WBN955L | Leyland Atlantean AN68/1R | Park Royal | O43/32F | 1972 |

Ancilliary vehicles:-

TV284	HSO284V	Leyland Atlantean AN68A/1R	Alexander AL	TV	1980	Grampian 1996
TV404	G62RND	Leyland Tiger TR2R62C16Z4	Alexander N	TV	1989	Timeline, 1998
TV405	G63RND	Leyland Tiger TR2R62C16Z4	Alexander N	TV	1989	Timeline, 1998
TV412	G70RND	Leyland Tiger TR2R62C16Z4	Alexander N	TV	1989	Timeline, 1998
TV1412	M412RND	Iveco TurboDaily 59.12	Marshall C 31	TV	1995	Citibus, Middleton, 1995
TV1415	M415RND	Iveco TurboDaily 59.12	Marshall C 31	TV	1995	Citibus, Middleton, 1995
TV1416	M416RND	Iveco TurboDaily 59.12	Marshall C 31	TV	1995	Citibus, Middleton, 1995
TV1422	DSA254T	Leyland Atlantean AN68A/1R	Alexander AL	TV	1979	Grampian, 1996
TV1423	DSA253T	Leyland Atlantean AN68A/1R	Alexander AL	TV	1979	Grampian, 1996
TV1440	TND102X	Ford R1114	Duple Dominant IV	TV	1983	Hulme Hall, Cheadle, 1994
TX1751	F636XMS	Mercedes-Benz 811D	Alexander Sprint	TV	1988	CentreWest, 1998
TX1752	F640XMS	Mercedes-Benz 811D	Alexander Sprint	TV	1988	CentreWest, 1998
TX1753	F642XMS	Mercedes-Benz 811D	Alexander Sprint	TV	1988	CentreWest, 1998
TX1754	F672XMS	Mercedes-Benz 811D	Alexander Sprint	TV	1988	CentreWest, 1998
TV4269	FVR269V	Leyland Atlantean AN68D/1R	Northern Counties	TV	1980	
TV4357	ORJ357W	Leyland Atlantean AN68D/1R	Northern Counties	TV	1981	
TV4447	SND447X	Leyland Atlantean AN68D/1R	Northern Counties	TV	1981	
TV4562	ANA562Y	Leyland Atlantean AN68D/1R	Northern Counties	TV	1980	
TV4580	ANA580Y	Leyland Atlantean AN68D/1R	Northern Counties	TV	1982	
TV4583	ANA583Y	Leyland Atlantean AN68D/1R	Northern Counties	TV	1982	
TV4642	ANA642Y	Leyland Atlantean AN68D/1R	Northern Counties	TV	1982	
TV5012	GBU12V	MCW Metrobus DR102/10	MCW	TV	1980	
TV5061	MRJ61W	MCW Metrobus DR102/21	MCW	TV	1981	
TV5062	MRJ62W	MCW Metrobus DR102/21	MCW	TV	1981	
S5086	ORJ86W	MCW Metrobus DR102/21	MCW	B43/30F	1981	
TV4768	HWT54N	Leyland Atlantean AN68/1R	Roe	TV	1975	Yorkshire Rider, 1997

Allocations

Bolton (Crook Street)

Mercedes-Benz	1721	1722	1723	1724	1831	1832	1833	1834
	1835							
Dart	6007	6008	6009	6010	6011	6012	6013	6014
	6015	6016	6017	6018	6019	6020	6021	6022
	6023	6024	6025	6040	6041	6042	6043	6044
	6045	6046	6047	6048	6049	6061	6062	6063
	6064	6065	6066	6067	6068	6069	6070	6071
	6072	6073	6077					
Excel	6602	6603	6604	6605	6606	6607	6608	6609
	6610							
Lynx	1401	1402	1403	1404				
Tiger	401	402	406					
Volvo B10BLE	580	581	582	583	584	585	586	587
	588	589	590	591	634	635	636	637
	638	639	640	641	642	643	644	645
	646	647	648	649	650	651	652	653
	654	655	657					
Atlantean	4416	4419	4441	4448	4458	4460	4461	4469
	4471	4474	4475	4486	4490	4491	4508	4517
	4523	4524	4529	4531	4532	4535	4539	4540
	4541	4547	4548	4549	4551	4554	4555	4561
	4563	4566	4567	4570	4573	4575	4584	4587
	4588	4594	4607	4611	4615	4617	4623	4626
	4633	4635	4640	4645	4648	4650	4652	4713
	4720	4721	4736	4739	4740	4746	4753	4758
	4763	7077						
Olympian	3037	3043	3044	3046	3047	3061	3066	3078
	3081	3083	3090	3092	3098	3099	3100	3105
	3120	3144	3151	3163	3177	3180	3190	3192
	3201	3211	3218	3219	3223	3227	3228	3231
	3232	3233	3237	3238	3239	3240	3241	3242
	3243	3244	3245	3252	3254	3256	3261	3262
	3263	3274	3275	3408	3409	3410		

Bury (Rochdale Road)

Dart	1101	1104	1123	1124	1125	1126	1127	1128
	1129	1130	1131	1132	1133	1134	1135	1136
	1137	1138	1139	1140	1141	1142	1143	1144
	1145	1146	1147	1148	1149	1150	1151	1152
	1153	6001	6002	6003	6004	6005	6006	6050
	6051	6052	6053	6054	6055	6056	6057	6058
	6059	6060						
Volvo B10B	501	504	508	509	512	519	520	521
	522	533	534	535	536	538	543	544
	545	546	547					
Volvo B10BLE	563	564	565	566	567	568		
Volvo B10M	701							
Volvo B10LA	2001	2002	2003	2004	2005	2006	2007	2008
	2009	2010	2011	2012	2013	2014	2015	
Atlantean	4438	4442	4444	4446	4497	4571	4606	4636
	4677	4697	4703	4717	4718	4728	4732	4755
Olympian	3038	3052	3054	3064	3068	3076	3096	3103
	3106	3108	3109	3112	3113	3116	3127	3128
	3134	3136	3141	3142	3152	3160	3168	3182
	3183	3188	3249	3250	3251	3253	3257	3259
	3271	3273	3276					
Volvo Citybus	1481	1482	1483	7003	7005	7008	7009	7010

Manchester (Queens Road)

Mercedes-Benz	1801	1803	1805	1806	1807	1808	1809	1810
	1811	1812	1818	1819				
Volvo B6	1043	1044	1047	1048	1049	1050	1051	1052
	1053	1054	1055	1056	1057	1058	1059	1060
	1061	1062	1063	1064	1065	1066	1067	1068
	1069	1070	1071	1072	1073	1074	1075	1076
	1077	1078	1079	1080	1081	1082	1083	1084
	1085	1086	1093	1094	1095	1096	1097	1098
Volvo B10B	502	503	505	506	507	510	511	513
	514	515	516	517	518	550	551	552
Volvo B10BLE	621	622	623	624	625	626	627	628
	628	630	631	632	633	656		
Metrobus	5013	5015	5032	5033	5034	5035	5082	5084
	5085	5096	5097	5114	5136	5139	5140	5149
	5152	5171	5172	5174	5316	5317	5318	5320
	5532	5541	5546	5547	5553	5555	5562	5564
	5565	5568	5569	5571	5572	5579		
Olympian	3042	3045	3050	3073	3075	3079	3093	3104
	3107	3115	3123	3129	3130	3131	3140	3157
	3159	3171	3187	3194	3222	3401	3402	3403
	3404	3405	3406	3407				

Rochdale (Miall Street) - Pioneer

Mercedes-Benz	1717	1731	1732	1733	1734	1841	1842	1843
Renault-Dodge	1998							
Dart	1171	1172	6512	6513	6514	6515	6516	
Tiger	407							

Oldham (Wallshaw Street)

Mercedes-Benz	1703	1704	1706	1707	1708	1709	1714	1719
	1802	1813	1814	1815	1816	1817	1820	
Dart	6501	6502	6503	6504	6505	6506	6507	6508
	6509	6510	6511	6517	6518	6519	6520	6521
	6522	6523	6524	6525	6526	6527	6528	6529
	6530							
Volvo B10B	523	524	525	526	527	528	529	530
	531	532	537	539	540	541	542	548
	549	553	554	556				
Volvo B10BLE	669	670	671	672	673			
Scania	101	102	103	104	105	106	107	108
	109	110	111	112	113	114	115	116
	117	118	119					
Atlantean	4558	4581	4610	4638	4656	4659	4663	4667
	4670	4672	4673	4676	4682	4686	4691	4692
	4709	4716	4727	4738	4765			
Metrobus	5050	5058	5060	5070	5101	5102	5103	5104
	5112	5115	5122	5126	5129	5130	5131	5133
	5147	5148	5150	5151	5166	5167	5168	5169
	5178	5181	5183	5184	5186	5187	5188	5201
	5202	5203	5204	5205	5206	5207	5208	5209
	5210	5301	5302	5303	5304	5305	5306	5307
	5308	5309	5310	5311	5312	5313	5314	5315
	5319							
Olympian	3040	3041	3048	3051	3059	3062	3063	3085
	3097	3102	3161	3162	3186	3189	3202	3203
	3204	3206	3209	3217	3220	3225	3229	3235
	3284							

Wigan (Melverley Street)

Mercedes-Benz	1804	1821	1822					
Dart	608	609	610	611	612	613	614	617
	618	1102	1103	1105	1106	1119	1120	1121
	1122	6026	6027	6028	6029	6030	6031	6032
	6033	6034	6035	6036	6037	6038	6039	6074
	6075	6076	6078	6079	6080	6091	6092	6093
Volvo B10L	557	558	559	561	562			
Volvo B10BLE	571	572	573	574	575	576	577	578
	579	587						
Tiger	408	409	410	411				
Excel	6601							
Atlantean	4374	4498	4502	4503	4522	4534	4542	4576
	4578	4590	4591	4595	4599	4603	4616	4621
	4622	4629	4641	4649	4654	4655	4658	4662
	4689	4701	4712	4729	4756	4760		
Olympian	3011	3012	3013	3014	3015	3071	3101	3111
	3148	3200	3246	3247	3248	3258	3264	3265
	3266	3267	3270	3278	3279	3280	3281	3286
	3287	3288	3290	3292	3293	3299	3302	3303
	3305							

Unallocated

Renault-Dodge	1997	1999				
Volvo B6	1087	1088	1089	1090	1091	1092

FISHWICK

John Fishwick & Sons Ltd, Golden Hill Garage, Golden Hill Lane, Leyland, PR5 2LE

2	A462LFV	Leyland Atlantean AN69/2L	Eastern Coach Works	B47/35F	1983	
3	J7JFS	Leyland Lynx LX2R11C15Z4R	Leyland Lynx 2	B47F	1991	
4	H64CCK	Leyland Lynx LX2R11C15Z4R	Leyland Lynx 2	B47F	1991	
5	H65CCK	Leyland Lynx LX2R11C15Z4R	Leyland Lynx 2	B51F	1991	
6	NFR559T	Leyland National 11351A/1R		B49F	1979	
7	GCK428W	Leyland National 2 NL116AL11/1R		B49F	1981	
8	GCK429W	Leyland National 2 NL116AL11/1R		B49F	1981	
9	WRN412V	Leyland National 2 NL116L11/1R		B49F	1980	
10	WRN413V	Leyland National 2 NL116L11/1R		B49F	1980	
11	NFR560T	Leyland National 11351A/1R [DAF]		B49F	1979	
12	GCK430W	Leyland National 2 NL116AL11/1R		B49F	1981	
14	J14JFS	Leyland Lynx LX2R11C15Z4R	Leyland Lynx 2	B51F	1992	
15	R845VEC	Dennis Dart SLF	Wright Crusader	N41F	1997	
16	OFV620X	Leyland National 2 NL116AL11/1R		B49F	1981	
17	R846VEC	Dennis Dart SLF	Wright Crusader	N41F	1997	
18	R847VEC	Dennis Dart SLF	Wright Crusader	N41F	1997	
19	R848VEC	Dennis Dart SLF	Wright Crusader	N41F	1997	
20	LUA714V	Bristol VRT/SL3/6LXB	Eastern Coach Works	B43/31F	1979	Northern Bus, Anston, 1994
21	DWU295T	Bristol VRT/SL3/6LXB	Eastern Coach Works	B43/31F	1979	Northern Bus, Anston, 1994
22	SRN103P	Leyland Atlantean AN68A/1R	East Lancashire	B43/32F	1976	
23	GRN895W	Leyland Atlantean AN69/1L	Eastern Coach Works	B43/31F	1981	
25	D25VCW	Leyland Lynx LX112TL11ZR1	Leyland	B47F	1986	
26	OFV621X	Leyland National 2 NL116AL11/1R		B49F	1981	
27	ABV939Y	Leyland National 2 NL116TL11/1R		B49F	1982	
28	FBV524S	Leyland National 11351A/1R		B49F	1978	
29	AAP651T	Bristol VRT/SL3/6LXB	Eastern Coach Works	B43/31F	1978	Partridge, Hadleigh, 1997
30	D30VCW	Leyland Lynx LX112TL11ZR1	Leyland	B47F	1986	
31	HJB461W	Bristol VRT/SL3/6LXB	Eastern Coach Works	B43/31F	1980	Partridge, Hadleigh, 1997
32	D32YCW	Leyland Lynx LX112TL11ZR1S	Leyland	B47F	1987	
33	D33YCW	Leyland Lynx LX112TL11ZR1S	Leyland	B47F	1987	
34	XCW957R	Leyland National 11351A/1R		B49F	1977	
	M664WCK	Volvo B10M-62	Plaxton Excalibur	C49FT	1995	
	M665WCK	Volvo B10M-62	Plaxton Excalibur	C49FT	1995	
	N662KCW	EOS E180Z	EOS 90	C49FT	1996	
	N985FWT	DAF DE33WSSB3000	Van Hool Alizée HE	C49FT	1996	
	P866PWW	DAF DE33WSSB3000	Van Hool Alizée HE	C49FT	1997	
	P867PWW	DAF DE33WSSB3000	Van Hool Alizée HE	C49FT	1997	
	R61GNW	DAF DE33WSSB3000	Van Hool Alizée 2	C48FT	1998	
	R62GNW	DAF DE33WSSB3000	Van Hool Alizée 2	C48FT	1998	
	T58AUA	DAF DE33WSSB3000	Van Hool Alizée 2	C48FT	1999	
	T59AUA	DAF DE33WSSB3000	Van Hool Alizée 2	C48FT	1999	
M1	F705WFV	Mercedes-Benz 609D	Reeve Burgess Beaver	BC19F	1989	
M2	F706WFV	Mercedes-Benz 609D	Reeve Burgess Beaver	BC19F	1989	
M5	E45HBV	Mercedes-Benz 609D	Reeve Burgess Beaver	B20F	1987	
M6	E46HBV	Mercedes-Benz 609D	Reeve Burgess Beaver	B20F	1987	
M7	E47HBV	Mercedes-Benz 609D	Reeve Burgess Beaver	B20F	1987	
M8	D84BLF	Mercedes-Benz 609D	Reeve Burgess Beaver	BC19F	1987	Mercedes-Benz demonstrator, 1987
M10	E100MFV	Mercedes-Benz 609D	Reeve Burgess Beaver	BC19F	1988	
M11	K5JFS	Mercedes-Benz 814D	Autobus Classique 2	C29F	1993	

Previous registrations:
K5JFS	K721GBE

Opposite:- **The family-owned operator, John Fishwick & Sons continues to provide passenger services from its base near the old Leyland works. Once, the entire fleet comprised Leyland products, but in recent years several other maufacturers have supplied vehicles. The Leyland National and Lynx are still the mainstay of the service fleet, while four Bristol VRs have joined the school fleet. It is expected that the first of the new DAF SB120 low floor midi-bus will be shown at the 1999 motor show. Shown here are Leyland National 10, WRN413V and R61GNW a DAF SB3000 with the mark 2 version of Van Hool Alizee bodywork.**
Cliff Beeton/Tony Wilson

HOLMESWOOD

Holmeswood Coaches Ltd, Fallowfields, Sandy Way, Holmeswood, Rufford, L40 1UB

BHF291A	AEC Reliance 2MU3RV	Plaxton Panorama Elite III (1973)	C41F	1960	Wimpey, 1973
ECK865E	Leyland Leopard PSU3/4R	Plaxton Supreme IV (1980)	C49F	1967	Hants & Dorset, 1980
ARC669T	Leyland Atlantean AN68A/1R	Northern Counties	B47/31D	1979	City of Nottingham, 1996
LCW411W	Leyland Tiger TRCTL11/3R	Duple Dominant II	C57F	1981	Mercers, Preston, 1993
ANA159Y	MCW Metrobus DR102/23	MCW	B43/30F	1982	Stagecoach Manchester, 1998
A914RRN	Leyland Tiger B43	Plaxton Paramount 3200	C49F	1984	Mercers, Longridge, 1984
AAX300A	Leyland Tiger TRCTL11/3R	Berkhof Excellence 1000L ('95)	C55F	1984	Tellings - Golden Miller, 1992
A20HWD	Van Hool TD824	Van Hool Astromega	C57/27F	1985	Duff, Sutton on the Forest, 1996
A4HWD	Leyland Olympian ONTL11/2R	Eastern Coach Works	C45/28F	1985	Cedric, Wivenhoe, 1998
OAZ9330	Leyland Olympian ONTL11/2RSp	Eastern Coach Works	C45/28F	1985	Ham, Flimwell, 1998
5AAX	Volvo B10M-61	Berkhof Excellence 1000 ('96)	C57F	1986	Shearings, 1993
A19HWD	Leyland Tiger TRCTL11/3R	Duple 320	C57F	1987	Bodman & Heath, Worton, 1999
D261FUL	Leyland Olympian ONLXB/1RH	Eastern Coach Works	BC42/29F	1987	London Central, 1998
YSU991	ACE Puma IV	Plaxton Paramount 3200 II	C34F	1988	The Londoners, Nunhead, 1993
YXI7923	Volvo B10M-61	Van Hool Alizée H	C55F	1988	Shearings, 1996
YTY867	Volvo B10M-60	Plaxton Paramount 3200 II	C57F	1989	Woodstones, Kidderminster, 1995
H2HWD	Scania K113TRB	Van Hool Astrobel	C57/14CT	1990	Birmingham Coach, Tividale, 1997
201SC	Scania K93CRB	Van Hool Alizée H	C49F	1991	
H927DRJ	Scania K93CRB	Plaxton Paramount 3200 III	C55F	1991	Shearings, 1995
J220XKY	Scania K93CRB	Van Hool Alizée H	C55F	1992	Pemico, South Bermondsey, 1998
J289NNC	Scania K93CRB	Plaxton Première 320	C57F	1992	Shearings, 1998
J294NNC	Scania K93CRB	Plaxton Première 320	C53F	1992	Shearings, 1998
J297NNC	Scania K93CRB	Plaxton Première 320	C53F	1992	Shearings, 1998
J298NNC	Scania K93CRB	Plaxton Première 320	C53F	1992	Shearings, 1998
J299NNC	Scania K93CRB	Plaxton Première 320	C53F	1992	Shearings, 1998

Holmeswood operate school services with older coaches and double-deck buses while a modern fleet of high-class coaches is employed on an extensive tours and excursions programme. Recent arrivals, including a new addition as we go to press, are based on Scania chassis and feature HWD index marks. Air conditioned Irizar MidiCentury S4HWD is seen in a multi-coloured scheme earlier in 1999. In addition, Holmeswood control Bostocks of Congleton which features in our Merseyside and Cheshire Bus Handbook. *Keith Grimes*

Enjoying a trip to Blackpool's Pleasure Beach is A20HWD from the Holmeswood fleet. This integral double-deck coach from Van Hool is marketed as the Astromega. The model has a Mercedes-Benz power unit and with seating for 84 passengers, is the highest capacity coach in the fleet. *Paul Wigan*

K4HWD	Scania K113TRA	Berkhof Excellence 2000HD	C57/19DT	1993	The Kings Ferry, Gillingham, 1998
L18HWD	Mercedes-Benz 711D	Plaxton Beaver	BC25F	1994	Hillary, Prudhoe, 1997
466YMG	Volvo B10M	Van Hool Alizée H	C53F	1994	
M6HWD	Scania K113CRB	Van Hool Alizée HE	C49F	1994	
M844LFP	Toyota Coaster HZB50R	Caetano Optimo III	C21F	1995	Marchwood, Totton, 1998
N784ORY	Dennis Javelin GX	Caetano Algarve II	C51F	1995	Allied Coachlines, Uxbridge, 1999
N839AOV	Renault Trafic	Jubilee	M8	1995	van, 1999
N91WVC	Scania K113TRB	Van Hool Astrobel	C57/17CT	1996	Harry Shaw, Coventry, 1999
P2HWD	MAN 11.220 HOCLR	Caetano Algarve II	C35F	1997	
P50HWD	Neoplan N116/3	Neoplan Cityliner	C49FT	1997	
P4HWD	Scania L94IB	Irizar Inter-Century 12.32	C50FT	1997	
P839RBX	Renault Master T35D	Cymric	M15	1997	
P5HWD	MAN 11.220 HOCLR	Berkhof Excellence 1000 Midi	C33FT	1997	
R3HWD	Dennis Javelin	Caetano Algarve II	C53F	1997	
R4HWD	Dennis Javelin	Caetano Algarve II	C53F	1997	
R5HWD	Scania K113CRB	Van Hool Alizée II	C49FT	1998	
R6HWD	Scania K113CRB	Van Hool Alizée II	C49FT	1998	
S4HWD	Scania L94IB	Irizar Midicentury 10.15	C38FT	1998	
V4HWD	Scania L94IB	Van Hool Alizée II	C49FT	1999	

Previous registrations:

5AAX	C336DND, SPR124, C449GVM	H2HWD	H134ACU, KSU464, H681FCU, H10WLE, H163POF
201SC	H812RWJ	K4HWD	K15KFC
466YMG	?	LCW411W	KHG184W, 1958PH
A4HWD	B694BPU	OAZ9330	B578LPE
A19HWD	E179WDV	YSU991	E923LCP
A20HWD	C256FHJ, A4HWD	YTY867	F460WFX
AAX300A	A257VWO	YXI7923	F746ENE
BHF291A	466YMG		

Depots: Fallowfields, Sandy Way, Holmeswood, Cowling Brow, Chorley and Derby Road, Southport

HULME HALL

Hulme Hall Coaches Ltd, 75 Hulme Hall Road, Cheadle Hulme, Stockport SK8 6LA

PFC514W	Bristol VRT/SL3/6LXB	Eastern Coach Works	B43/27D	1981	Oxford Bus Company, 1993
PFC515W	Bristol VRT/SL3/6LXB	Eastern Coach Works	B43/27D	1981	Oxford Bus Company, 1993
MEF823W	Bristol VRT/SL3/6LXB	Eastern Coach Works	B43/31F	1981	Arriva North East, 1999
VEX291X	Bristol VRT/SL3/6LXB	Eastern Coach Works	BC41/25F	1981	GHA, Bettws Gwerfil Goch, 1999
VUA472X	Bristol VRT/SL3/6LXB	Eastern Coach Works	B43/31F	1981	West Riding, 1994
SND288X	Leyland Leopard PSU5D/4R	Duple Dominant IV	C53F	1982	North Western, 1990
RJI8918	Leyland Tiger TRCTL11/3R	Duple 340	C49FT	1986	Matthews, Croydon, 1994
SIB2014	Volvo B10M-61	Plaxton Paramount 3500 II	C49FT	1986	National Holidays, 1998
VJI6855	Iveco Daily 49.10	Robin Hood City Nippy	BC21F	1987	Vale, Cheetham, 1997
515VTB	Volvo B10M-61	Plaxton Paramount 3500 III	C53F	1988	National Holidays, 1999
OTK802	Volvo B10M-61	Plaxton Paramount 3500 III	C49FT	1988	National Holidays, 1998
VJI6850	Iveco Daily 49.10	Robin Hood City Nippy	BC25F	1989	Stagecoach Midland Red, 1997
WJI2823	Iveco Daily 49.10	Carlyle Dailybus 2	B25F	1989	Midland Fox, 1998

Previous registrations:

515VTB	E574UHS, PXI7915	SIB2014	C106AFX	VJI6855	E878LHV
OTK802	E578UHS, PJI8916	VJI6850	F872UAC	WJI2823	G238GCC
RJI8918	C75KLG				

Depot:- Lower Bent Farm, Stanley Road, Cheadle Hulme

The annual school break provides operators with an opportunity to prepare the fleet for the next term. At Hulme Hall the summer of 1999 was used to repaint Bristol VR VEX291X, and is seen here after being completed. A feature of the Hulme Hall operation is that vehicles are allocated to routes for the whole year.
Cliff Beeton

JP TRAVEL

City Nippy - JP Executive Travel - Hail & Ride

P V Walsh, Cromer Garage, John Lee Fold, Middleton, Rochdale, M24 2LR

JIL6526	Ford R1014	Duple Dominant II	C35F	1979	County Carriages, 1999
TJI6878	Freight Rover Sherpa	Optare	B16F	1987	Jones, Eccles, 1998
D337VBB	Mercedes-Benz 307D	Mercedes-Benz	M12	1987	
LIL2830	Renault-Dodge S56	Northern Counties	B22F	1987	Stagecoach South, 1993
LIL2831	Renault-Dodge S56	Northern Counties	B22F	1987	Stagecoach South, 1993
E129KYW	MCW MetroRider MF150/38	MCW	B25F	1987	Daybird Roadline, Killamarsh, 1997
E357KPO	Iveco Daily 49.10	Robin Hood City Nippy	B25F	1988	
F639HVU	Renault-Dodge S56	Northern Counties	B22F	1988	
F145UFR	Renault-Dodge S56	Northern Counties	B27F	1988	Blackpool, 1996
F893XOE	Freight Rover Sherpa	Carlyle Citybus 2	BC9FL	1988	Proctor, Bedale, 1998
F820FWE	Mercedes-Benz 609D	Whittaker Europa	BC24F	1989	A&C Luxury, Motherwell, 1998
G888TJA	Mercedes-Benz 709D	Phoenix	B29F	1990	
G889TJA	Mercedes-Benz 709D	Phoenix	B29F	1990	
H147CBU	Mercedes-Benz 709D	Phoenix	B29F	1991	
H691FNB	Mercedes-Benz 709D	Phoenix	B29F	1991	
J20JPT	Mercedes-Benz 609D	Made-to-Measure	B21F	1992	
K84UND	Mercedes-Benz 609D	Made-to-Measure	B21F	1992	
K757PUT	Toyota Coaster HDB30R	Caetano Optimo	C21F	1992	Henning, Wheatley Hill, 1997
K123AJA	Mercedes-Benz 709D	Wright NimBus	B27F	1993	
L196DVM	Mercedes-Benz 709D	Wright NimBus	B27F	1993	
L707LKY	Mercedes-Benz 711D	Plaxton Beaver	B23F	1993	Mercedes-Benz demonstrator, 1996
L708LKY	Mercedes-Benz 811D	Wright NimBus	B29F	1993	Mercedes-Benz demonstrator, 1996

JPT is one of the current trading names for J P Travel, though many will be more familiar with the *City Nippy* name that has been on minibuses in the Middleton and Bury areas for some years. The fleet is dominated by Mercedes-Benz minibuses. Pictured at Bury interchange is P6JPT, an 811D which carries Plaxton bodywork. *Paul Wigan*

Marshall supplied bodywork on six Mercedes-Benz 700-series vehicles now in the fleet. The C19 model is illustrated by M8JPT as it leaves Bury for Crumpsall. In this view *Hail & Ride* and *City Nippy* names can be seen. *Tony Wilson*

L5BUS	Mercedes-Benz 709D	Plaxton Beaver	B27F	1993	Jim Stones, Leigh, 1997
L502FVU	Mercedes-Benz 709D	Marshall C19	BC27F	1994	
LIB283	Mercedes-Benz 711D	Marshall C19	B27F	1994	Glossopdale, Dukinfield, 1998
M1JPT	Mercedes-Benz 711D	Marshall C19	B27F	1994	Glossopdale, Dukinfield, 1998
M2JPT	Mercedes-Benz 709D	Marshall C19	B27F	1994	
M7JPT	Mercedes-Benz 709D	Marshall C19	B27F	1995	
M8JPT	Mercedes-Benz 709D	Marshall C19	B27F	1995	
P876PWW	Dennis Dart SLF	Plaxton Pointer	N29F	1997	Valet Parking, Luton Airport, 1999
P1JPT	Mercedes-Benz 709D	Plaxton Beaver	B27F	1997	
P2JPT	Mercedes-Benz Vario O814	Plaxton Beaver 2	B29F	1997	Mercedes-Benz demonstrator, 1998
P3JPT	Mercedes-Benz 709D	Plaxton Beaver	B27F	1997	
P6JPT	Mercedes-Benz 811D	Plaxton Beaver	B31F	1997	
P8JPT	Mercedes-Benz 811D	Plaxton Beaver	B31F	1997	
R2JPT	Mercedes-Benz Vario O810	Plaxton Beaver 2	B31F	1997	
R3JPT	Mercedes-Benz Vario O810	Plaxton Beaver 2	B31F	1997	
S3JPT	Mercedes-Benz Vario O814	Plaxton Beaver 2	B31F	1998	
S6JPT	Mercedes-Benz Vario O814	Plaxton Beaver 2	B31F	1998	
S979TBA	Mercedes-Benz Vario O814	Plaxton Cheetah	C32F	1998	

Previous registrations:

JIL6526	JMJ121V	LIL2831	E408EPE	P2JPT	P296JHE
LIB283	M635FJF	M1JPT	M636FJF	TJI6875	D309PEJ
LIL2830	E406EPE	J20JPT	J615PNE		

Livery: Silver and blue

JIM STONES COACHES

J B Stones, The Bus Garage, Hope Carr Way, Leigh WN7 3DE

A499MHG	Leyland-DAB Tiger Cub	Leyland	B43F	1984	Leyland demonstrator, 1986
B500MPY	Leyland-DAB Tiger Cub	DAB / Eastern Coach Works	B46F	1985	Tees & District, 1993
B10JYM	Leyland Tiger TRCTL11/3LZ	East Lancashire Spryte (1998)	B53F	1985	MoD, 1996 (37KC41)
B11JYM	Leyland Tiger TRCTL11/3RZ	East Lancashire Spryte (1998)	B53F	1986	MoD, 1998 (69KE46)
B16TYG	Leyland Tiger TRCTL11/3LZM	Plaxton Derwent	B54F	1989	MoD, 1996 (03KJ36)
M55BUS	Mercedes-Benz 709D	Plaxton Beaver	B27F	1995	
N967ENA	Mercedes-Benz 709D	Plaxton Beaver	B27F	1996	
BUS1N	Dennis Dart SLF	Plaxton Pointer MPD	N28F	1999	
BUS1T	Dennis Dart SLF	Plaxton Pointer MPD	N28F	1999	
B1BUS	Dennis Dart SLF	Plaxton Pointer MPD	N28F	1999	
M1 BUS	Dennis Dart SLF	Plaxton Pointer MPD	N28F	1999	
T291 ROF	Mercedes-Benz Vario O814	Plaxton Beaver 2	B31F	1999	
T292 ROF	Mercedes-Benz Vario O814	Plaxton Beaver 2	B31F	1999	
T293 ROF	Mercedes-Benz Vario O814	Plaxton Beaver 2	B31F	1999	
T294 ROF	Mercedes-Benz Vario O814	Plaxton Beaver 2	B31F	1999	

Previous registrations:

A499MHG	A499MHG, BUS1T	N967ENA	M1BUS
B500MPY	B500MPY, B1BUS		

J55BUS, shown here in Leigh, has recently left the fleet as a delivery of new minibuses has displaced it, these being four new Mercedes-Benz Vario buses. Interestingly, several index marks are held on retention. These are H1JYM, B1JYM, J5BUS, BUS1S, and T1KET.

KEN ROUTLEDGE TRAVEL

K J Routledge, 1A St Helens Street, Cockermouth, Cumbria, CA13 9HX

J712BAO	Mercedes-Benz 811D	Autobus Classique	C33F	1991
L435KHH	Mercedes-Benz 711D	Plaxton Beaver	BC25F	1993
L743MAO	Ford Transit VE6	Deansgate	M12	1994
P882CHH	Mercedes-Benz 814D	Crystals	BC33F	1996
P884CHH	Mercedes-Benz 711D	Crest	BC24F	1996
R484YVV	Mercedes-Benz 412D	Onyx	M16	1997
R776PRM	Ford Transit VE6	Ford	M8	1997
S193UAO	Ford Transit VE6	Crest	M12	1998
S299JRM	Mercedes-Benz Vario O814	Autobus Nouvelle 2	C33F	1998

Livery: White

The Cumbrian town of Cockermouth is home to Ken Routledge Travel. The fleet of minibuses perform Cumbria County Council contracts, mostly for schools in the north of the county. A Crest conversion is illustrated in this view of P884CHH, which is based on a Mercedes-Benz 711 van. *Bill Potter*

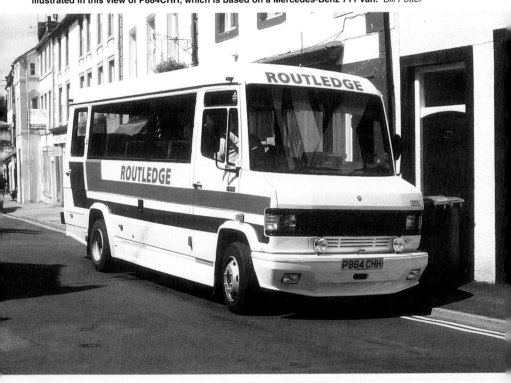

The Lancashire, Cumbria and Manchester Bus Handbook

KIRKBY LONSDALE MINI COACHES

S J Sutton, Twenty Acres, Moor End, Hutton Roof, Kirkby Lonsdale, Cumbria, LA6 2PF

PIL7237	Volvo B58-61	Plaxton Supreme IV	C50FT	1981	Hunter, Grange, 1998
KAZ4127	Leyland Tiger TRCTL11/3R	Duple Laser	C51F	1983	Nu-Venture, Aylesford, 1996
B909BGA	Mercedes-Benz L608D	PMT Hanbridge	BC21F	1984	Cunningham, Carlisle, 1993
TAZ5285	Mercedes-Benz 609D	PMT Burslem	BC26F	1988	Smith, Ledbury, 1994
E76MHG	Renault-Dodge S56	Northern Counties	B25F	1988	Preston, 1996
TAZ5284	Mercedes-Benz 609D	Scott/Olympic	BC24F	1988	Tidbury, St Helens, 1998
H81PTG	Mercedes-Benz 811D	Optare StarRider	B33F	1991	Silverwing, Bristol, 1998
H85PTG	Mercedes-Benz 811D	Optare StarRider	B33F	1991	Silverwing, Bristol, 1999
RIL1026	Mercedes-Benz 814D	Crystals	BC33F	1994	Courtney, Bracknell, 1999
M465RVO	Volkswagen Transporter	Kirkham	M8	1995	private owner, 1997
N657AEO	Mercedes-Benz 609D	Onyx	B24F	1996	

Previous registrations:

KAZ4127	HBH427Y, 9GUV, SWN753Y, 3558RU, JKM117Y	TAZ5284	F259VCS
PIL7237	CYS868X	TAZ5285	E430YLG
RIL1026	L89 EWO		

Livery: White

The rolling countryside around the Lune Valley is the area in which Kirkby Lonsdale Mini Coaches operate. Pictured at rest in Lancaster is Mercedes-Benz 609, N657AEO. This vehicle has bodywork by Onyx and is currently the only vehicle in the fleet purchased new. *Paul Wigan*

LAKELAND COACHES

J Lakeland, Smithy Row, Hurst Green, Lancashire

K833HUM	Volvo B10M-60	Jonckheere Deauville 45L	C50F	1993	Wallace Arnold, 1997
K834HUM	Volvo B10M-60	Jonckheere Deauville 45L	C50F	1993	Wallace Arnold, 1996
FDZ362	Volvo B10M-60	Van Hool Alizée H	C50F	1993	Wallace Arnold, 1997
ESU926	Volvo B10M-62	Van Hool Alizée HE	C53F	1996	Park's of Hamilton, 1999
N955DWJ	Volvo B10M-62	Plaxton Première 350	C53F	1996	
P405MDT	Mercedes-Benz 814D	Plaxton Beaver	BC32F	1997	
P962SFR	Mercedes-Benz 814D	Plaxton Beaver	BC32F	1996	
R672NFR	Scania L113CRL	East Lancashire European	N49F	1997	
T487CCK	Mercedes-Benz Vario O814	Plaxton Cheetah	C29F	1999	
T486CCK	Volvo B10M-62	Plaxton Excalibur	C49F	1999	
T436EBD	Mercedes-Benz Vario O814	Plaxton Beaver 2	B F	1999	

Previous registrations:

ESU926	HSK649, N516PYS	FDZ362	K801HUM, WA3399, K619KWT

The only low-floor vehicle in the Lakeland fleet is East Lancashire-bodied Scania L113 R672NFR. The bus can be found on route 211 from Preston to Chipping, near Clitheroe, which operates as a Lancashire County Council tender. *Paul Wigan*

LANCASTER BUS

Lancaster Bus Ltd, 16a Braganza Way, Lune Industrial Estate, Lancaster LA1 5QP

1	E570MAC	Peugeot-Talbot Pullman	Talbot	B20F	1988	Woodhead, Morecambe, 1996
2	B56AOP	Ford Transit 190D	Carlyle	B16F	1984	Woodhead, Morecambe, 1996
3	D70OKG	Freight Rover Sherpa	Carlyle	B20F	1987	Woodhead, Morecambe, 1996
4	D641MDB	MCW MetroRider MF151/3	MCW	B25F	1987	G M South, 1997
5	D646NOE	MCW MetroRider MF150/4	MCW	B23F	1987	Valles, Wallasey, 1998
6	E979DNK	MCW MetroRider MF150/81	MCW	B25F	1988	The Shires, 1998
7	WAZ3866	DAF MB200DKFL600	Van Hool Alizée H	C48FT	1984	Ramm, Sudden, 1998
8	A618FCD	Bedford YNT	Plaxton Paramount 3200	C49F	1984	Smithyman, Maltby, 1996
9	YSE666Y	Bedford YNT	Plaxton Paramount 3200	C53F	1983	Ennis, Middleton, 1997
10	C200WGV	Renault-Dodge S56	East Lancashire	B26F	1986	Wren, Saltburn, 1997
11	SSU780W	Leyland Leopard PSU3F/4R	Duple Dominant	B55F	1981	Wealden, Five Oak Green, 1997
12	JSJ429W	Volvo B58-56	Duple Dominant	B53F	1980	James, Sutton Coldfield, 1998
13	PSO32W	Leyland Leopard PSU3G/4R	Duple Dominant II Express	C49F	1981	Bluebird Buses, 1998
14	TVN585	Volvo B10M-61	LAG Galaxy	C49FT	1983	Ashall, Clayton, 1998
15	D130NON	Freight Rover Sherpa	Carlyle	B20F	1986	MTL (Heysham Travel), 1998
16	H169WWT	Optare MetroRider MR03	Optare	B26F	1991	Stagecoach London, 1999

Previous registrations:

PSO32W	ORS110W, TSV722, PSO32W, 866NHT	WAZ3866	B360DWF, WOI504, WSV488, B940MKP, A7HOU
TVN585	FAC10Y		

Competition for Stagecoach Lancaster can be found in the form of Lancaster Bus who operate city services using a variety of vehicles painted in an all-white livery. Pictured outside the shopping arcade is MetroRider 6, E979DNK. *Bill Potter*

MANCHESTER INTERNATIONAL AIRPORT

Manchester Airport plc, Manchester International Airport, Ringway, Manchester, M22 5PA

N1	NHH358W	Leyland National 2 NL116AL11/3R		B30T	1981
N2	NHH359W	Leyland National 2 NL116AL11/3R		B30T	1981
N3	Q580GRJ	Leyland National 2 NL116AL11/3R		B30T	1981
N4	unreg	Leyland National 2 NL116AL11/3R		B30T	1981
N5	unreg	Leyland National 2 NL116AL11/3R		B30T	1981
N6	unreg	Leyland National 2 NL116AL11/3R		B30T	1981
N7	unreg	Leyland National 2 NL116AL11/3R		B30T	1981
N8	unreg	Leyland National 2 NL116AL11/3R		B30T	1981
	H199ENC	Mercedes-Benz 709D	Reeve Burgess Beaver	B20F	1990
	H201ENC	Mercedes-Benz 709D	Reeve Burgess Beaver	B20F	1990
	H726LOL	Mercedes-Benz 811D	Carlyle	B27F	1990
	K125TCP	DAF SB220LC550	Ikarus Citibus	B26DL	1993
	K126TCP	DAF SB220LC550	Ikarus Citibus	B26DL	1993
	K127TCP	DAF SB220LC550	Ikarus Citibus	B26DL	1993
	K977JWW	Optare MetroRider MR03	Optare	B23F	1993
	K978JWW	Optare MetroRider MR03	Optare	B23F	1993
	M958VWY	Optare MetroRider MR03	Optare	B23F	1995
	M359OBU	Dennis Dart 9SDL3053	Plaxton Pointer	B29F	1994
	M360OBU	Dennis Dart 9SDL3053	Plaxton Pointer	B29F	1994
	M361OBU	Dennis Dart 9SDL3053	Plaxton Pointer	B29F	1994
	M362OBU	Dennis Dart 9SDL3053	Plaxton Pointer	B29F	1994
	N962WJA	Dennis Dart 9SDL3053	Marshall C36	B27F	1995
	N963WJA	Dennis Dart 9SDL3053	Marshall C36	B27F	1995
	N964WJA	Dennis Dart 9SDL3053	Marshall C36	B27F	1995
	N599XRJ	Dennis Dart 9SDL3053	Marshall C36	B25F	1995
	N601XRJ	Dennis Dart 9SDL3053	Marshall C36	B25F	1995
	N602XRJ	Dennis Dart 9SDL3053	Marshall C36	B25F	1995
	T522JCA	Mercedes-Benz Vario O814	Balmoral	C29F	1999
	T284PVM	Dennis Dart SLF	Plaxton Pointer 2	N34F	1999

Neoplan airside buses

1	unreg	Neoplan N9022	Neoplan	B10D	1994
2	unreg	Neoplan N9022	Neoplan	B10D	1994

Airside coach

1	unreg	Dennis Dart SLF	East Lancashire Flyte	N29F	1998
2	unreg	Dennis Dart SLF	East Lancashire Flyte	N29F	1998
3	unreg	Dennis Dart SLF	East Lancashire Flyte	N29F	1998
4	unreg	Dennis Dart SLF	East Lancashire Flyte	N29F	1998
5	unreg	Dennis Dart SLF	East Lancashire Flyte	N27F	1998

Livery: White, red and blue. Numbered vehicles operate airside at Manchester International Airport.

Depot: Melbourne Avenue, Manchester Airport

Opposite: **Manchester International Airport has increased the number of internal bus routes following the opening of Terminal 2, and Terminal 3's inauguration this year. Services are provided for car park users, transfers as well as air-side links for aircraft parked away from the central piers. Vehicles dedicated to these latter duties are unregistered, but carry fleet numbers in large letters. All the fleet are fitted with airside lighting and communications systems. Pictured outside the Radisson/SAS hotel is Plaxton-bodied Dennis Dart M361OVU, while Marshall-bodied Dart N962WJA is seen entering Terminal 2.**
Bill Potter/Cliff Beeton

MANCHESTER METROLINK

Greater Manchester Metro Ltd, Metrolink House, Queens Road,
Manchester, M8 7RY

1001-1026		GEC Alsthom		Firema		86-seat	1991-92
1001	1005	1009	1012	1015	1018	1021	1024
1002	1006	1010	1013	1016	1019	1022	1025
1003	1007	1011	1014	1017	1020	1023	1026
1004	1008						

2001-2008		GEC Alsthom		Firema		86-seat	1999
2001	2002	2003	2004	2005	2006	2007	2008

Livery: Ivory and turquoise

Named trams:
1002 Manchester Arndale Voyager; 1003 The Robert Owen; 1005 Greater Altrincham Enterprise; 1007 The Guiness Record Breaker; 1009 Co-operative Insurance; 1010 Manchester Champion; 1014 Manchester 2000; 1015 Sparky; 1016 Signal Express; 1017 Rosie; 1019 The Eric Black; 1024 The John Greenwood; 1025 Christie Metro Challenger.

An extension of the Bury-Altrincham Metrolink is progressing. It is envisaged that trams will be running to Broadway, Salford Quays by the end of 1999 and all the way to Eccles by Spring 2000. For this extension eight further trams have been ordered, the first now undergoing trials from the depot in Queens Road. Shown near Piccadilly rail station is 1005. *Tony Wilson*

MAYNE

A Mayne and Son Ltd, Ashton New Road, Clayton, Manchester M11 4PD
Maynes's Coaches Ltd, The Coach Station, Battersby Lane, Warrington WA2 7ET

1	P101HNC	Scania N113DRB	East Lancashire Cityzen	B45/31F	1996	
2	P102HNC	Scania N113DRB	East Lancashire Cityzen	B45/31F	1996	
3	P103HNC	Scania N113DRB	East Lancashire Cityzen	B45/31F	1996	
4	P104HNC	Scania N113DRB	East Lancashire Cityzen	B45/31F	1996	
5	IAZ4775	Leyland Fleetline FE30AGR	Northern Counties	B43/32F	1980	Barry Cooper, 1995
6	IAZ4776	Leyland Fleetline FE30AGR	Northern Counties	B43/32F	1980	Barry Cooper, 1995
8	R108YBA	Scania N113DRB	East Lancashire Cityzen	B45/33F	1997	
9	R109YBA	Scania N113DRB	East Lancashire Cityzen	B45/33F	1997	
10	M210NDB	Scania N113DRB	East Lancashire	B45/31F	1995	
11	M211NDB	Scania N113DRB	East Lancashire	B45/31F	1995	
12	F112HNC	Scania N113DRB	Northern Counties	B47/32F	1989	
13	F113HNC	Scania N113DRB	Northern Counties	BC47/30F	1989	
14	L114DNA	Scania N113DRB	East Lancashire	B47/31F	1993	
15	G115SBA	Scania N113DRB	Northern Counties	B47/32F	1989	
16	G116SBA	Scania N113DRB	Northern Counties	B47/32F	1989	
17	G117SBA	Scania N113DRB	Northern Counties	B47/32F	1989	
21	A101DPB	Dennis Falcon HC SD407	W Stringer Vanguard (1987)	BC49F	1983	Wycombe Bus, 1991
24	R24YNC	Dennis Dart	Marshall Capital	B39F	1997	
25	V125DJA	Dennis Trident	East Lancashire	N51/30F	1999	
26	V126DJA	Dennis Trident	East Lancashire	N51/30F	1999	
27	V127DJA	Dennis Trident	East Lancashire	N51/30F	1999	
28	V128DJA	Dennis Trident	East Lancashire	N51/30F	1999	
29	V129DJA	Dennis Trident	East Lancashire	N51/30F	1999	
32	NIL8256	Leyland Atlantean AN68A/1R	Northern Counties	B43/32F	1982	G M South, 1996
36	BVR100T	Leyland Fleetline FE30AGR	Northern Counties	B43/32F	1979	Barry Cooper, 1996
37	KDB137V	Leyland Fleetline FE30AGR	Northern Counties	B43/32F	1980	Barry Cooper, 1996
38	NIL8258	Leyland Atlantean AN68A/1R	Northern Counties	B43/32F	1981	G M South, 1996
42	M42ONF	Scania L113CRL	Northern Counties Paladin	B51F	1994	
43	M113RNK	Scania L113CRL	Northern Counties Paladin	B51F	1994	Scania demonstrator, 1995

45-49		Dennis Dart SLF	Marshall Capital	N37F	1998	
45	R45CDB	46	R46CDB	47	R47CDB	48	R48CDB	49	R49CDB

50	403BGO	Leyland Tiger TRCTLXCT/3RZ	Plaxton Paramount 3200	C55F	1985	
51	SIW 6251	Dennis Javelin 8.5SDA1903	Duple 320	C37F	1991	
52	PIL7752	DAF MB230DKFL615	Plaxton Paramount 3200 III	C55F	1987	Trent, 1998
53	CLZ8353	DAF MB230DKFL615	Plaxton Paramount 3200 III	C55F	1987	Trent, 1998
56	N56CNF	Bova FLC 12-280	Bova Futura Club	C55F	1996	
57	S57TNA	Bova FHD 12-340	Bova Futura	C49FT	1998	
58	T58JDB	Bova FHD 12-340	Bova Futura	C49FT	1999	
60	RIL8160	Volvo B10M-61	Plaxton Paramount 3500 III	C40FT	1992	
62	NIB4162	Leyland Leopard PSU5C/4R	Plaxton Supreme IV	C57F	1982	
63	S63TNA	Scania L94IB	Irizar InterCentury 12.32	C55F	1998	
64	T64JDB	Scania L94IB	Irizar InterCentury 12.32	C55F	1999	
65	T65JDB	Scania L94IB	Irizar InterCentury 12.32	C55F	1999	
66	MJI5766	Leyland Leopard PSU3E/4R	Plaxton Supreme IV Express	C53F	1980	
67	N67YVR	Dennis Javelin 12SDA2155	UVG UniStar	C57F	1996	
68	N68YVR	Dennis Javelin 12SDA2155	UVG UniStar	C57F	1996	
69	SSV269	Leyland Tiger TRCTL11/3R	Plaxton Paramount 3500 Exp	C55F	1983	
71	RAZ5171	DAF MB230LB615	Plaxton Paramount 3200 III	C55F	1988	Trent, 1997
72	RAZ5172	DAF MB230DKFL615	Plaxton Paramount 3200 III	C55F	1987	Trent, 1997
73	NIL9773	DAF MB230DKFL615	Plaxton Paramount 3200 III	C55F	1987	Trent, 1997
74	NIL9774	DAF MB230DKFL615	Plaxton Paramount 3200 III	C55F	1987	Trent, 1997
75	P75JND	Volvo B10M-62	Plaxton Première 320	C55F	1997	
76	P76JND	Volvo B10M-62	Plaxton Première 320	C55F	1997	
77	LIB6437	Leyland Tiger TRCTLXCT/3RZ	Plaxton Paramount 3500 II	C53F	1986	
79	LIB6439	Leyland Tiger TRCTLXCT/3RZ	Plaxton Paramount 3200 II	C57F	1986	

Maynes Coaches Ltd (Warrington allocation)

2	TET747S	Leyland Fleetline FE30AGR	Roe	B43/33F	1977	Stott, Oldham, 1997
3	ULS 663T	Leyland Fleetline FE30AGR	Eastern Coach Works	B43/32F	1979	Clydeside 2000, 1992
4	GND505N	Daimler Fleetline CRG6LXB	Northern Counties	B43/32F	1974	Greater Manchester, 1988
5	OJD163R	Leyland Fleetline FE30AGR	Park Royal	B44/29F	1976	Stevensons, 1985
6	ULS666T	Leyland Fleetline FE30AGR	Eastern Coach Works	B43/32F	1979	Clydeside 2000, 1992
7	THX555S	Leyland Fleetline FE30ALR Sp	Park Royal	B44/31F	1978	London Buses, 1991
8	THX303S	Leyland Fleetline FE30ALR Sp	MCW	B44/31F	1978	London Buses, 1991
9	TET746S	Leyland Fleetline FE30AGR	Roe	B43/33F	1977	Stott, Oldham, 1997
10	THX601S	Leyland Fleetline FE30ALR Sp	Park Royal	B44/31F	1978	London Buses, 1991
11	THX594S	Leyland Fleetline FE30ALR Sp	Park Royal	B44/31F	1978	London Buses, 1991
18	YPL764	Leyland Tiger TRCTL11/3R	Plaxton Paramount 3500	C57F	1983	
19	R119CNE	Volvo B10M-62	Plaxton Première 320	C57FT	1998	
20	R120CNE	Volvo B10M-62	Plaxton Première 320	C57FT	1998	
21	P121JNF	Volvo B10M-62	Plaxton Première 320	C55F	1997	
22	P122JNF	Volvo B10M-62	Plaxton Première 320	C55F	1997	
23	T223JND	Scania L94IB	Irizar InterCentury 12.32	C55F	1999	
24	T224JND	Scania L94IB	Irizar InterCentury 12.32	C55F	1999	
25	UOL337	Leyland Tiger TRCTL11/3R	Plaxton Paramount 3200 II	C53F	1985	
41	GDZ3841	Leyland Leopard PSU3B/4R	Willowbrook Warrior (1990)	B51F	1974	Bromyard Omnibus Co, 1990
60	GIL2160	Leyland Leopard PSU5C/4R	Plaxton Supreme IV	C57F	1981	
64	MJI5764	Leyland Leopard PSU5C/4R	Plaxton Supreme IV	C57F	1982	
65	MJI5765	Leyland Leopard PSU5C/4R	Plaxton Supreme IV	C57F	1982	
66	UCE665	Leyland Leopard PSU4A/4R	Plaxton Supreme IV (1982)	C53F	1968	Midland Red, 1982
70	TKU540	Leyland Tiger TRCTL11/3R	Plaxton Paramount 3500	C49FT	1984	
	EUK978	Leyland Tiger TRCTL11/3R	Plaxton Paramount 3500	C53FT	1984	
	OED201	Leyland Tiger TRCTL11/3R	Plaxton Paramount 3200 II	C53F	1985	
	NMX643	Leyland Leopard PSU3F/5R	Plaxton Supreme IV	C53F	1980	
	NIB3261	Leyland Leopard PSU5C/4R	Plaxton Supreme IV	C57F	1981	

Previous registrations:

403BGO	B350RNA	MJI5765	SNC365X	OED201	B424RNA
CLZ8353	D640WNU	MJI5766	MRJ358W	PIL7752	D639WNU
EUK978	A421KBA	NIB3261	SNC361X	RAZ5171	E644DAU
GDZ3841	JVS928N	NIB4162	SNC362X	RAZ5172	D634WNU
GIL2160	MRJ360W	NIL8256	SND483X	SIW6251	H51DVR
IAZ4775	MNC487W	NIL8257	SND453X	SSV269	ANA368Y
IAZ4776	MNC488W	NIL8258	SND425X	TKU540	A370HNC
LIB6437	C347YBA	NIL9773	D637WNU	UCE665	WHA236H, SNC355X,
LIB6439	B349RNA	NIL9774	D643WNU	UOL337	B425RNA
MJI5764	SNC364X	NMX643	HDB355V	YPL764	A418HND

Mayne's now operate over a larger area of Manchester than they did prior to deregulation. The fleet has also seen a steady influx of new vehicles represented here by Dennis Dart 47, R47CDB; East-Lancashire-bodied Scania 4, P104HNC and Scania coach 65, T65JDB. The first of four low-floor double-decks is due from Dennis, and these will carry bodywork from East Lancashire.
Cliff Beeton/Tony Wilson/Paul Wigan.

THE MOUNTAIN GOAT

Mountain Goat Holidays and Tours, 10 Victoria Street, Windermere, Cumbria, LA23 1AD

M10MGH	Renault Master T35D	Cymric	M16	1994	
M6MGH	Renault Master T35D	Dobson	M16	1995	
M8MGH	Renault Master T35D	Dobson	M16	1995	
M20MGH	Renault Master T35D	CSM	M15	1995	private owner, 1998
M6OAT	Renault Master T35D	Dobson	M16	1996	
N829REC	Renault Master T35D	Dobson	M16	1996	
N103YHH	Renault Master T35D	Cymric	M16	1996	
N554SOA	Renault Master T35D	Jubilee	M16	1996	
YAZ7315	Renault Master T35D	CSM	M16	1999	

Previous registration

M20MGH   M185OBU

Livery: White, green and red

Depot: Chestnut Road Garage, Windermere

Mountain Goat provide links to English Lakeland, from the hiker who uses the services to access the fells to the Japanese tourist decanted from larger touring coaches using the minibuses to get nearer the sensitive byeways and gills. Pictured at Windermere is M6MGH, a Renault with locally converted bodywork. *Bill Potter*

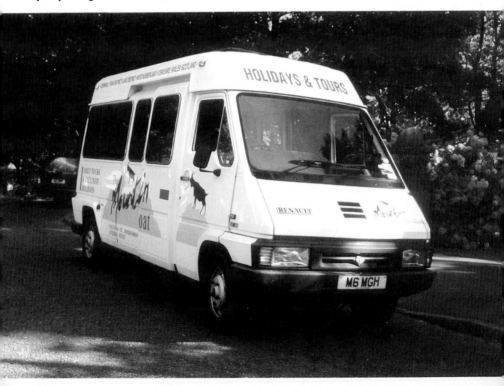

PHOENIX

HandyBus - Phoenix

Phoenix North West Ltd, Unit 5, Sycamore Trading Estate, Squires Gate, Blackpool FY4 3RL

801	H611CGG	Mercedes-Benz 709D	Dormobile Routemaker	B29F	1991	Lofty's, Mickle Trafford, 1995
802	H612CGG	Mercedes-Benz 709D	Dormobile Routemaker	B29F	1991	Lofty's, Mickle Trafford, 1995
803	H613CGG	Mercedes-Benz 709D	Dormobile Routemaker	B29F	1991	Lofty's, Mickle Trafford, 1995
804	H804SFP	Mercedes-Benz 709D	Dormobile Routemaker	B29F	1992	Kinchbus, Barrow-on-Soar, 1995
805	J227HDS	Mercedes-Benz 811D	Dormobile Routemaker	B33F	1992	Wilson, Carnwath, 1998
806	K106RNS	Mercedes-Benz 709D	Dormobile Routemaker	B29F	1991	Lofty's, Mickle Trafford, 1996
807	L808YBC	Mercedes-Benz 709D	Dormobile Routemaker	B27F	1993	Kinchbus, Barrow-on-Soar, 1996
808	J608KGB	Mercedes-Benz 709D	Dormobile Routemaker	B27F	1992	D & N Travel, Ystradgynlais, 1996
809	L138XDS	Mercedes-Benz 709D	Dormobile Routemaker	BC29F	1994	Pathfinder, Newark, 1996
810	L257VSU	Mercedes-Benz 709D	Dormobile Routemaker	B29F	1993	Pathfinder, Newark, 1996
811	L805YBC	Mercedes-Benz 709D	Dormobile Routemaker	B27F	1993	A2B, Prenton, 1997
812	L848WDS	Mercedes-Benz 709D	Dormobile Routemaker	B29F	1994	Pathfinder, Newark, 1996
813	L806YBC	Mercedes-Benz 709D	Dormobile Routemaker	B27F	1993	A2B, Prenton, 1997
814	R814LFV	Mercedes-Benz Vario O810	Plaxton Beaver 2	B27F	1997	
815	R816LFV	Mercedes-Benz Vario O810	Plaxton Beaver 2	B27F	1997	
816	R815LFV	Mercedes-Benz Vario O810	Plaxton Beaver 2	B27F	1997	
817	R107GNW	Mercedes-Benz Vario O814	Plaxton Beaver 2	B27F	1998	
818	R108GNW	Mercedes-Benz Vario O814	Plaxton Beaver 2	B27F	1998	
819	M152LPL	Mercedes-Benz 709D	Plaxton Beaver	B25F	1995	Metrobus, 1998

Previous registrations:

R815LFV   R816LFV   R816LFV   R815LFV

Livery: Yellow and red; yellow and black (HandyBus).

Knott End is the setting for this picture of Phoenix M152LPL, a 1998 acquisition from Metrobus. The all-Mercedes fleet operate a franchise for Blackpool Buses and the vehicles involved on this route carry *HandyBus* livery and lettering. *Paul Wigan*

PILKINGTON

R M & J Pilkington, 135 Blackburn Road, Accrington, BB5 0AA

7	PIB5507	Leyland National 10351/1R		B41F	1975	Transol, Handsworth, 1994
12	PIL7012	Leyland National 11351A/1R		B49F	1978	Arriva North West, 1998
13	PIL7013	Leyland National 2 NL116L11/1R		B52F	1980	Arriva North West, 1998
14	PIB7014	Leyland National 10351B/1R		B44F	1979	North Western, 1996
17	PIL6617	Leyland National 11351A/1R		B49F	1979	Brewers, 1998
23	PIB5823	Leyland National 11351A/1R		B49F	1978	Stagecoach East Midland, 1997
33	PIB4033	Leyland National 10351B/1R		B44F	1979	North Western, 1996
34	PIB6434	Leyland National 10351B/1R		B44F	1978	Stagecoach Midland Red, 1997
41	PIL5941	Leyland National 2 NL106AL11/1R		B44F	1981	Arriva North West, 1998
45	PIB6945	Leyland National 11351/1R		B49F	1975	Brook, Werneth, 1993
46	PIL9546	Leyland National 2 NL106AL11/1R		B44F	1981	Arriva North West, 1998
51	PIB9051	Leyland National 2 NL116L11/1R		B49F	1980	Cherry, Bootle, 1998
52	PIB5952	Leyland National 11351A/1R		B49F	1979	Thamesway, 1995
56	PIB7256	Leyland National 10351A/1R		B44F	1979	Glynn Williams, Crosskeys, 1997
60	PIL8560	Leyland National 2 NL116HLXB/1R		B52F	1982	Stagecoach North West, 1999
67	PIB6667	Leyland National 11351/1R		B52F	1973	Cooper, Dukinfield, 1995
76	PIB8076	Leyland National 11351A/1R		B49F	1977	MTL (Merseybus), 1995
82	PIB9482	Leyland National 11351A/1R		B49F	1977	Glyn Williams, Crosskeys, 1997
83	PIL2083	Leyland National 11351A/1R		B49F	1979	Brewers, 1998
86	PIL2086	Leyland National 11351A/1R		B49F	1978	Britannia Travel, Telford, 1998
88	PIB3488	Leyland National 11351A/1R(Volvo)		B49F	1979	Black Prince, Morley, 1998
125	PIB1125	Leyland Leopard PSU3B/4R	Duple Dominant IV (1981)	C51F	1975	Barry Raybould, Walsall, 1996
301	PIB8301	Bedford YLQ	Duple Dominant II	C45F	1978	Bond, Willington, 1992
514	TJI7514	Leyland Tiger TRCTL11/2R	Eastern Coach Works B51	BC49F	1982	Hellyers, Fareham, 1998
M90	PIB4290	Renault-Dodge S56	Alexander AM	B25F	1987	Stephenson, Easingwold, 1996

Pictured passing through Rawtenstall is Pilkington's B51XFV, a Dennis Falcon latterly with Arriva North West. As we went to press this vehicle received the inevitable PIL mark - PIL9738. Route 464 is the principal Accrington to Bacup service on which Pilkington now operate together, in part, with Rossendale and First Manchester. *Paul Wigan*

The Leyland National dominates the Pilkington fleet. Most of these now carry index plates in the PIB/PIL series. Number 46, PIL9546, is seen on the 464 service and was new to Ribble, becoming North Western when the fleet was divided under NBC management. *Paul Wigan*

GLJ682N	Leyland National 11351/1R		DP48F	1975	Zak's, Birmingham, 1999
HNL157N	Leyland National 11351/1R		B52F	1975	Zak's, Birmingham, 1999
OOX807R	Leyland National 11351/1R (DAF)		B50F	1977	Arriva North West, 1999
XYS596S	Leyland National 11351A/1R (DAF)		B52F	1978	Arriva North West, 1999
GMB379T	Leyland National 11353A/1R		B49F	1978	Arriva North West, 1998
MIL5581	Leyland National 10351/1R		B41F	1978	Arriva North West, 1999
PIL2108	Leyland National 10351B/1R		B44F	1979	Linkstar, Craven Arms, 1998
BYW402V	Leyland National 10351A/2R (Volvo)		B44F	1979	Arriva North West, 1999
ODM680V	Leyland National 10351B/1R		B44F	1979	McLaughlin, Penwortham, 1999
YRN815V	Leyland National 2 NL106L11/1R		B44F	1980	Cherry, Bootle, 1999
DBV835W	Leyland National 2 NL106L11/1R		B44F	1980	Cherry, Bootle, 1999
PIB8225	Leyland Leopard PSU3F/4R	Willowbrook 008	C47F	1981	Red & White, 1992
PIL9738	Dennis Falcon H SDA413	East Lancashire	BC40F	1985	Arriva Manchester, 1999
PIB1433	Freight Rover Sherpa	Carlyle	B20F	1986	Ashworth, Moreton, 1994
PIB3705	Renault-Dodge S56	Alexander AM	B25F	1987	Stephenson, Easingwold, 1996
PIB6485	Renault-Dodge S56	Northern Counties	BC20F	1987	Fylde, 1994
PIB8991	Renault-Dodge S56	Northern Counties	B20F	1987	Mapleshaw, Newcastle, 1993
PIB9062	Freight Rover Sherpa	Dormobile	B16F	1987	Russell, Darwen, 1994
D429NNA	Renault-Dodge S46	Northern Counties	B22F	1987	Midland, Cannock, 1997

Previous registrations:

MIL5581	LPB209P	PIB6667	MAN14A, CNB432M	PIL2083	AWN812V
PIB1125	KDB672P, SND88X, PIB5073	PIB6945	GVV888N	PIL2086	TOF683S
PIB1433	D55TLV	PIB7014	MCA675T	PIL2108	MCA678T
PIB3488	BVP766V	PIB7256	YDW401T	PIL5941	LFR869X
PIB3705	D898DSF	PIB8076	XCW956R	PIL6617	OEP794R
PIB4033	JTU 582T	PIB8225	KWO559X	PIL7012	GMB386T
PIB4290	D830RYS	PIB8301	APT891S	PIL7013	AFM2W
PIB5507	HJA129N, PIB7382	PIB8991	D884MDB	PIL8560	WAO398Y
PIB5823	VKU73S	PIB9051	VBG95V	PIL9546	LFR867X
PIB5952	BNO669T, PIB5513	PIB9062	D743LKE	PIL9738	B51XFV
PIB6434	WFR392V	PIB9482	CBV790S	TJI7514	TPC111X
PIB6485	D106AFV				

Depot: Argyle Street

PRESTON

Preston Bus Ltd, 221 Deepdale Road, Preston, PR1 6NY

1-10			Optare MetroRider MR37		Optare			B25F	1994-95		
1	M401TCK	3	M403TCK	5	M405TCK	7	M407TCK	9	M409TCK
2	M402TCK	4	M404TCK	6	M406TCK	8	M408TCK	10	M410TCK

11-16			Optare MetroRider MR37		Optare			B25F	1996		
11	P411TFR	13	P413TFR	14	P414TFR	15	P415TFR	16	P416TFR
12	P412TFR								

17-40			Optare MetroRider MR17		Optare			B29F	1995-98		
17	R417RCW	22	N422GBV	27	N427GBV	32	R432NFR	37	R437NFR
18	R418RCW	23	N423GBV	28	N428GBV	33	R433NFR	38	R438RCW
19	R419RCW	24	N424GBV	29	N429GBV	34	R434NFR	39	R439RCW
20	N420GBV	25	N425GBV	30	N430GBV	35	R435NFR	40	R440RCW
21	N421GBV	26	N426GBV	31	N431GBV	36	R436NFR		

43-74			Renault-Dodge S56		Northern Counties			B22F	1987-88		
43	D43AFV	54	D754YCW	62	D762YCW	72	D72AFV	74	D74AFV
51	D751YCW	61	D761YCW	64	D764YCW	73	D73AFV		

Recent developments at Preston Bus have seen Renault-Dodge minibuses replaced byOptare MetroRiders, and as we go to press the first of seven Dennis Tridents are awaited. Pictured opposite are MetroRider 19, R419RCW and Leyland Lynx 212, F212YHG. Pictured below is Eastern Coach Works-bodied Leyland Olympian 135, G35OCK, one of four purchased in 1990. *Paul Wigan*

77-92

		Renault-Dodge S56		Northern Counties		B25F		1988-89	
77	E77LFR	89	F89UHG	90	F90UHG	91	F91AHG	92	F92AHG
88	F88UHG								

101	H101BFR	Leyland Olympian ON2R50C13Z4 Northern Counties Palatine	B47/30F	1991	
102	H102BFR	Leyland Olympian ON2R50C13Z4 Northern Counties Palatine	B47/30F	1991	
103	H103BFR	Leyland Olympian ON2R50C13Z4 Northern Counties Palatine	B47/30F	1991	
104	H104BFR	Leyland Olympian ON2R50C13Z4 Northern Counties Palatine	B47/30F	1991	
106	J976PRW	Leyland Olympian ON2R50C13Z4 Leyland	B47/31F	1991	Volvo bus demonstrator, 1992

107-114

		Leyland Olympian ON2R50C13Z4 Leyland			B47/31F*		1991-92	*107/14 are BC43/29F	
107	J107KCW	109	J109KCW	112	J112 KCW	113	J113 KCW	114	J114 KCW
108	J108KCW	110	J110KCW						

132	F32AHG	Leyland Olympian ONCL10/2RZ Northern Counties	B51/34F	1989	
133	A33MRN	Leyland Olympian ONTL11/2R Eastern Coach Works	B47/25F	1984	
134	G34OCK	Leyland Olympian ONCL10/1RZ Eastern Coach Works	BC43/29F	1990	
135	G35OCK	Leyland Olympian ONCL10/1RZ Eastern Coach Works	BC43/29F	1990	
136	G36OCK	Leyland Olympian ONCL10/1RZ Eastern Coach Works	B47/31F	1990	
137	G37OCK	Leyland Olympian ONCL10/1RZ Eastern Coach Works	B47/31F	1990	

141-150

		Leyland Atlantean AN68A/2R		Alexander AL		B49/36F		1980	
141	UHG141V	143	UHG143V	145	UHG145V	148	UHG148V	150	UHG150V
142	UHG142V	144	UHG144V	147	UHG147V	149	UHG149V		

152	GBV152W	Leyland Atlantean AN68B/2R	East Lancashire	B50/36F	1981	
156	GBV156W	Leyland Atlantean AN68B/2R	East Lancashire	B50/36F	1981	

158-165

		Leyland Atlantean AN68C/2R		East Lancashire		B50/36F		1982	
158	OBV158X	161	OBV161X	163	OBV163X	164	OBV164X	165	OBV165X
159	OBV159X	162	OBV162X						

166-177

		Leyland Atlantean AN68D/2R		East Lancashire		B50/36F		1982-83	
166	URN166Y	169	URN169Y	172	URN172Y	174	DRN174Y	176	DRN176Y
167	URN167Y	170	URN170Y	173	DRN173Y	175	DRN175Y	177	DRN177Y
168	URN168Y	171	URN171Y						

181	DRN1Y	Leyland Atlantean AN68D/2R	East Lancashire	B45/29F	1983	
182	DRN2Y	Leyland Atlantean AN68D/2R	East Lancashire	B45/29F	1983	

190-196

		Dennis Trident 2		East Lancashire		N / F		1999	
190	V190EBV	192	V192EBV	194	V194EBV	195	V195EBV	196	V196EBV
191	V191EBV	193	V193EBV						

210	F210YHG	Leyland Lynx LX112L10ZR1R	Leyland	B47F	1989	
211	F211YHG	Leyland Lynx LX112L10ZR1R	Leyland	B47F	1989	
212	F212YHG	Leyland Lynx LX112L10ZR1R	Leyland	BC45F	1989	
213	F213YHG	Leyland Lynx LX112L10ZR1R	Leyland	BC45F	1989	

214-218

		Leyland Lynx LX2R11C15Z4R		Leyland		BC45F		1989	
214	G214KRN	215	G215KRN	216	G216KRN	217	G217KRN	218	G218KRN

223-229

		Leyland Lynx LX2R11C15Z4R		Leyland		BC45F		1990	
223	H23YBV	226	H26YBV	227	H27YBV	228	H28YBV	229	H29YBV
224	H24YBV								

309	PRN 909	Leyland Tiger TRBTL11/2RP	Duple 320	C51F	1987	

Previous Registrations:

PRN909	D40AFV

Livery: Blue and ivory

REDLINE COACHES

R G H & S R Nuttall, 83 Bispham Avenue, Leyland, PR5 3QE

LRN695N	Leyland AN68/1R	Roe	B43/33F	1975	Whittaker, Penwortham, 1998
LFR399W	Volvo B58-56	Plaxton Supreme IV	C53F	1980	Whittaker, Penwortham, 1999
LFJ854W	Bristol VRT/SL3/6LXB	Eastern Coach Works	B43/31F	1980	Tim's Travel, Sheerness, 1998
LFJ868W	Bristol VRT/SL3/6LXB	Eastern Coach Works	B43/31F	1981	Tim's Travel, Sheerness, 1999
12RED	Volvo B10M-61	Plaxton Supreme V	C53F	1982	McKendry, Loanhead, 1998
D210OKY	Mercedes-Benz 709D	Reeve Burgess	B20F	1986	Fishwick, Leyland, 1996
LIL4492	Volvo B10M-61	Plaxton Paramount 3500 III	C53FT	1987	Patterson, Birmingham, 1995
E183GRG	Leyland TRCTL11/3RZ	Plaxton Paramount 3500 III	C48FT	1987	Go-Ahead (OK), 1998
F744FDV	Mercedes-Benz 709D	Reeve Burgess Beaver	BC25F	1988	Stagecoach Devon, 1999
44NN	Volvo B10M-61	Plaxton Paramount 3500 III	C57F	1989	School Bus Scotland, 1999
15RED	Volvo B10M-60	Van Hool Alizée HE	C53F	1993	Clarkes of London, 1994
6RED	Volvo B10M-62	Van Hool Alizée HE	C51FT	1995	
16RED	Volvo B10M-62	Plaxton Premiere 350	C51FT	1995	
R18RED	Volvo B10M-62	Van Hool Alizée HE	C49FT	1997	
R22RED	Scania L94IB	Irizar InterCentury 12.32	C49FT	1998	
R60RED	Volvo B10M-62	Van Hool Alizée HE	C49F	1998	
S18RED	Mercedes-Benz Vario O810	Plaxton Beaver 2	B27F	1999	
T9RED	Scania L94IB	Van Hool Alizée II	C49FT	1999	

Previous registrations:

6RED	M137SKY	E183GRG	E131CTN, JSK327, E183GRG, ESK982
12RED	VWX367X, 4831WA, BUA158X, 8868VC, OUH578X	LIL4492	D782SGB
15RED	KDZ6277, KSK953, L755YNS	LRN695N	HWT45N, PAZ5463
16RED	N684BEO, 44SN	44NN	F644UVT

Depot: 4 Crossley House Trading Estate, Penwortham

In addition to its coaching activities, Redline provide vehicles for several school contracts in the Preston and Leyland areas for which three double-deck buses are owned. Shown here during a heavy burst of rain are Bristol VR LFJ868W and Roe-bodied Atlantean LRN695N.

ROBINSONS

Ribblesdale Coachways Ltd, Park Garage, Great Harwood, Lancashire, BB6 7SP

237	H237AFV	DAF MB230LT615	Van Hool Alizée H	C49FT	1991
238	H238AFV	DAF MB230LT615	Van Hool Alizée H	C49FT	1991
239	H239AFV	DAF MB230LT615	Van Hool Alizée H	C49FT	1991
240	H240AFV	DAF MB230LT615	Van Hool Alizée H	C49FT	1991
241	H241AFV	DAF MB230LT615	Van Hool Alizée H	C49FT	1991
242	H242AFV	DAF MB230LT615	Van Hool Alizée H	C49FT	1991
243	J243LFR	DAF MB230LT615	Van Hool Alizée H	C49FT	1992
243	J244LFR	DAF MB230LT615	Van Hool Alizée H	C49FT	1992
244	J245LFR	DAF MB230LT615	Van Hool Alizée H	C49FT	1992
246	J246LFR	DAF MB230LT615	Van Hool Alizée H	C49FT	1992
247	J247LFR	DAF MB230LT615	Van Hool Alizée H	C49FT	1992
248	L248JBV	Volvo B10M-62	Jonckheere Deauville 45	C48FT	1994
249	L249JBV	Volvo B10M-62	Jonckheere Deauville 45	C48FT	1994
250	L250JBV	Volvo B10M-62	Jonckheere Deauville 45	C48FT	1994
251	N251KFR	Volvo B10M-62	Plaxton Première 350	C49FT	1996
252	N252KFR	Volvo B10M-62	Plaxton Première 350	C49FT	1996
253	N253KFR	Volvo B10M-62	Plaxton Première 350	C49FT	1996
254	N254KFR	Volvo B10M-62	Plaxton Première 350	C49FT	1996
255	P255YFR	Volvo B10M-62	Plaxton Première 350	C49FT	1997
256	P256YFR	Volvo B10M-62	Plaxton Première 350	C49FT	1997
257	P257YFR	Volvo B10M-62	Plaxton Première 350	C49FT	1997
258	S258JFR	Volvo B10M-62	Plaxton Excalibur	C49FT	1998
259	S259JFR	Volvo B10M-62	Plaxton Excalibur	C49FT	1998
260	S260JFR	Volvo B10M-62	Plaxton Excalibur	C49FT	1998

Livery:- Green and black or blue and black

Respected for its distinctive livery, even after a 1990's make-over and its quality touring programme, Robinsons coaches can be found across the British Isles and on European Tours. Pictured while on tour in Tenby is Plaxton Première 350 number 252, N252KFR. *Byron Gage*

ROBINSON'S

P R Elliott, Station Road Garage, Appleby-in-Westmorland, Cumbria CA16 6TX

CHA460K	Leyland Leopard PSU3B/4R	Plaxton Panorama	C47F	1971	Midland Red, 1981
SWS768S	Bristol LH6L	Eastern Coach Works	B45F	1978	Bristol, 1984
KBD21V	Bristol LHS6L	Eastern Coach Works	BC35F	1979	Bedlington, Ashington, 1994
4761TR	DAF MB200DKTL600	Plaxton Supreme IV	C57F	1980	Harris Bus, West Thurrock, 1991
3927TR	Volvo B58-56	Plaxton Supreme IV	C53F	1980	Hilton, Newton-le-Willows, 1995
NUS333Y	Bedford YNT	Wright TT	B53F	1983	Goodwin, Stockport, 1991
A745DRM	Volkswagen Transporter	Devon Conversions	M10	1984	private owner, 1990
9884TR	DAF MB200DKFL600	LAG Galaxy	C51F	1985	
F842EHH	Ford Transit VE6	Mellor	M16	1988	Swallow, Sheffield, 1989
990ENR	Volvo B10M-61	Van Hool Alizée H	C53F	1988	Excelsior, 1991
M785PAO	LDV 400	LDV	M16	1995	
R357URM	LDV Convoy	LDV	M16	1998	

Previous registrations:

990ENR	E303OPR, XEL55S, E406SEL	4761TR	NEV773V, SIB2632
3927TR	LUA255V, AJF405A, SIB2633	9884TR	From new

Livery: Silver, green and black

The depot of Robinson's, Appleby-in-Westmorland, is located near one of the rail stations on the Settle-Carlisle line. The fleet includes two Bristol LH buses that are used on school services and Van Hool Alizée-bodied Volvo 990ENR is pictured here. *Bill Potter*

ROSSENDALE

Rossendale Transport Ltd ; Ellen Smith (Tours) Ltd, 35 Bacup Road, Rawtenstall, BB4 7NG

7	E674DCU	MCW MetroRider MF150/62	MCW	B23F	1987	Moor-Dale, Newcastle, 1990
8	E248UWR	MCW MetroRider MF150/80	MCW	B23F	1988	Yorkshire Rider, 1993
11	L911ECW	Optare MetroRider MR09	Optare	B23F	1993	
12	L912ECW	Optare MetroRider MR09	Optare	B23F	1993	
13	L813KCW	Optare MetroRider MR31	Optare	B25F	1994	
14	L814KCW	Optare MetroRider MR31	Optare	B25F	1994	
15	P915XUG	Optare MetroRider MR31	Optare	B23F	1997	
16	P916XUG	Optare MetroRider MR31	Optare	B23F	1997	

17-26

				Dennis Dart 8.5SDL3003	Carlyle Dartline		B25F	1990	Metroline, 1997-98

17	H117MOB	19	H119MOB	21	H621MOM	23	H110MOB	25	H115MOB
18	H611MOM	20	H620MOM	22	H108MOB	24	H113MOB	26	H116MOB

29	M529RHG	Volvo Olympian YN2RV18Z4	Alexander Royale	B43/29F	1994	
30	M530RHG	Volvo Olympian YN2RV18Z4	Alexander Royale	B43/29F	1994	
31	B101PHC	Leyland Olympian ONLXCT/2R	East Lancashire	B47/35F	1985	Stevensons, 1993
32	B102PHC	Leyland Olympian ONLXCT/2R	East Lancashire	B47/35F	1985	Stevensons, 1993
33	B183FDM	Volvo Citybus B10M-50	East Lancashire	BC45/33F	1985	The Wright Company, Wrexham,'93

34-38

				Leyland Olympian ON2R50C13Z4*	Leyland		B47/51F	1989	London United, 1999
									*34 is ONCL10/1RZ

34	G304UYT	35	G307UYT	36	G312UYT	37	G313UYT	38	G314UYT

39-150

				Leyland Olympian ONLXB/1RH	Eastern Coach Works		B42/30F	1986	London Central, 1998

39	C39CHM	41	C34CHM	44	C84CHM	46	C96CHM	49	C89CHM
40	C40CHM	43	C93CHM	45	C85CHM	48	C88CHM	50	C90CHM

42	F115YWO	MCW MetroRider MF151/103	MCW	BC23F	1988	Rhondda, 1995
51	NSU181	MCW MetroRider MF150/9	MCW	BC25F	1986	Patrick Collection, Bimingham, 1992
54	J584CUB	Optare MetroRider MR07	Optare	BC25F	1992	Apcoa, Sunbury, 1999
57	J587CUB	Optare MetroRider MR07	Optare	BC25F	1992	Apcoa, Sunbury, 1999
58	J588CUB	Optare MetroRider MR07	Optare	BC25F	1992	Apcoa, Sunbury, 1999
59	J589CUB	Optare MetroRider MR07	Optare	BC25F	1992	Apcoa, Sunbury, 1999
64	F164DET	MCW MetroRider MF150/120	MCW	B25F	1989	Liverbus, 1993
66	G728JJC	Volvo B10M-55	Plaxton Derwent 2	BC53F	1989	Goodwin, Eccles, 1999
67	G727JJC	Volvo B10M-55	Plaxton Derwent 2	BC53F	1989	Goodwin, Eccles, 1999
68	F338VSD	Volvo B10M-56	Duple 300	B53F	1988	Hutchison, Overtown, 1997
69	F339VSD	Volvo B10M-56	Duple 300	B53F	1988	Hutchison, Overtown, 1997
70	PJI9170	Leyland Leopard PSU4D/2R	East Lancashire EL2000 (1993)	B47F	1977	National Welsh, 1989
71	PJI9171	Leyland Leopard PSU4D/2R	East Lancashire EL2000 (1993)	B47F	1977	National Welsh, 1989
72	PJI9172	Volvo B10M-61	Duple Dominant	B53F	1987	Allander, Milngavie, 1997
73	PJI9173	Volvo B10M-61	East Lancashire EL2000 (1992)	B51F	1981	Allander, Milngavie, 1997
74	PJI9174	Leyland Tiger TRCTL11/3R	East Lancashire EL2000 (1993)	B53F	1981	Allander, Milngavie, 1997
75	PJI9175	Leyland Leopard PSU3E/4R	East Lancashire EL2000 (1993)	BC49F	1980	Blue Bus, Horwich1993
76	PJI9176	Leyland Leopard PSU3E/4R	East Lancashire EL2000 (1992)	B51F	1977	South Lancs, St Helens, 1993
77	PJI9177	Leyland Leopard PSU3C/4R	East Lancashire EL2000 (1992)	B51F	1977	Ellen Smith, Rochdale, 1991
78	PJI9178	Leyland Leopard PSU3E/4R	East Lancashire EL2000 (1992)	B51F	1979	Ribble, 1987
79	PJI9179	Leyland Leopard PSU3E/4R	East Lancashire EL2000 (1992)	B51F	1980	Cooper, Stockton Heath, 1980

Opposite: **Representing the Rossendale fleet are two East Lancashire-bodied Leylands. The upper picture shows Tiger 92, F92XBV at Burnley, while the lower view shows Olympian 32, B102PHC which was new to Stevensons of Burton on Trent. The Rossendale fleet has undergone several changes recently, including the disposal of some MetroRiders and the re-numbering of former London Buses Olympians so the fleet numbers match their index marks.** *Bill Potter/Paul Wigan*

Pictured in the Derbyshire village of Tideswell is Volvo Olympian 29, M529RHG. One of a pair that carry Alexander Royale bodywork, it was heading for Crich as part of the Peak Bus network. Noticeably, the lower deck appears rather full, while many seats remain unoccupied on the upper deck. *Tony Wilson*

80-91				Dennis Dart 8.5SDL3003			Carlyle Dartline			B25F	1990	Metroline, 1997-98	
80	H118MOB	83	H109MOB	86	H114MOB	88	H128MOB	90	H130MOB				
81	H102MOB	84	H120MOB	87	H127MOB	89	H129MOB	91	H131MOB				
82	H104MOB	85	H112MOB										

92	F92XBV	Leyland Tiger TRBTL11/2RP	East Lancashire	BC49F	1989	
93	F93XBV	Leyland Tiger TRBTL11/2RP	East Lancashire	B51F	1989	
94	F94XBV	Leyland Tiger TRBTL11/2RP	East Lancashire	B51F	1989	
95	F95XBV	Leyland Tiger TRBTL11/2RP	East Lancashire	B51F	1989	
101	H101VFV	Dennis Dart 9.0SDL3002	Duple/Carlyle Dartline	B36F	1990	
102	H102VFV	Dennis Dart 9.0SDL3002	Duple/Carlyle Dartline	B36F	1990	
103	H103VFV	Dennis Dart 9.0SDL3002	Duple/Carlyle Dartline	B36F	1990	
104	H104CHG	Dennis Dart 9.0SDL3002	Reeve Burgess Pointer	B35F	1991	
105	H105CHG	Dennis Dart 9.0SDL3002	Reeve Burgess Pointer	B35F	1991	

106-113				Dennis Dart SLF			East Lancashire Spryte			N28F	1996-97	
106	N106LCK	108	N108LCK	110	N110LCK	112	P212DCK	113	P213DCK			
107	N107LCK	109	N109LCK	111	P211DCK							

114-123				Dennis Dart SLF			Plaxton Pointer SPD			N40F	1998	
114	S114KRN	116	S116KRN	118	S118KRN	120	S120KRN	122	S122KRN			
115	S115KRN	117	S117KRN	119	S119KRN	121	S121KRN	123	S123KRN			

126	L26FNE	Dennis Dart 9.8SDL3035	Marshall C37	B40F	1994	Mayne, Clayton, 1998
127	L27FNE	Dennis Dart 9.8SDL3035	Marshall C37	B40F	1994	Mayne, Clayton, 1998
128	K28XBA	Dennis Dart 9.8SDL3012	Marshall C27	B40F	1992	Mayne, Clayton, 1998
129	K29XBA	Dennis Dart 9.8SDL3012	Marshall C27	B40F	1993	Mayne, Clayton, 1998

130	A752NNA	Leyland Atlantean AN68D/1R	Northern Counties	B43/32F	1984	Stagecoach Manchester, 1997
131	A741NNA	Leyland Atlantean AN68D/1R	Northern Counties	B43/32F	1984	Stagecoach Manchester, 1997
133	FVR259V	Leyland Atlantean AN68A/1R	Northern Counties	B43/32F	1979	GM South, 1996
134	MNC521W	Leyland Atlantean AN68A/1R	Northern Counties	B43/32F	1980	GM South, 1996
199	E764KJX	Peugeot Talbot Freeway	Talbot	B15FL	1988	Employment Service, 1995
231	T231JNC	Volkswagen Caravelle	Volkswagen	M8	1999	
232	T232JNC	Volkswagen Caravelle	Volkswagen	M8	1999	
300	N300EST	Dennis Javelin 12SDA2159	Plaxton Première 350	C48FT	1995	
303	OIB5403	Leyland Tiger TRCTL11/3RZ	Plaxton Paramount 3200 II	C53F	1985	Ellen Smith, Rochdale, 1991
312	NXI 812	Volvo B10MT-53	Van Hool Astral	C48FT	1989	Viscount Central, Burnley, 1999
320	RJI8720	Volvo B10M-61	Van Hool Alizée H	C53F	1989	Shearings, 1993
322	RJI8722	Volvo B10M-61	Van Hool Alizée H	C53F	1987	Clarkson, South Elmsall, 1993
323	RJI8723	Volvo B10M-61	Van Hool Alizée H	C49FT	1989	Limebourne, Battersea, 1994
333	N333EST	Dennis Javelin 12SDA2171	Neoplan Transliner	C50FT	1996	
341	T341NBV	Bova FHD 12.340	Bova Futura	C49FT	1999	
342	T342NBV	Bova FHD 12.340	Bova Futura	C49FT	1999	
343	T343NBV	Bova FHD 12.340	Bova Futura	C49FT	1999	
343	R343HCW	Ford Galaxy	Ford	M7	1997	
344	T344NBV	Bova FHD 12.340	Bova Futura	C49FT	1999	
347	M347MCY	Dennis Javelin 12SDA2134	Berkhof Excellence 1000L	C50FT	1994	Diamond-Glantawe, Morriston, 1998
348	M348MCY	Dennis Javelin 12SDA2134	Berkhof Excellence 1000L	C50FT	1994	Diamond-Glantawe, Morriston, 1998
380	LIB1180	Leyland Leopard PSU5D/4R	Plaxton Paramount 3200 III('88)	C53F	1980	Border Buses, Burnley, 1993
382	VOY182X	Leyland Tiger TRCTL11/2R	Plaxton Viewmaster IV Express	C53F	1981	Border Buses, Burnley, 1996
570	R570ANB	Volkswagen Caravelle	Volkswagen	M8	1998	
980	P980JEC	Ford Galaxy	Ford	M7	1997	

Previous Registrations:

G727JJC	G900MNS, WSV553	G728JJC	G899MNS, WSV550	RJI8720	F763ENE
LIB1180	BUH225V, AAL468A	PJI9173	NCS117W	PJI9176	VAJ784S
NSU181	D87EDH	PJI9174	BSG551W	PJI9178	WCK123V
NXI812	G827UMU	PJI9177	UGG369R	PJI9179	GRF268V
N333EST	N585AWJ	PJI9170	PHB362R	RJI8722	D561MVR, MIW2422, D709 NYG
OIB5403	B887WRJ	PJI9171	PHB363R	RJI8723	F887SMU
PJI9172	D376RHS	PJI9175	WCK139V		

Named Vehicles:- 114 *Valley Tourer*, 115 *Valley Tripper*, 116 *Valley Shopper*, 117 *Valley Wanderer*, 118 *Valley Traveller*, 119 *Valley Venturer*, 120 *Valley Rover*, 121 *Valley Commuter*, 122 *Valley Explorer*, 123 *Valley Rambler*

Livery: Cream and maroon (buses) ; red and white (coaches)

Allocations: Rochdale (Mandale Park) and Buxton outstaion: 54/8, 66/7, 70/2-8, 80-91, 101-13, 231/2, 300-82, 570, 980. Rawtenstall (Bacup Road) and Burnley outstation - remainder

Valley Traveller **is the name applied to low-floor Dennis Dart 118, S118KRN, one of a batch of eight delivered in 1998. These Darts carry Plaxton Pointer SPD bodywork, a product commisioned by Plaxton using a special specification of the Dennis Dart SLF chassis.**
Paul Wigan

SHEARINGS

Shearings Ltd, Miry Lane, Wigan WN3 4AG

101-116

Volvo B10M-62 · Van Hool Alizée II · C46FT · 1999

101	T101JBA	105	T105JBA	108	T108JBA	111	T197JBA	114	T114JBA
102	T102JBA	106	T106JBA	109	T109JBA	112	T112JBA	115	T115JBA
103	T103JBA	107	T107JBA	110	T110JBA	113	T113JBA	116	T116JBA
104	T104JBA								

117-122

Volvo B10M-62 · Jonckheere Mistral 45 · C46FT · 1999

117	T117JBA	119	T119JBA	120	T120JBA	121	T198JBA	122	T122JBA
118	T118JBA								

123-132

Volvo B10M-62 · Jonckheere Mistral 45 · C50F · 1999

123	T199JBA	125	T125JBA	127	T127JBA	129	T129JBA	131	T131JBA
124	T124JBA	126	T126JBA	128	T128JBA	130	T130JBA	132	T132JBA

451-476

Volvo B10M-60 · Van Hool Alizée HE · C46FT · 1993

451	K451VVR	457	K457VVR	462	K462VVR	467	K467VVR	472	K472VVR
452	K452VVR	458	K458VVR	463	K463VVR	468	K468VVR	473	K473VVR
453	K453VVR	459	K459VVR	464	K464VVR	469	K469VVR	474	K474VVR
454	K454VVR	460	K460VVR	465	K465VVR	470	K470VVR	475	K475VVR
455	K455VVR	461	K461VVR	466	K466VVR	471	K471VVR	476	K476VVR
456	K456VVR								

486-495

Volvo B10M-60 · Van Hool Alizée HE · C53F · 1993

486	K486VVR	488	K488VVR	490	K490VVR	492	K492VVR	494	K494VVR
487	K487VVR	489	K489VVR	491	K491VVR	493	K493VVR	495	K495VVR

496	K496VVR	Volvo B10M-62	Van Hool Alizée HE	C53F	1993

561-569

Scania K113CRB · Van Hool Alizée HE · C46FT · 1994

561	L561FND	563	L563FND	565	L565FND	567	L567FND	569	L569FND
562	L562FND	564	L564FND	566	L566FND	568	L568FND		

570	L570FND	Volvo B10M-62	Plaxton Excalibur	C46FT	1994

631-688

Volvo B10M-62 · Van Hool Alizée HE · C46FT · 1995

631	M631KVU	643	M643KVU	655	M655KVU	667	M667KVU	678	M678KVU
632	M632KVU	644	M644KVU	656	M656KVU	668	M668KVU	679	M679KVU
633	M633KVU	645	M645KVU	657	M657KVU	669	M669KVU	680	M680KVU
634	M634KVU	646	M646KVU	658	M658KVU	670	M670KVU	681	M681KVU
635	M635KVU	647	M647KVU	659	M659KVU	671	M671KVU	682	M682KVU
636	M636KVU	648	M648KVU	660	M660KVU	672	M672KVU	683	M683KVU
637	M637KVU	649	M649KVU	661	M661KVU	673	M673KVU	684	M684KVU
638	M638KVU	650	M650KVU	662	M662KVU	674	M674KVU	685	M685KVU
639	M639KVU	651	M651KVU	663	M663KVU	675	M675KVU	686	M686KVU
640	M640KVU	652	M652KVU	664	M664KVU	676	M676KVU	687	M687KVU
641	M641KVU	653	M653KVU	665	M665KVU	677	M677KVU	688	M688KVU
642	M642KVU	654	M654KVU	666	SPR35				

Opposite: **Shearings offer a large programme of UK and continental tours. For the latter air conditioning and additional comforts are provided. The principal chassis provider is Volvo with recent bodywork awards being placed with rival Belgian coachbuilders Van Hool and Jonckheere. Both bodybuilders are represented here with (upper picture) the first from the 1997 delivery, 801, P801GBA and 954, R954YNF, displaying the continental door. A fleet of Ford Tourneo GLX minibuses are also used to provide occasional feeder work, and to provide crew transport.** *Cliff Beeton/Philip Stephenson*

701-720 — Volvo B10M-62 — Van Hool Alizée HE — C46FT — 1996

701	N701UVR	705	N705UVR	709	N709UVR	713	N713UVR
702	N702UVR	706	N706UVR	710	N710UVR	714	N714UVR
703	N703UVR	707	N707UVR	711	N711UVR	715	N715UVR
704	N704UVR	708	N708UVR	712	N712UVR	716	N716UVR

717	N717UVR
718	N718UVR
719	N719UVR
720	N720UVR

721-35 — Volvo B10M-62 — Jonckheere Deauville 45 — C46FT — 1996

721	N721UVR	724	N724UVR	727	N727UVR	730	N730UVR
722	N722UVR	725	N725UVR	728	N728UVR	731	N731UVR
723	N723UVR	726	N726UVR	729	N729UVR	732	N732UVR

733	N733UVR
734	N734UVR
735	N735UVR

801-35 — Volvo B10M-62 — Van Hool Alizée HE — C46FT — 1996

801	P801GBA	808	P808GBA	815	P815GBA	822	P822GBA
802	P802GBA	809	P809GBA	816	P816GBA	823	P823GBA
803	P803GBA	810	P810GBA	817	P817GBA	824	P824GBA
804	P804GBA	811	P811GBA	818	P818GBA	825	P825GBA
805	P805GBA	812	P812GBA	819	P819GBA	826	P826GBA
806	P806GBA	813	P813GBA	820	P820GBA	827	P827GBA
807	P807GBA	814	P814GBA	821	P821GBA	828	P828GBA

829	P829GBA
830	P830GBA
831	P831GBA
832	P832GBA
833	P833GBA
834	P834GBA
835	P835GBA

901-915 — Volvo B10M-62 — Van Hool Alizée HE — C46FT — 1998

901	R901YBA	904	R904YBA	907	R907YBA	910	R910YBA
902	R902YBA	905	R905YBA	908	R908YBA	911	R991ANB
903	R903YBA	906	R906YBA	909	R909YBA	912	R912YBA

913	R913YBA
914	R914YBA
915	R915YBA

916-934 — Volvo B10M-62 — Plaxton Excalibur — C50F — 1998

916	R916YBA	920	R920YBA	924	R924YBA	928	R928YBA
917	R917YBA	921	R921YBA	925	R925YBA	929	R929YBA
918	R918YBA	922	R922YBA	926	R926YBA	930	R930YBA
919	R919YBA	923	R923YBA	927	R927YBA	931	R931YBA

932	R932YBA
933	R933YBA
934	R934YBA

935-954 — Volvo B10M-62 — Jonckheere Mistral 45 — C50F — 1998

935	R935YNF	939	R939YNF	943	R943YNF	947	R947YNF
936	R936YNF	940	R940YNF	944	R944YNF	948	R948YNF
937	R937YNF	941	R941YNF	945	R945YNF	949	R949YNF
938	R938YNF	942	R942YNF	946	R946YNF	950	R950YNF

951	R951YNF
952	R952YNF
953	R953YNF
954	R954YNF

Crew transporters

M596WCW	Volkswagen Caravelle	Volkswagen	M8	1995
M771VCW	Volkswagen Caravelle	Volkswagen	M8	1995
M772VCW	Volkswagen Caravelle	Volkswagen	M8	1995
M773VCW	Volkswagen Caravelle	Volkswagen	M8	1995
M774VCW	Volkswagen Caravelle	Volkswagen	M8	1995
M776VCW	Volkswagen Caravelle	Volkswagen	M8	1995
N973JFR	Volkswagen Caravelle	Volkswagen	M8	1996
N974JFR	Volkswagen Caravelle	Volkswagen	M8	1996
N975JFR	Volkswagen Caravelle	Volkswagen	M8	1996
P652VBV	Volkswagen Caravelle	Volkswagen	M8	1996
P653VBV	Volkswagen Caravelle	Volkswagen	M8	1996
R638OTN	Ford Tourneo GLX	Ford	M8	1998
R639OTN	Ford Tourneo GLX	Ford	M8	1998
R641OTN	Ford Tourneo GLX	Ford	M8	1998
R652OTN	Ford Tourneo GLX	Ford	M8	1998
T	Ford Tourneo GLX	Ford	M8	1998
T	Ford Tourneo GLX	Ford	M8	1998
T	Ford Tourneo GLX	Ford	M8	1998
T	Ford Tourneo GLX	Ford	M8	1998

Previous Registrations:

205CCH	on retention	ESU121	on retention	WSV528	on retention
5140RU	on retention	SPR35	from new	XTW359	on retention
ESU117	on retention				

Livery: Miami blue, orange and white

SIM'S TRAVEL

William Sim & Son, Hunholme Garage, Boot, Holmrock, Cumbria, CA19 1TF

ENF555Y	Volvo B10M-61	Duple Dominant IV	C53F	1983	Shearings, 1988
F130AEL	Volvo B10M-60	Plaxton Paramount 3200 III	C57F	1989	Excelsior, Bournemouth, 1995
219DLV	DAF MB230LB615	Caetano Algarve H-NDH	C53F	1989	Abbeyways, Halifax, 1991
WXI5865	Van Hool T815H	Van Hool Alizée H	C49F	1990	Peter Carol, Bristol, 1994
H538EVM	Mercedes-Benz 408D	Made to Measure	M15	1991	
A15TVL	Volvo B10M-60	Van Hool Alizée H	C49FT	1992	Shearings, 1999
N298VRM	Mercedes-Benz 609D	Onyx	C21F	1995	
N256THO	Volvo B10M-62	Plaxton Première 320	C49FT	1996	Excelsior, Bouremouth, 1998
P505GHH	Mercedes-Benz 814D	Autobus Classique Nouvelle	BC33F	1997	
R853WRM	Ford Tourneo	Ford	M8	1997	
T953JAO	Mercedes Benz 410D	Autobus	BC16F	1999	

Previous registrations:

219DLV	F234RJX	N256THO	XEL31
A15TVL	J242NNC	WXI5865	G731XHY
F130AEL	F458WFX, A18EXC		

Livery: Red and white

A detour from the Cumbria coast, along the track of the Ravenhead and Eskdale railway brings one to the depot of Sim's Travel. This attractive part of the Lake District is home to a smart fleet of white and red coaches. Illustrated here is J242NNC, recently re-registered A15TVL, a former Shearings Volvo B10M with Van Hool Alizée bodywork. The company provide services to BNFL, the atomic energy company, both with staff transport and the operation of BNFL's own coaches used for visitors to the site. *Bill Potter*

SOUTH LANCS TRAVEL

South Lancs Travel - Green Triangle - B & D Coaches

Green Triangle Buses Ltd; B&D Coaches Ltd, Printshop Lane, Atherton, M46 9BJ

1	T11SLT	Dennis Dart SLF	Plaxton Pointer MPD	N28F	1999	
2	V2SLT	Dennis Dart SLF	Plaxton Pointer MPD	N28F	1999	
3	V3SLT	Dennis Dart SLF	Plaxton Pointer MPD	N28F	1999	
6	N796XRA	Mercedes-Benz 709D	Plaxton Beaver	B23F	1995	
7	P417HVR	Iveco TurboDaily 59.12	Mellor Solo	B27F	1997	
8	P248KND	Iveco TurboDaily 59.12	Mellor Solo	B27F	1996	
9	R399CVR	Iveco TurboDaily 59.12	Mellor Solo	B29F	1998	
10	H101EKR	Iveco Daily 49.10	Phoenix	B23F	1991	Stagecoach South (EK), 1997
11	J118LKO	Iveco Daily 49.10	Dormobile Routemaker	B25F	1991	Stagecoach South (EK), 1997
14	F914XWY	Mercedes-Benz 811D	Optare StarRider	B26F	1988	London Central, 1998
19	F919YWY	Mercedes-Benz 811D	Optare StarRider	B26F	1988	London Central, 1998
21	G121PGT	Mercedes-Benz 811D	Alexander AM	B28F	1990	HMB Services, Gateshead, 1998
30	F30CWY	Mercedes-Benz 811D	Optare StarRider	B26F	1989	London Central, 1998
42	F42CWY	Mercedes-Benz 811D	Optare StarRider	B26F	1989	London Central, 1998
48	R948AMB	Mercedes-Benz Vario O814	Plaxton Beaver 2	B31F	1998	
49	R949AMB	Mercedes-Benz Vario O814	Plaxton Beaver 2	B31F	1998	
58	N258DUR	Mercedes-Benz 709D	Plaxton Beaver	B27F	1995	Pete's Travel, West Bromwich, 1999
59	J229JJR	Renault S75	Plaxton Beaver	B28F	1991	MK Metro (Border), 1999
60	J230JJR	Renault S75	Plaxton Beaver	B28F	1991	Classic Bus, Annfield Plain, 1999
61	R661GCA	Mercedes-Benz Vario O814	Plaxton Beaver 2	B31F	1998	
65	R165ESG	Mercedes-Benz Vario O810	Plaxton Beaver 2	B29F	1997	G Bell, Silksworth, 1999
66	R166ESG	Mercedes-Benz Vario O810	Plaxton Beaver 2	B29F	1997	G Bell, Silksworth, 1999
72	M672RAJ	Mercedes-Benz 709D	ARB	B25F	1994	Go-Ahead (OK), 1999

South Lancs Travel is the newly-revived name encompassing the operations of B&D Coaches, and Green Triangle Buses which hold the operator's licences. Green Triangle names are carried on S775RNE, pictured shortly after entering service on the Leigh-Trafford Centre service. *Paul Wigan*

The latest arrival for South Lancs Transport is Dennis Dart T11SLT, which carries the new livery of yellow and dark blue. Bodywork is a Plaxton Pointer MPD, the shortened version of this popular low floor bus, which returns us full circle to the size of the original Darts in 1989. *Cliff Beeton*

111	G911RPN	Dennis Javelin 11SDL1914	Duple 300	B55F	1989	Eastbourne, 1999
112	G621CPS	Dennis Javelin 11SDL1914	Duple 300	B55F	1990	Leask, Lerwick, 1999
114	G914RPN	Dennis Javelin 11SDL1914	Duple 300	B55F	1990	Eastbourne, 1999
115	G25HDW	Dennis Javelin 11SDL1914	Duple 300	B55F	1990	Eastbourne, 1999
126	B26ADW	Leyland Tiger TRBTL11/2RP	East Lancashire	B49F	1984	South Lancashire, 1998
127	B27ADW	Leyland Tiger TRBTL11/2RP	East Lancashire	BC47F	1984	South Lancashire, 1998
154	MBZ6454	Volvo B10M-61	East Lancashire EL2000 (1991)	B55F	1985	Arriva The Shires, 1998
159	G59RND	Leyland Tiger TR2R62C16Z4	Alexander Q	B55F	1989	Border Buses, Burnley, 1999
161	G61RND	Leyland Tiger TR2R62C16Z4	Alexander Q	B55F	1989	Border Buses, Burnley, 1999
167	HIL7467	Volvo B10M-61	East Lancashire EL2000 (1991)	B55F	1983	Arriva The Shires, 1998
192	G492 XWS	Leyland Tiger TRCTL11/3LZM	Plaxton Derwent II	B54F	1989	MoD (03 KJ 25), 1998
466	AFB597V	Bristol LH6L	Eastern Coach Works	B43F	1980	Arriva North West, 1998

Previous registrations:

HIL6747	FUA387Y, 3408WY, NRV859Y	MBZ6454	B572AVW, URY598

Depots: Printshop Lane, Atherton and Findlay Street, Leigh

Note: 466 is on long term loan to MK Metro.

SPRINGFIELD COACHWAYS

W & E Trezise, 24 Douglas Bank Drive, Wigan WN6 7NH

XBF58S	Leyland Leopard PSU3E/4R	Duple Dominant I	C49F	1978	PMT, 1990
MFR420T	Ford R1114	Plaxton Supreme III	C53F	1978	Ericsway, Eccles, 1988
HIL6956	Leyland Tiger TRCTL11/2R	Plaxton Supreme V	C46F	1982	Ogden, St Helens, 1995
OIJ2645	Leyland Leopard PSU3B/4R	Duple Dominant IV	C49F	1982	Ogden, St Helens, 1995
NIW2399	Leyland Tiger TRCTL11/3RH	Duple 320	C57F	1986	Finglands, Manchester, 1996
SIB1832	Leyland Tiger TRCTL11/3RH	Duple 320	C57F	1986	Finglands, Manchester, 1996
C150LWA	Leyland Royal Tiger RT	Plaxton Paramount 3500 II	C49FT	1986	Roe, Stainforth, 1993
D359JUM	Volkswagen LT55	Optare City Pacer	B23F	1986	London Buses, 1992
RXJ318	DAF SB2300DHS585	Duple 340	C53F	1987	Crawshaw, Mansfield W, 1990
H129YGG	Mercedes-Benz 709D	Dormobile Routemaker	B29F	1991	Timeline, Bolton, 1995
P741YCK	Optare MetroRider MR15	Optare	B29F	1997	
P310XCW	Optare MetroRider MR15	Optare	B29F	1997	
R641MBV	Optare L1000	Optare Excel	N32F	1997	
R642MBV	Optare L1000	Optare Excel	N32F	1997	
R643MBV	Optare L1000	Optare Excel	N32F	1997	
R183OCW	Mercedes-Benz Vario O814	Plaxton Beaver 2	B27F	1998	
R184OCW	Mercedes-Benz Vario O814	Plaxton Beaver 2	B27F	1998	
R185OCW	Mercedes-Benz Vario O814	Plaxton Beaver 2	B27F	1998	
S764RNE	Dennis Dart SLF	Plaxton Pointer MPD	N28F	1999	
S765RNE	Dennis Dart SLF	Plaxton Pointer MPD	N28F	1999	
S766RNE	Dennis Dart SLF	Plaxton Pointer MPD	N28F	1999	

Previous registrations

HIL6956	NHL261X, JOI2949	OIJ2645	RHG911X	SIB1832	C312ENA
NIW2399	C309ENA	RJX318	D624YCX		

Depot: Frith Street, Wigan

Springfield coaches operate the *Easylink* service 630 on behalf of Wigan Metropolitan Council. Three of the vehicles in the livery for the service are Optare Excels, with three Dennis Darts being added during 1999. Pictured here is R641MBV.
Cliff Beeton

STAGECOACH CUMBERLAND

Stagecoach (North West) Ltd; Stagecoach Lancaster
2/F Broadacre House, 16-20 Lowther Street, Carlisle, CA3 8DA

1-15
Mercedes-Benz 709D　　Alexander Sprint　　B23F　　1995

1	N201UHH	4	N204UHH	7	N207UHH	10	N210UHH	13	N213UHH
2	N202UHH	5	N205UHH	8	N208UHH	11	N211UHH	14	N214UHH
3	N203UHH	6	N206UHH	9	N209UHH	12	N212UHH	15	N215UHH

16-33
Mercedes-Benz 709D　　Alexander Sprint　　B23F　　1996

16	N116YHH	20	N120YHH	24	N124YHH	28	N128YRM	31	N131YRM
17	N117YHH	21	N121YHH	25	N125YHH	29	N129YRM	32	N132YRM
18	N118YHH	22	N122YHH	26	N126YRM	30	N130YRM	33	N133YRM
19	N119YHH	23	N123YHH	27	N127YRM				

36w	D36UAO	Mercedes-Benz L608D	Reeve Burgess	B20F	1986
44w	D44UAO	Mercedes-Benz L608D	Reeve Burgess	B20F	1987
45w	D45UAO	Mercedes-Benz L608D	Reeve Burgess	B20F	1987

47-53
Mercedes-Benz 709D　　Alexander Sprint　　B25F　　1988　　51-53 ex Hampshire Bus, 1989

| 47 | E47CHH | 49 | E49CHH | 51 | E511PVV | 52 | E512PVV | 53 | E510PVV |
| 48 | E48CHH | 50 | E50CHH | | | | | | |

54-70
Mercedes-Benz 709D　　Alexander Sprint　　B23F*　　1990-91　　55-70 ex Magicbus, 1990-91
*57-9/61-4 are B25F

54	G178PAO	58	G268TSL	61	G263TSL	64	G266TSL	67	G295TSL
55	G299TSL	59	G269TSL	62	G264TSL	65	G297TSL	68	G294TSL
56	G300TSL	60	G296TSL	63	G265TSL	66	G298TSL	70	G293TSL
57	G267TSL								

71-78
Mercedes-Benz 709D　　Alexander Sprint　　B25F　　1993

| 71 | K871GHH | 73 | K873GHH | 75 | K875GHH | 77 | K877GHH | 78 | K878GHH |
| 72 | K872GHH | 74 | K874GHH | 76 | K876GHH | | | | |

The last of the Mercedes-Benz L608D minibuses are destined to depart after later models from Cambus have been transferred. Pictured at Appleby-in-Westmorland is 203, N619VSS, one of those involved. *Bill Potter*

79-86		Mercedes-Benz 709D	Alexander Sprint	B25F	1993	Ribble, 1994

79	K626UFR	81	K622UFR	83	K121XHG	85	L123DRN	86	K113XHG
80	K623UFR	82	K114XHG	84	L126DRN				

87	N327XRP	Mercedes-Benz 709D	Alexander Sprint	BC23F	1996	
88	N328XRP	Mercedes-Benz 709D	Alexander Sprint	BC23F	1996	
89	N329XRP	Mercedes-Benz 709D	Alexander Sprint	BC23F	1996	

90-96		Mercedes-Benz Vario O814	Alexander ALX100	B29F	1998	

90	S190RAO	92	S192RAO	94	S194RAO	95	S195RAO	96	S196RAO
91	S191RAO	93	S193RAO						

97	N645VSS	Mercedes-Benz 709D	Alexander Sprint	B25F	1996	Stagecoach Manchester, 1998
98	N646VSS	Mercedes-Benz 709D	Alexander Sprint	B25F	1996	Stagecoach Manchester, 1998
101	109DRM	Leyland Tiger TRCTL11/2R	Duple Laser	C50F	1984	
102	A102DAO	Leyland Tiger TRCTL11/2R	Duple Laser	C50F	1984	
103	B103HAO	Leyland Tiger TRCTL11/3RH	Duple Laser 2	C50F	1984	
105	B105HAO	Leyland Tiger TRCTL11/3RH	Duple Laser 2	C53F	1984	
106	B106HAO	Leyland Tiger TRCTL11/3RH	Duple Laser 2	C49F	1984	
109	WLT706	Leyland Tiger TRCTL11/3RH	Plaxton Paramount 3500 II	C48FT	1986	
110	WLT824	Leyland Tiger TRCTL11/3RH	Plaxton Paramount 3500 II	C46FT	1986	
111	VRR447	Leyland Tiger TRCTL11/3RH	Plaxton Paramount 3500 II	C48FT	1985	Hampshire Bus, 1988
114	PSU787	Leyland Tiger TRCTL11/3RZ	Duple Caribbean 2	C49FT	1986	East Midland, 1995
120	J120AHH	Volvo B10M-60	Plaxton Expressliner	C46FT	1991	
121	J121AHH	Volvo B10M-60	Plaxton Expressliner	C46FT	1991	

126-132		Volvo B10M-62	Plaxton Expressliner 2	C46FT	1994-95	

126	L126NAO	128	N128VAO	130	N130VAO	131	N131VAO	132	N132VAO
127	L127NAO	129	N129VAO						

133	S133KRM	Volvo B10M-62	Jonckheere Mistral 50	C44FT	1998	
134	S134KRM	Volvo B10M-62	Jonckheere Mistral 50	C44FT	1998	
135	F135SPX	Dennis Javelin 11SDL1914	Duple 300	B63F	1989	Ribble, 1997
136	F136SPX	Dennis Javelin 11SDL1914	Duple 300	B63F	1989	Ribble, 1997
137	F137SPX	Dennis Javelin 11SDL1914	Duple 300	B63F	1989	Ribble, 1997
143	L143BFV	Dennis Javelin 11SDL2129	Plaxton Première Interurban	BC47F	1993	Stagecoach Ribble, 1998
152	L152BFV	Dennis Javelin 11SDL2133	Plaxton Première Interurban	BC47F	1993	Ribble, 1997
154	L154BFV	Dennis Javelin 11SDL2133	Plaxton Première Interurban	BC47F	1993	Ribble, 1997
156	PCK335	Leyland Tiger TRCTL11/3RH	Duple Laser 2	C53F	1985	Ribble, 1989
158	DSV943	Volvo B10M-61	Plaxton Paramount 3500 III	C48FT	1987	Wallace Arnold, 1990
159	LJY145	Volvo B10M-61	Plaxton Paramount 3500 III	C48FT	1987	Ribble, 1995
160	YDG616	Volvo B10M-61	Plaxton Paramount 3500 III	C48FT	1987	Ribble, 1995
161	JPU817	Volvo B10M-61	Plaxton Paramount 3500 III	C53F	1987	Wallace Arnold, 1990
162	B162WRN	Leyland Tiger TRCTL11/3RH	Duple Laser 2	C53F	1985	Ribble, 1991
163	RIL5084	Volvo B10M-60	Plaxton Paramount 3500 III	C48FT	1990	Stagecoach Oxford, 1999

200-211		Mercedes-Benz 709D	Alexander Sprint	B25F	1996	Stagecoach Cambus, 1999

200	N614VSS	202	N617VSS	204	N641VSS	205	N613VSS	206	N616VSS
201	N615VSS	203	N619VSS						

270	L270LHH	Volvo B6-9.9M	Alexander Dash	B40F	1993	
275	L275JAO	Volvo B6-9.9M	Alexander Dash	B40F	1993	
276	L276JAO	Volvo B6-9.9M	Alexander Dash	B40F	1993	
282	L282JAO	Volvo B6-9.9M	Alexander Dash	B40F	1993	
283	M460VHE	Volvo B6-9.9M	Alexander Dash	B40F	1993	Manchester, 1997
373w	HHH373V	Leyland National 2 NL116L11/1R		B52F	1980	Ribble, 1997

Opposite: **A batch of MAN single-decks with Alexander ALX400 bodywork are currently being delivered for use on Carlisle city services. These will displace Alexander PS buses to Lancaster. Shown here are two double-deck buses. The number of Bristol VRs continues to reduce, though they can be found on normal service on West Cumbria workings. Pictured in Cockermouth while operating local service is 431, KRM431W. The lower picture shows one of the Olympians, 2192, H192WFR, in Uni-Sprint colours. This service links Morecambe with the University of Lancaster.** *Bill Potter*

Stagecoach Cumberland have lettered Plaxton Paramount 158, DSV943, for service X35 between Kendal and Barrow. The vehicle sides carry displays for several of the sponsoring firms, which are placed on a white vehicle. *Phillip Stephenson*

420-437

		Bristol VRT/SL3/6LXB		Eastern Coach Works		B43/31F	1980		
420w	FAO420V	424w	FAO424V	427	FAO427V	432	KRM432W	435	KRM435W
421w	FAO421V	425w	FAO425V	428	FAO428V	433	KRM433W	436w	KRM436W
422w	FAO422V	426w	FAO426V	431	KRM431W	434w	KRM434W	437w	KRM437W
423w	FAO423V								

449	K449YCW	Optare MetroRider MR01	Optare	B31F	1992	Ribble, 1997	
450	K450YCW	Optare MetroRider MR01	Optare	B31F	1992	Ribble, 1997	

455-463

		Volvo B10M-55		Alexander PS		B48F	1995	Ribble, 1997	
455	M455VCW	457	M457VCW	459	M459VCW	461	M461VCW	463	M463VCW
456	M456VCW	458	M458VCW	460	M460VCW	462	M462VCW		

505	LUA273V	Leyland Leopard PSU3F/4R	Plaxton Supreme IV	C51F	1980	Yeowart, Whitehaven, 1988

528-560

		Mercedes-Benz L608D		Reeve Burgess		B20F	1986	Ribble, 1989	
528	D528RCK	529	D529RCK	533	D533RCK	559	D559RCK	560	D560RCK

565	G665PHH	Mercedes-Benz 709D	Alexander Sprint	B23F	1990	Ribble, 1997
566	G566PRM	Mercedes-Benz 709D	Alexander Sprint	B23F	1990	Ribble, 1997
567	G567PRM	Mercedes-Benz 709D	Alexander Sprint	BC25F	1990	Ribble, 1997
569w	LUA275V	Leyland Leopard PSU3E/4R	Plaxton Supreme IV	C51F	1980	Kirkpatrick, Brigham, 1988
570	G570PRM	Mercedes-Benz 709D	Alexander Sprint	BC25F	1990	Stagecoach Ribble, 1998
571	G571PRM	Mercedes-Benz 709D	Alexander Sprint	BC25F	1990	Stagecoach Ribble, 1998
572	G572PRM	Mercedes-Benz 709D	Alexander Sprint	BC25F	1990	Stagecoach Ribble, 1998
592	G192PAO	Mercedes-Benz 709D	Alexander Sprint	B23F	1990	Ribble, 1997

Three Duple-bodied Dennis Javelin buses transferred from Ribble with the Lancaster and Morecambe depots, the trio spending much of their time outstationed at Garstang. Number 137, F137SPX is seen in Lancaster. Interestingly, the coloured stripes are not carried onto the roof on this vehicle. *Phillip Stephenson*

597-625

| | | | | | | Mercedes-Benz 709D | Alexander Sprint | B25F | 1993 | Ribble, 1997-98 |

597	K117XHG	604	K124XHG	615	K615UFR	619	K619UFR	625	K625UFR
602	L122DRN	607	L127DRN	618	K618UFR				

645	WAO645Y	Leyland Tiger TRCTL11/2R	Alexander TE	BC47F	1983	Ribble, 1997
649	N649VSS	Mercedes-Benz 709D	Alexander Sprint	B25F	1996	Manchester, 1998
650	N650VSS	Mercedes-Benz 709D	Alexander Sprint	B25F	1996	Manchester, 1998
651	N651VSS	Mercedes-Benz 709D	Alexander Sprint	B25F	1996	Manchester, 1998
652	N652VSS	Mercedes-Benz 709D	Alexander Sprint	B25F	1996	Manchester, 1998

699-788

| | | | | | | | | | | Volvo B10M-55 | Alexander PS | B49F* | 1992-93 | *772-788 are BC48F |

699	K699ERM	717	K717DAO	735	K735DAO	754	K754DAO	771	K771DAO
700	K700DAO	718	K718DAO	736	K736DAO	755	K755DAO	772	K772DAO
701	K701DAO	719	K719DAO	737	K737DAO	756	K756DAO	773	K773DAO
702	K702DAO	720	K720DAO	738	K738DAO	757	K757DAO	774	K774DAO
703	K703DAO	721	K721DAO	739	K739DAO	758	K758DAO	775	K775DAO
704	K704ERM	722	K722DAO	741	K741DAO	759	K759DAO	776	K776DAO
705	K705DAO	723	K723DAO	742	K742DAO	760	K760DAO	777	K777DAO
706	K706DAO	724	K724DAO	743	K743DAO	761	K761DAO	778	K778DAO
707	K707DAO	725	K725DAO	744	K744DAO	762	K762DAO	779	K779DAO
708	K708DAO	726	K726DAO	745	K745DAO	763	K763DAO	780	K780DAO
709	K709DAO	727	K727DAO	746	K746DAO	764	K764DAO	781	K781DAO
710	K710DAO	728	K728DAO	748	K748DAO	765	K765DAO	783	K783DAO
711	K711DAO	729	K729DAO	749	K749DAO	766	K766DAO	784	K784DAO
712	K712DAO	730	K730DAO	750	K750DAO	767	K767DAO	785	K785DAO
713	K713DAO	731	K731DAO	751	K751DAO	768	K768DAO	786	K786DAO
714	K714DAO	732	K732DAO	752	K752DAO	769	K769DAO	787	K787DAO
715	K715DAO	733	K733DAO	753	K753DAO	770	K770DAO	788	K788DAO
716	K716DAO	734	K734DAO						

789	N789VRM	Volvo B10M-55	Alexander PS	BC48F	1995	
790	N790VRM	Volvo B10M-55	Alexander PS	BC48F	1995	
791	R791PAO	Volvo B10M-62	Plaxton Premiere Interurban	BC51F	1997	
792	R792PAO	Volvo B10M-62	Plaxton Premiere Interurban	BC51F	1997	
793	R793URM	Volvo B10M-55	Alexander PS	B49F	1998	
794	R794URM	Volvo B10M-55	Alexander PS	B49F	1998	
795	R795URM	Volvo B10M-55	Alexander PS	B49F	1998	
796	S796KRM	Volvo B10M-62	Jonckheere Modulo	BC51F	1998	
797	S797KRM	Volvo B10M-62	Jonckheere Modulo	BC51F	1998	
798	S798KRM	Volvo B10M-62	Jonckheere Modulo	BC51F	1998	
799	S799KRM	Volvo B10M-62	Jonckheere Modulo	BC51F	1998	

801-809

		MAN 18.220 HOCLR	Alexander ALX300	N42F	1999	

801	V801DFV	803	V803DFV	806	V806DFV	808	V808DFV	809	V809DFV
802	V802DFV	804	V804DFV	807	V807DFV				

810w	TRN810V	Leyland National 10351B/1R		B44F	1979	Ribble, 1986
811	V811DFV	MAN 18.220 HOCLR	Alexander ALX300	N42F	1999	
812	V812DFV	MAN 18.220 HOCLR	Alexander ALX300	N42F	1999	
879	RHG884X	Leyland National 2 NL116AL11/1R		B52F	1982	Ribble, 1997
888w	ARN888Y	Leyland National 2 NL116HLXB/1R		B52F	1983	Ribble, 1997
900	B900WRN	Leyland Tiger TRCTL11/1R	Duple Dominant	B49F	1984	Ribble, 1997
1001	URM801Y	Leyland Olympian ONLXB/1R	Eastern Coach Works	BC45/30F	1982	
1002	URM802Y	Leyland Olympian ONLXB/1R	Eastern Coach Works	B45/32F	1982	

1003-1011

		Leyland Olympian ONLXB/2RZ	Alexander RL	B51/36F	1988	

1003	F803FAO	1005	F805FAO	1007	F807FAO	1009	F809FAO	1011	F811FAO
1004	F804FAO	1006	F806FAO	1008	F808FAO	1010	F810FAO		

1012-1019

		Leyland Olympian ON2R56G13Z4	Alexander RL	B51/34F	1990	

1012	H112SAO	1014	H114SAO	1016	H116SAO	1018	H118SAO	1019	H119SAO
1013	H113SAO	1015	H115SAO	1017	H117SAO				

1020-1027

		Leyland Olympian ON2R56G13Z4	Alexander RL	BC47/27F	1991	

1020	J120AAO	1022	J122AAO	1024	J124XHH	1026	J126XHH	1027	J127XHH
1021	J121AAO	1023	J123XHH	1025	J125XHH				

1028-1035

		Leyland Olympian ON2R50G13Z4	Alexander RL	BC43/27F	1992	

1028	K128DAO	1030	K130DAO	1032	K132DAO	1034	K134DAO	1035	K135DAO
1029	K129DAO	1031	K131DAO	1033	K133DAO				

1090	C382SAO	Leyland Olympian ONLXB/1RV	Alexander RL	B47/30F	1986	Bluebird, 1991
1091	C383SAO	Leyland Olympian ONLXB/1RV	Alexander RL	B47/30F	1986	Bluebird, 1991
1092	D384XAO	Leyland Olympian ONLXB/1RV	Alexander RL	B47/30F	1987	Bluebird, 1991
1093	D380XRS	Leyland Olympian ONLXB/1RV	Alexander RL	B47/30F	1987	Bluebird, 1992
1094	D381XRS	Leyland Olympian ONLXB/1RV	Alexander RL	B47/30F	1987	Bluebird, 1992
1103	KRN103T	Leyland Leopard PSU3E/4R	Duple Dominant II	C47F	1978	Ribble, 1989
1105	KRN105T	Leyland Leopard PSU3E/4R	Duple Dominant II	C47F	1978	Ribble, 1989
1113	KRN113T	Leyland Leopard PSU3E/4R	Duple Dominant II	C47F	1979	Ribble, 1989
1119	KRN119T	Leyland Leopard PSU3E/4R	Duple Dominant II	C47F	1979	Ribble, 1986
1120	G520LWU	Volvo B10M-60	Plaxton Paramount 3500 III	C49FT	1990	Cambus (Premier), 1997
1125	GRM625V	Leyland Leopard PSU3F/4R	Duple Dominant II	C49F	1980	
1149	PSU788	Leyland Tiger TRCTL11/3RZ	Duple Caribbean 2	C48FT	1985	Ribble, 1997
1151	B151WRN	Leyland Tiger TRCTL11/2RH	Duple Laser 2	C49F	1985	Ribble, 1991
1153	B153WRN	Leyland Tiger TRCTL11/2RH	Duple Laser 2	C53F	1985	Ribble, 1991
1154	B154WRN	Leyland Tiger TRCTL11/2RH	Duple Laser 2	C53F	1985	Ribble, 1991
1155	B43MAO	Leyland Tiger TRCTL11/3RH	Duple Laser 2	C53F	1985	Ribble, 1991
1160	L160CCW	Dennis Javelin 11SDL2133	Plaxton Premiére Interurban	BC47F	1993	Ribble, 1997
1161	L161CCW	Dennis Javelin 11SDL2133	Plaxton Premiére Interurban	BC47F	1993	Stagecoach Ribble, 1998
1162	WLT980	Volvo B10M-61	Plaxton Paramount 3500 II	C48F	1986	Ribble, 1994
1175	MRJ275W	Leyland Leopard PSU5D/4R	Plaxton Supreme IV	C50F	1981	Ribble, 1989
1199	FDV799V	Leyland Leopard PSU3E/4R	Plaxton Supreme IV Exp	C49F	1980	Ribble, 1989
1201	F201FHH	Leyland Olympian ONLXCT/3RZ	Alexander RL	BC55/41F	1989	
1202	F202FHH	Leyland Olympian ONLXCT/3RZ	Alexander RL	BC55/41F	1989	
1253	HNE253V	Leyland Leopard PSU5C/4R	Duple Dominant II	C53F	1980	Ribble, 1989
1528	N885AVV	Mercedes-Benz 709D	Alexander Sprint	B25F	1996	Stagecoach Manchester, 1998

One of the first tri-axle double-deck buses for the UK market was 1201, F201FHH in the Cumberland fleet. Currently based at Barrow, they have replaced two vehicles on a school service. With a seated capacity of 96, a figure more associated with those of articulated vehicles. The two tri-axles may be seen in Ulverston operating the link into Barrow. Here, 1201 is seen on an excursion. *Cliff Beeton*

2017	B117TVU	Leyland Olympian ONLXB/1R	Northern Counties	O43/30F	1985	Stagecoach Manchester, 1999
2024w	DBV24W	Bristol VRT/SL3/6LXB	Eastern Coach Works	B43/31F	1980	Ribble, 1986
2032w	DBV32W	Bristol VRT/SL3/6LXB	Eastern Coach Works	B43/31F	1980	Ribble, 1986
2035	UWV610S	Bristol VRT/SL3/6LXB	Eastern Coach Works	O43/31F	1977	Southdown, 1990
2036	UWV612S	Bristol VRT/SL3/6LXB	Eastern Coach Works	O43/31F	1977	Southdown, 1990
2037	UWV618S	Bristol VRT/SL3/6LXB	Eastern Coach Works	O43/31F	1978	Southdown, 1990
2038	UWV620S	Bristol VRT/SL3/6LXB	Eastern Coach Works	O43/31F	1978	Southdown, 1990
2075	XRR175S	Bristol VRT/SL3/6LXB	Eastern Coach Works	O43/27F	1980	Ribble, 1995
2076	UWV622S	Bristol VRT/SL3/6LXB	Eastern Coach Works	O43/31F	1980	Ribble, 1996
2100	DBV100W	Leyland Olympian B45.02	Eastern Coach Works	B45/33F	1980	Ribble, 1997
2102	JFR2W	Leyland Olympian ONLXB/1R	Eastern Coach Works	O45/32F	1981	Ribble, 1997
2116	OFV16X	Leyland Olympian ONLXB/1R	Eastern Coach Works	B45/32F	1982	Ribble, 1997
2117	OFV17X	Leyland Olympian ONLXB/1R	Eastern Coach Works	B45/32F	1982	Ribble, 1997
2129	VRN829Y	Leyland Olympian ONLXBT/1R	Eastern Coach Works	O45/32F	1982	Ribble, 1997
2134	DBV134Y	Leyland Olympian ONLXB/1R	Eastern Coach Works	B45/32F	1983	Ribble, 1989
2138	A138MRN	Leyland Olympian ONLXB/1R	Eastern Coach Works	B45/32F	1984	Ribble, 1997
2170	C170ECK	Leyland Olympian ONLXB/1R	Eastern Coach Works	BC42/30F	1985	Ribble, 1997
2174	C174ECK	Leyland Olympian ONLXB/1R	Eastern Coach Works	BC42/30F	1985	Ribble, 1997
2175	C175ECK	Leyland Olympian ONLXB/1R	Eastern Coach Works	BC42/30F	1985	Ribble, 1989
2176	C176ECK	Leyland Olympian ONLXB/1R	Eastern Coach Works	BC42/30F	1985	Ribble, 1989
2177	C177ECK	Leyland Olympian ONLXB/1R	Eastern Coach Works	BC42/30F	1986	Ribble, 1989
2179	C179ECK	Leyland Olympian ONLXB/1R	Eastern Coach Works	BC41/26F	1985	Ribble, 1997

2180-2189

		Leyland Olympian ON2R56G16Z4 Alexander RL		BC51/31F	1989	Ribble, 1997
2180	G180JHG	2182	G182JHG	2184	G184JHG	2186	G186JHG	2189	G189JHG
2181	G181JHG	2183	G183JHG	2185	G185JHG		

2191	H191WFR	Leyland Olympian ON2R56G16Z4 Alexander RL	B47/30F	1990	Ribble, 1997
2192	H192WFR	Leyland Olympian ON2R56G16Z4 Alexander RL	B47/30F	1990	Ribble, 1997
2194	H194WFR	Leyland Olympian ON2R56G16Z4 Alexander RL	B47/30F	1990	Ribble, 1997

2199-2210 Leyland Olympian ON2R56G13Z4 Alexander RL   BC43/27F* 1991   Ribble, 1997
*2204-6/10 are BC47/27F

2199	J199HFR	2203	J203HFR	2205	J205HFR	2207	J207HFR	2209	J209HFR
2201	J201HFR	2204	J204HFR	2206	J206HFR	2208	J208HFR	2210	J210HFR
2202	J202HFR								

2211-2223 Leyland Olympian ONLXB/1R   Alexander RL   B45/32F   1984-85   Ribble, 1997

| 2211 | A975OST | 2216 | B892UAS | 2217 | B893UAS | 2219 | B895UAS | 2223 | B899UAS |

Ancilliary vehicles

3002	VLF578	Leyland Leopard PSU3/3R	Alexander AY	TV	1974	Magicbus, 1990
3003	RUT842	Leyland Leopard PSU3/3R	Alexander AYS	TV	1974	Magicbus, 1990
3004	TCK841	Leyland Leopard PSU3/3R	Alexander AY	TV	1974	Ribble, 1997
3005	EGB52T	Leyland Leopard PSU3/3R	Alexander AY	TV	1978	Stagecoach Busways, 1998
3006	D513VAO	Dodge Commando G13	Reeve Burgess	TV	1986	MoD, 1999 (80KF60)
3007	A247GAU	Dodge Commando G13	Reeve Burgess	TV	1984	MoD, 1999 (30KB44)

Previous Registrations

109DRM	A101DAO	PSU787	C495LJV
B43MAO	B155WRN, PCK335	PSU788	B146ACK
C382SAO	C473SSO, GSO3V	PCK335	B156WRN
		RIL5084	G545LWU, 9258VC
C383SAO	C474SSO, GSO4V	RUT842	OGM608M
D384XAO	D375XRS, GSO5V	TCK841	SCS355M
D560RCK	D561RCK	VLF578	SCS359M
DSV943	D203LWX	VRR447	B180RLJ
JPU817	D207LWX	WLT380	C105DWR
K449YCW	K300LCT	WLT706	C109OHH
K450YCW	K200LCT	WLT824	C110OHH
LJY145	D205LWX	YDG616	D206LWX

Allocations:-

Barrow (Walney Road) - Stagecoach Cumberland

Outstations - Millom; Coniston; Ulverston; Askam and Haverthwaite

Mercedes-Benz	5	16	17	18	19	20	21	22
	23	24	26	54	55	56	68	70
	71	72	87	89	90	91	92	93
	94	95	96	98	567	618	652	1528
Volvo Coach	120	126	127	128	1120			
Tiger	101							
Javelin	152	154						
Volvo PS	702	754	755	756	757	758	759	760
	761	762	778	780	786	787		
Olympian	1001	1002	1003	1005	1090	1091	1092	1093
	1094	1201	1202	2177				

Carlisle (Willowholme Ind Est) - Stagecoach Cumberland

Outstation - Penrith

Mercedes-Benz	6	76	77	78	79	80	81	82
	83	84	97	206	619			
Tiger	102	106	111	156	1153	1154		
Volvo coach	1162							
Volvo PS	710	711	712	713	714	715	716	717
	718	719	720	721	722	723	724	725
	726	727	728	729	730	731	732	733
	734	735	736	737	738	739	741	745
	746	766	772	773	781	783	784	785
	788	789	790					
Volvo Interurban	791	792						
Volvo Modulo	799							
MAN	801	802	803	804	806	807	808	809
	811	812						

Leopard	505	1103	1125	1175	1253			
National	810							
Volvo B6	270	283						
Bristol VR	2076							
Olympian	1006	1009	1010	1011	1028	1029	1030	1031
	1032	2100						

Kendal (Station Road) - Stagecoach Cumberland

Outstations - Ambleside; Appleby and Grange

Mercedes-Benz	1	2	3	7	8	9	10	11
	12	13	14	15	49	50	51	65
	200	201	202	203	204	205	651	
Volvo B6	275	276	282					
Leopard	1105	1113	1119	1199				
Tiger	103	105	162	1149	1151	1155		
Volvo Coach	160	161						
Volvo PS	705	774	775	776				
Bristol VR	435	2036	2038					
Olympian	1008	1012	1019	1020	1021	1022	1023	1024
	1025	1026	1027	2102	2129	2175		

Morecambe (Heysham Road) - Stagecoach Lancaster

Outstations - Garstang; Ingleton and Lancaster

Mercedes-Benz	565	566	570	592	597	602	604	607
	615	625						
MetroRider	449	450						
Tiger	109	645	900					
Javelin	135	136	137	143	1160	1161		
Volvo Coach	158	163						
Volvo PS	460	461	462	463	699	700	701	703
	704	706	707	742	743	744	748	749
	750	751	752	793	794	795		
Olympian	1004	1007	1035	2117	2138	2170	2174	2179
	2180	2181	2182	2183	2184	2185	2186	2189
	2191	2192	2194	2199	2201	2202	2204	2205
	2206	2207	2208	2209	2210	2211	2216	2217
	2219	2223						

Workington (Lillyhall) - Stagecoach Cumberland

Mercedes-Benz	4	25	27	28	29	30	31	32
	33	48	57	58	59	60	61	62
	63	64	66	67	73	74	75	85
	86	88	571	572	649	650		
Tiger	110	114						
Volvo Coach	121	129	130	131	132	133	134	159
Volvo PS	455	456	457	458	459	708	809	753
	763	764	765	767	768	769	770	771
	777	779						
Volvo Modulo	796	797	798					
Bristol VR	427	428	431					
Olympian	1013	1014	1015	1016	1017	1018	1033	1034
	2116	2134	2176	2203				

Unallocated and stored

Mercedes-Benz	36	44	45	47	52	53	528	529
	533	559	560					
Leopard	569							
National	373	810	879	888				
Bristol VR	420	421	422	423	424	425	426	433
	434	436	437	2024	2032	2035	2037	2075

STAGECOACH MANCHESTER

Manchester - Magic Bus

Stagecoach Manchester, Daw Bank, Stockport, SK3 0DU

| 1 | L105SDY | Dennis Javelin 11SDL2133 | Plaxton Premiére Interurban | BC47F | 1994 | Stagecoach Ribble, 1998 |
| 2 | L107SDY | Dennis Javelin 11SDL2133 | Plaxton Premiére Interurban | BC47F | 1994 | Stagecoach Ribble, 1998 |

101-159   MAN 18.220 HOCLR   Alexander ALX300   N42F   1998

101	S101TRJ	114	S114TRJ	126	S126TRJ	137	S137TRJ	148	S148TRJ
102	S102TRJ	115	S115TRJ	127	S127TRJ	138	S138TRJ	149	S149TRJ
103	S103TRJ	116	S116TRJ	128	S128TRJ	139	S139TRJ	150	S150TRJ
104	S104TRJ	117	S117TRJ	129	S129TRJ	140	S140TRJ	151	S151TRJ
105	S105TRJ	118	S118TRJ	130	S130TRJ	141	S141TRJ	152	S152TRJ
106	S106TRJ	119	S119TRJ	131	S131TRJ	142	S142TRJ	153	S153TRJ
107	S107TRJ	120	S120TRJ	132	S132TRJ	143	S143TRJ	154	S154TRJ
108	S108TRJ	121	S121TRJ	133	S133TRJ	144	S144TRJ	156	S156TRJ
109	S109TRJ	122	S122TRJ	134	S134TRJ	145	S145TRJ	157	S157TRJ
110	S110TRJ	124	S124TRJ	135	S135TRJ	146	S146TRJ	158	S158TRJ
112	S112TRJ	125	S125TRJ	136	S136TRJ	147	S147TRJ	159	S159TRJ
113	S113TRJ								

160-215   MAN 18.220 HOCLR   Alexander ALX300   N42F   1999

160	T160MVM	172	T172MVM	185	T185MVM	195	T195MVM	206	T206TND
161	T161MVM	173	T173MVM	186	T186MVM	196	T196MVM	207	T207TND
162	T162MVM	174	T174MVM	187	T187MVM	197	T197MVM	208	T208TND
163	T163MVM	178	T178MVM	188	T188MVM	198	T198TND	209	T209TND
164	T164MVM	179	T179MVM	189	T189MVM	199	T199TND	210	T210TND
165	T165MVM	180	T180MVM	190	T190MVM	201	T201TND	211	T211TND
166	T166MVM	181	T181MVM	191	T191MVM	202	T202TND	212	T212TND
167	T167MVM	182	T182MVM	192	T192MVM	203	T203TND	213	T213TND
168	T168MVM	183	T183MVM	193	T193MVM	204	T204TND	214	T214TND
169	T169MVM	184	T184MVM	194	T194MVM	205	T205TND	215	T215TND

401-430   Mercedes-Benz 811D   Alexander Sprint   B31F   1995-96

401	N401WVR	407	N407WVR	413	N413WVR	419	N419WVR	425	N425WVR
402	N402WVR	408	N408WVR	414	N414WVR	420	N420WVR	426	N426WVR
403	N403WVR	409	N409WVR	415	N415WVR	421	N421WVR	427	N427WVR
404	N404WVR	410	N410WVR	416	N416WVR	422	N422WVR	428	N428WVR
405	N405WVR	411	N411WVR	417	N417WVR	423	N423WVR	429	N429WVR
406	N406WVR	412	N412WVR	418	N418WVR	424	N424WVR	430	N430WVR

431	H881NFS	Mercedes-Benz 410D	Crystals	M15	1991	Glossopdale, Dukinfield, 1999
433	N746YVR	Mercedes-Benz 711D	Marshall C19	B27F	1995	Glossopdale, Dukinfield, 1999
434	N748YVR	Mercedes-Benz 711D	Marshall C19	B27F	1995	Glossopdale, Dukinfield, 1999

Opposite: **Stagecoach Manchester has one of the more modern fleets in the country considering its size. One of two Dennis Tridents from the 1998 order is 613, T613MNF, shown here at Hazel Grove. This pair are to be joined by more from the 1999 order shortly. Latterly with Stagecoach Kenya, Dennis Dragons have been entering service on Wilmslow Road services in Magic Bus livery. Seen in Piccadilly about to head for Northenden is 685, M685TDB.** *Tony Wilson/Cliff Beeton*

509-527   Mercedes-Benz 709D   Alexander Sprint   B25F   1996

509	N653VSS	513	N657VSS	517	N661VSS	521	N665VSS	525	N882AVV
510	N654VSS	514	N658VSS	518	N662VSS	522	N879AVV	526	N883AVV
511	N655VSS	515	N659VSS	519	N663VSS	523	N880AVV	527	N884AVV
512	N656VSS	516	N660VSS	520	N664VSS	524	N881AVV		

530-566   Mercedes-Benz Vario O814   Plaxton Beaver 2   B27F   1997

530	P530PNE	537	P537PNE	544	P544PNE	551	P551PNE	559	P559PNE
531	P531PNE	538	P538PNE	545	P545PNE	552	P552PNE	561	P561PNE
532	P532PNE	539	P539PNE	546	P546PNE	553	P553PNE	562	P562PNE
533	P533PNE	540	P540PNE	547	P547PNE	554	P554PNE	563	P563PNE
534	P534PNE	541	P541PNE	548	P548PNE	556	P556PNE	564	P564PNE
535	P535PNE	542	P542PNE	549	P549PNE	557	P557PNE	565	P565PNE
536	P536PNE	543	P543PNE	550	P550PNE	558	P558PNE	566	P566PNE

567	R276CBU	Mercedes-Benz Vario O814	Plaxton Beaver 2	B31F	1998	Glossopdale, Dukinfield, 1999
568	R277CBU	Mercedes-Benz Vario O814	Plaxton Beaver 2	B31F	1998	Glossopdale, Dukinfield, 1999
569	R446YNF	Mercedes-Benz Vario O814	Plaxton Beaver 2	B31F	1997	Glossopdale, Dukinfield, 1999
570	R447YNF	Mercedes-Benz Vario O814	Plaxton Beaver 2	B31F	1997	Glossopdale, Dukinfield, 1999
571	R899AVM	Mercedes-Benz Vario O814	Plaxton Beaver 2	B27F	1997	Glossopdale, Dukinfield, 1999
572	R898AVM	Mercedes-Benz Vario O814	Plaxton Beaver 2	B27F	1997	Glossopdale, Dukinfield, 1999
573	R901AVM	Mercedes-Benz Vario O814	Plaxton Beaver 2	B27F	1997	Glossopdale, Dukinfield, 1999

612-624   Dennis Trident   Alexander ALX400   N47/27F   1999

612	T612MNF	615	V615DJA	618	V618DJA	621	V621DJA	623	V623DJA
613	T613MNF	616	V616DJA	619	V619DJA	622	V622DJA	624	V624DJA
614	V614DJA	617	V617DJA	620	V620DJA				

680-699   Dennis Dragon DDA1820   Duple Metsec/AVA   B51/37F   1995   Stagecoach Kenya, 1998-99

680	M680TDB	684	M684TDB	688	M688TDB	692	M692TDB	696	M696TDB
681	M681TDB	685	M685TDB	689	M689TDB	693	M693TDB	697	M697TDB
682	M682TDB	686	M686TDB	690	M690TDB	694	M694TDB	698	M698TDB
683	M683TDB	687	M687TDB	691	M691TDB	695	M695TDB	699	M699TDB

716-730   Volvo Olympian   Alexander RL   B51/36F   1996

716	P716GND	719	P719GND	722	P722GND	725	P725GND	728	P728GND
717	P717GND	720	P720GND	723	P723GND	726	P726GND	729	P729GND
718	P718GND	721	P721GND	724	P724GND	727	P727GND	730	P730GND

731-743   Volvo Olympian   Alexander RL   B51/36F   1997   Stagecoach Oxford, 1998

731	R501UWL	734	R504UWL	737	R507UWL	740	R510UWL	742	R512UWL
732	R502UWL	735	R505UWL	738	R508UWL	741	R511UWL	743	R513UWL
733	R503UWL	736	R506UWL	739	R509UWL				

744-782   Volvo Olympian   Alexander RL   B51/36F   1998

744	R744DRJ	753	R753DRJ	761	R761DRJ	768	S768SVU	775	S775RVU
745	R745DRJ	754	R754DRJ	762	R762DRJ	769	S769RVU	776	S776RVU
746	R746DRJ	755	R755DRJ	763	R763DRJ	770	S770RVU	778	S778RVU
747	R747DRJ	756	R756DRJ	764	S764SVU	771	S771RVU	779	S779RVU
748	R748DRJ	757	R757DRJ	765	R765DRJ	772	S772RVU	780	S780RVU
749	R749DRJ	758	R758DRJ	766	S766SVU	773	S773RVU	781	S781RVU
751	R751DRJ	759	R759DRJ	767	S767SVU	774	S774RVU	782	S782RVU
752	R752DRJ	760	R760DRJ						

837-868   Volvo B10M-55   Alexander PS   B49F   1996

837	P837GND	844	P844GND	851	P851GND	857	P857GND	863	P863GND
838	P838GND	845	P845GND	852	P852GND	858	P858GND	864	P864GND
839	P839GND	846	P846GND	853	P853GND	859	P859GND	865	P865GND
840	P840GND	847	P847GND	854	P854GND	860	P860GND	866	P866GND
841	P841GND	848	P848GND	855	P855GND	861	P861GND	867	P867GND
842	P842GND	849	P849GND	856	P856GND	862	P862GND	868	P868GND
843	P843GND	850	P850GND						

Manchester International Airport and local transport operators have introduced SkyLine services. Selected vehicles from Stagecoach, Arriva and Trent display the vinyls. The services offer special rates aimed to encourage airport staff and passengers to travel to the airport on public transport. Just taking off for Manchester on the Gatley service 196 is 547, P547PNE. *Bill Potter*

869-894

Volvo B10M-55 Northern Counties Paladin B48F* 1997 *869-74/83-5/90/1 are BC47F

869	P869MNE	874	P874MNE	879	P879MNE	884	P884MNE	890	P890MNE
870	P870MNE	875	P875MNE	880	P880MNE	885	P885MNE	891	P891MNE
871	P871MNE	876	P876MNE	881	P881MNE	886	P886MNE	892	P892MNE
872	P872MNE	877	P877MNE	882	P882MNE	887	P887MNE	893	P893MNE
873	P873MNE	878	P878MNE	883	P883MNE	889	P889MNE	894	P894MNE

895-984

Volvo B10M-55 Alexander PS B49F 1997-98

895	R895XVM	915	R915XVM	933	R933XVM	951	R951XVM	968	R968XVM
896	R896XVM	916	R916XVM	934	R934XVM	952	R952XVM	969	R969XVM
897	R897XVM	917	R917XVM	935	R935XVM	953	R953XVM	970	R970XVM
898	R898XVM	918	R918XVM	936	R936XVM	954	R954XVM	971	R971XVM
899	R899XVM	919	R919XVM	937	R937XVM	955	R955XVM	972	R972XVM
901	R901XVM	920	R920XVM	938	R938XVM	956	R956XVM	973	R973XVM
902	R902XVM	921	R921XVM	939	R939XVM	957	R957XVM	974	R974XVM
903	R903XVM	922	R922XVM	940	R940XVM	958	R958XVM	975	R975XVM
904	R904XVM	923	R923XVM	941	R941XVM	959	R959XVM	976	R976XVM
905	R905XVM	924	R924XVM	942	R942XVM	960	R960XVM	977	R977XVM
906	R906XVM	925	R925XVM	943	R943XVM	961	R961XVM	978	R978XVM
907	R907XVM	926	R926XVM	944	R944XVM	962	R962XVM	979	R979XVM
908	R908XVM	927	R927XVM	945	R945XVM	963	R963XVM	980	R980XVM
909	R909XVM	928	R928XVM	946	R946XVM	964	R964XVM	981	R981XVM
910	R910XVM	929	R929XVM	947	R947XVM	965	R965XVM	982	R982XVM
912	R912XVM	930	R930XVM	948	R948XVM	966	R966XVM	983	R983XVM
913	R913XVM	931	R931XVM	949	R949XVM	967	R967XVM	984	R984XVM
914	R914XVM	932	R932XVM	950	R950XVM				

985-996

Volvo B10M-55 Plaxton Paladin B48F 1998

985	R985XVM	988	R988XVM	991	R991XVM	993	R993XVM	995	R995XVM
986	R986XVM	989	R989XVM	992	R992XVM	994	R994XVM	996	R996XVM
987	R987XVM	990	R990XVM						

Thirty Dennis Dominators were delivered in 1985 with a further ten joining the fleet six years later. These are all now allocated to Princess Road depot. Numerically the first, 2001, B901TVR, is seen on Princes Street in Manchester while operating to Southern Cemetary. *Tony Wilson*

1463-1467
Scania N113DRB   Northern Counties Palatine   B47/28F   1991   GMS Buses, 1994

1463	H463GVM	**1464**	H464GVM	**1465**	H465GVM	**1466**	H466GVM	**1467**	H467GVM

2001-2030
Dennis Dominator DDA1003   Northern Counties   B43/32F   1985   GMS Buses, 1994

2001	B901TVR	**2007**	B907TVR	**2013**	B913TVR	**2019**	B919TVR	**2025**	B25TVU
2002	B902TVR	**2008**	B908TVR	**2014**	B914TVR	**2020**	B920TVR	**2026**	B26TVU
2003	B903TVR	**2009**	B909TVR	**2015**	B915TVR	**2021**	B21TVU	**2027**	B27TVU
2004	B904TVR	**2010**	B910TVR	**2016**	B916TVR	**2022**	B22TVU	**2028**	B28TVU
2005	B905TVR	**2011**	B911TVR	**2017**	B917TVR	**2023**	B23TVU	**2029**	B29TVU
2006	B906TVR	**2012**	B912TVR	**2018**	B918TVR	**2024**	B24TVU	**2030**	B30TVU

2031-2040
Dennis Dominator DDA2033   Northern Counties Palatine   B43/29F   1991   GMS Buses, 1994

2031	H131GVM	**2033**	H133GVM	**2035**	H135GVM	**2037**	H137GVM	**2039**	H139GVM
2032	H132GVM	**2034**	H134GVM	**2036**	H136GVM	**2038**	H138GVM	**2040**	H140GVM

3004-3010
Leyland Olympian ONTL11/1R   Northern Counties   B43/30F   1982   GMS Buses, 1994

3004	ANA4Y	**3007**	ANA7Y	**3008**	ANA8Y	**3009**	ANA9Y	**3010**	ANA10Y
3006	ANA6Y								

3016-3025
Leyland Olympian ONLXCT/1R   Northern Counties   B43/30F   1983-84   GMS Buses, 1994

3016	A581HDB	**3018**	A583HDB	**3020**	A585HDB	**3022**	A22HNC	**3024**	A24HNC
3017	A582HDB	**3019**	A584HDB	**3021**	A21HNC	**3023**	A23HNC	**3025**	A25HNC

3026-3035
Leyland Olympian ONLXB/1R   Northern Counties   B43/30F   1984   GMS Buses, 1994

3026	A26ORJ	**3028**	A28ORJ	**3030**	A30ORJ	**3032**	A32ORJ	**3034**	B34PJA
3027	A27ORJ	**3029**	A29ORJ	**3031**	A31ORJ	**3033**	A33ORJ	**3035**	B35PJA

3036-3236

Leyland Olympian ONLXB/1R — Northern Counties — B43/30F* — 1984-86 — *3198/213/14 are BC43/26F — GMS Buses, 1994

3036	B36PJA	3086	B86SJA	3133	B133WNB	3166	C166YBA	3197	C197YBA
3039	B39PJA	3087	B87SJA	3135	B135WNB	3167	C167YBA	3198	C198YBA
3049	B49PJA	3088	B88SJA	3137	B137WNB	3169	C169YBA	3199	C199YBA
3053	B53PJA	3089	B89SJA	3138	B138WNB	3170	C170YBA	3205	C205CBU
3055	B55PJA	3091	B91SJA			3172	C172YBA	3207	C207CBU
3056	B56PJA	3094	B94SJA	3143	B143WNB	3173	C173YBA	3208	C208CBU
3057	B57PJA	3095	B95SJA	3145	B145WNB	3174	C174YBA	3210	C210CBU
3058	B58PJA	3110	B110SJA	3146	B146XNA	3175	C175YBA	3212	C212CBU
3060	B60PJA	3114	B114SJA	3147	B147XNA	3176	C176YBA	3213	C213CBU
3065	B65PJA			3149	B149XNA	3178	C178YBA	3214	C214CBU
3067	B67PJA	3118	B118TVU	3150 *	B150XNA	3179	C179YBA	3215	C215CBU
3069	B69PJA	3119	B119TVU	3153	B153XNA	3181	C181YBA	3216	C216CBU
3070	B70PJA	3121	B121TVU	3154	B154XNA	3184	C184YBA	3221	C221CBU
3072	B72PJA	3122	B122TVU	3155	B155XNA	3185	C185YBA	3224	C224CBU
3074	B74PJA	3124	B124TVU	3156	C156YBA	3191	C191YBA	3226	C226ENE
3077	B77PJA	3125	B125TVU	3158	C158YBA	3193	C193YBA	3230	C230ENE
3080	B80PJA	3126	B126WNB	3164	C164YBA	3195	C195YBA	3234	C234ENE
3082	B82PJA	3132	B132WNB	3165	C165YBA	3196	C196YBA	3236	C236EVU
3084	B84PJA								

3255-3277

Leyland Olympian ONLXB/1R — Northern Counties — BC43/26F — 1986-87 — GMS Buses, 1994

3255	C255FRJ	3268	D268JVR	3269	D269JVR	3272	D272JVR	3277	D277JVR
3260	D260JVR								

3282-3304

Leyland Olympian ONLXB/1RZ — Northern Counties — B43/30F* — 1988-89 — GMS Buses, 1994 — *3291 is BC43/25F

3282	F282DRJ	3289	F289DRJ	3295	F295DRJ	3298	F298DRJ	3301	F301DRJ
3283	F283DRJ	3291	F291DRJ	3296	F296DRJ	3300	F300DRJ	3304	F304DRJ
3285	F285DRJ	3294	F294DRJ	3297	F297DRJ				

5040-5173

MCW Metrobus DR102/21* — MCW — B43/30F — 1981-83 — GMS Buses, 1994 — *5120-73 are DR102/23

5040	MRJ40W	5055	MRJ55W	5120	SND120X	5158	ANA158Y	5173	ANA173Y
5048	MRJ48W								

Ancilliary Vehicles

4451	SND451X	Leyland Atlantean AN68A/1R	Northern Counties	TV	1982	GMS Buses, 1994
4452	SND452X	Leyland Atlantean AN68A/1R	Northern Counties	TV	1982	GMS Buses, 1994
4455	SND455X	Leyland Atlantean AN68A/1R	Northern Counties	TV	1982	GMS Buses, 1994
4472	SND472X	Leyland Atlantean AN68A/1R	Northern Counties	TV	1982	GMS Buses, 1994
TV05	LIB1182	Leyland Leopard PSU3F/4R	Plaxton Supreme IV Exp	TV	1981	Evans, Tregaron, 1995
TV06	ETC310W	Leyland Leopard PSU3F/5R	Plaxton Supreme IV Exp	TV	1981	Miller, Calderbank, 1995
TV07	GSU859T	Leyland Leopard PSU3E/2R	Alexander AYS	TV	1979	Graham, Perth, 1997
TV08	GLJ490N	Bristol LH6L	Eastern Coach Works	TV	1975	Town & Country SoM 1997
TV09	VDV105S	Bristol LH6L	Eastern Coach Works	TV	1978	United (Teeside), 1997
TV11	YAE516V	Bristol LH6L	Eastern Coach Works	TV	1979	United (Teeside), 1997
TV12	C293PDC	Dodge Commando G13	Wadham Stringer Vanguard	TV	1987	MoD, 1998 (93KF69)
TV13	D240SNC	Dodge Commando G13	Wadham Stringer Vanguard	TV	1987	MoD, 1998 (92KF94)
TV14	D41SNE	Dodge Commando G13	Wadham Stringer Vanguard	TV	1987	MoD, 1998 (80KF70)
TV15	D56SNE	Dodge Commando G13	Wadham Stringer Vanguard	TV	1986	MoD, 1998 (80KF54)
TV16	E968CVM	Dodge Commando G13	Wadham Stringer Vanguard	TV	1987	MoD, 1998 (93KF41)
A035	D35UAO	Mercedes-Benz L608D	Reeve Burgess	TV	1986	Cumberland, 1997

Previous Registrations:

JIL7608	XRB416L	M684TDB	KAG542J (Kenya)	M692TDB	KAG025X (Kenya)
LIB1182	GBO245W				
LIL3317	EUM900T	M685TDB	KAG770V (Kenya)	M693TDB	KAG601M (Kenya)
LIL4612	WFM806L	M686TDB	KAG060M (Kenya)	M694TDB	KAG470T (Kenya)
SJI2054	FNS161T	M687TDB	KAG292E (Kenya)	M695TDB	KAG544J (Kenya)
SJI4558	CFM352S	M688TDB	KAG543J (Kenya)	M696TDB	KAG264R (Kenya)
M680TDB	KAG933E (Kenya)	M689TDB	KAG471T (Kenya)	M69 TDB	KAG602M (Kenya)
M681TDB	KAH560B (Kenya)	M690TDB	KAG522X (Kenya)	M69 TDB	KAG472T (Kenya)
M682TDB	KAG931E (Kenya)	M691TDB	KAG405W (Kenya)	M69 TDB	KAG932E (Kenya)
M683TDB	KAG544H (Kenya)				

Allocations:-

Manchester (Hyde Road)

MAN - ALX300	135	136	137	138	139	140	144	145
	160	162	163	164	178	179	182	190
	195	196	197	198				
Volvo B10M Bus	837	838	839	840	847	848	849	850
	862	863	864	865	866	867	895	896
	897	898	899	901	902	903	904	905
	906	907	908	909	910	912	913	914
	915	916	917	918	919	920	921	922
	923	924	925	926	927	928	929	930
	931	932	933	934	935	936	971	972
	973	974	975	976	977	978	979	980
	981	982	983	984				
Scania	1463	1464	1465	1466	1467			
Olympian	731	732	733	734	735	736	737	738
	739	740	741	742	743	744	745	746
	747	748	749	751	752	753	754	755
	756	757	758	759	760	761	762	763
	764	765	766	3004	3006	3007	3008	3009
	3010	3016	3017	3018	3019	3020	3021	3022
	3023	3036	3039	3049	3053	3055	3056	3057
	3082	3084	3086	3087	3137	3150	3153	3154
	3155	3164	3165	3166	3167	3169	3170	3173
	3174	3175	3178	3179	3181	3191	3195	3196
	3212	3213	3214	3216	3221	3255	3260	3268
	3269							

More than a hundred MAN 18.220s are now in service with Stagecoach Manchester, the latest arrivals displacing Volvo B10Bs to Cambus and B6s to Ribble. One of the 1999 order is 167, T167MVM seen leaving the city centre for Flixton.
Tony Wilson

The final delivery of Volvo B10M buses were bodied by Plaxton at Scarborough to Northern Counties drawings. The twelve, including 990, R990XVM, are based at Stockport where this picture was taken. The rural service from Stockport to Marple, Hyde and Ashton is the regular employment for the type. *Cliff Beeton*

Manchester (Princess Road)

Mercedes-Benz	541	542	543	544	545	546	547	548
	566							
MAN - ALX300	146	148	149	153	154	156	157	158
	159	161	165	166	167	168	169	172
	173	174	180	181	189	193	199	201
	202	203	204	205	206	207	208	209
	210	211	212	213				
Volvo B10M Bus	841	842	843	844	845	846	855	856
	857	858	859	860	861	937	938	939
	940	941	942	943	944	945	946	947
	948	949	950	951	952	953	954	955
	956	957	958	959	960	961	962	963
	964	965	966	967	968	969	970	
Olympian	716	717	718	719	720	721	722	723
	724	725	726	727	728	729	730	767
	768	769	770	771	772	773	774	775
	776	778	779	780	781	782	3024	3025
	3026	3027	3028	3029	3030	3031	3032	3033
	3034	3035	3058	3060	3065	3067	3069	3070
	3110	3272	3277					
Dominator	2001	2002	2003	2004	2005	2006	2007	2008
	2009	2010	2011	2012	2013	2014	2015	2016
	2017	2018	2019	2020	2021	2022	2023	2024
	2025	2026	2027	2028	2029	2030	2031	2032
	2033	2034	2035	2036	2037	2038	2039	2040
Dragon	680	681	682	683	684	685	686	687
	688	689	690	691	692	693	694	695
	696							

Glossop (York Street)

Mercedes-Benz	401	431	509	549	550	551	552	553
	562	563	565	567	568	569	570	571
	572	573						
Olympians	3199	3207	3224	3226	3230	3236	3282	3283
	3285	3289	3291	3294	3295	3296	3297	3298
	3299	3301	3304					

Stockport (Daw Bank)

Coach	1	2						
MAN	101	102	103	104	105	106	107	108
	109	110	112	113	114	115	116	117
	118	119	120	121	122	124	125	126
	127	128	129	130	131	132	133	134
	142	143	147	150	151	152	183	184
	185	186	187	188	191	192	194	214
	215							
Volvo B10M Bus	851	852	853	854	868	869	870	871
	872	873	874	875	876	877	878	879
	880	881	882	883	884	885	886	887
	889	890	891	892	893	894	985	986
	987	988	989	990	991	992	993	994
	995	996						
Olympian	3088	3089	3091	3094	3095	3114	3118	3119
	3121	3122	3124	3125	3126	3132	3133	3135
	3138	3143	3145	3146	3147	3149	3156	3158
	3172	3176	3184	3185	3193	3197	3198	3205
	3208	3210	3215	3234	3298	3300		
Dennis Tridents	612	613	614	615	616	617	618	619
	620	621	622	623	624			

Stockport (Charles Street)

Mercedes-Benz	402	403	404	405	406	407	408	409
	410	411	412	413	414	415	416	417
	418	419	420	421	422	423	424	425
	426	427	428	429	430	433	434	515
	516	517	518	519	520	521	522	523
	524	525	526	527	530	531	532	533
	534	535	536	537	538	539	540	554
	556	557	558	559	561	564		

Unallocated

Mercedes-Benz	432	510	511	512	513	514
Olympian	3072	3074	3077	3080		
Metrobus	5040	5048	5055	5120	5158	5173

The Lancashire, Cumbria and Manchester Bus Handbook

STAGECOACH RIBBLE

Ribble - Burnley & Pendle

Stagecoach Ribble, Burnley & Pendle Transport Co Ltd,
Daw Bank, Stockport, Cheshire, SK3 0DU

105	P977UBV	Volvo B10M-62	Plaxton Premiére Interurban	BC51F	1996
106	P978UBV	Volvo B10M-62	Plaxton Premiére Interurban	BC51F	1996
107	P979UBV	Volvo B10M-62	Plaxton Premiére Interurban	BC51F	1996

108-114
Volvo B10M-62 — Plaxton Premiére Interurban — BC51F — 1997

| 108 | P108DCW | 110 | P110DCW | 112 | P112DCW | 113 | P113DCW | 114 | P114DCW |
| 109 | P109DCW | | | | | | | | |

| 123 | S269KHG | Volvo B10M-62 | Jonckheere Modulo | BC51F | 1998 |
| 124 | S270KHG | Volvo B10M-62 | Jonckheere Modulo | BC51F | 1998 |

138-144
Dennis Javelin 11SDL2129 — Plaxton Premiére Interurban — BC47F — 1993

| 138 | L138BFV | 140 | L140BFV | 141 | L141BFV | 142 | L142BFV | 144 | L144BFV |
| 139 | L139BFV | | | | | | | | |

145-160
Dennis Javelin 11SDL2133 — Plaxton Premiére Interurban — BC47F — 1993

145	L145BFV	149	L149BFV	153	L153BFV	156	L156BFV	158	L158BFV
146	L146BFV	150	L150BFV	155	L155BFV	157	L157BFV	159	L159CCW
148	L148BFV	151	L151BFV						

162-166
Dennis Javelin 11SDL2133 — Plaxton Premiére Interurban — BC47F — 1994 — Stagecoach South, 1994

| 162 | L101SDY | 163 | L103SDY | 164 | L104SDY | 165 | L106SDY | 166 | L102SDY |

176-180
Dennis Lance SLF 11SDA3201 — Berkhof 2000 — N35F — 1996

| 176 | N176LCK | 177 | N177LCK | 178 | N178LCK | 179 | N179LCK | 180 | N180LCK |

181-196
Dennis Lance 11SDA3101 — Alexander PS — B45F — 1992 — East London, 1997

181	J101WSC	185	J105WSC	188	J108WSC	191	J411WSC	194	J114WSC
182	J102WSC	186	J106WSC	189	J109WSC	192	J112WSC	195	J115WSC
183	J103WSC	187	J107WSC	190	J110WSC	193	J113WSC	196	J116WSC
184	J104WSC								

Seen in Red Lion Street, Burnley is Stagecoach Ribble's Leyland Swift 293, J263KRN. Bodywork is the Reeve Burgess Harrier model and it is one of four Swifts purchased from Hyndburn. The type are expected to be sold following the arrival of Volvo B6s from Stagecoach Manchester.
Tony Wilson

200-215

Volvo B6LE — Alexander ALX200 — N36F — 1997 — Stagecoach Manchester, 1999

200	P335JND	203	P338JND	207	P342JND	210	P345JND	213	P348JND
201	P336JND	204	P339JND	208	P343JND	211	P346JND	214	P349JND
202	P337JND	205	P340JND	209	P344JND	212	P347JND	215	P341JND

237-256

Volvo B6-9.9M — Alexander Dash — BC40F — 1993

237	L237CCW	240	L240CCW	251	L251CCK	253	L253CCK	256	L256CCK
239	L239CCW	241	L241CCK	252	L252CCK	255	L255CCK		

257-265

Volvo B6-9.9M — Alexander Dash — BC40F — 1993 — Fife Scottish, 1994

257	L667MSF	259	L669MSF	261	L661MSF	263	L663MSF	265	L665MSF
258	L668MSF	260	L660HKS	262	L662MSF	264	L664MSF		

277-287

Volvo B6-9.9M — Alexander Dash — B40F — 1993 — Cumberland 1994-96

277	L277JAO	279	L279JAO	283	L283JAO	285	L272LHH	287	L274LHH
278	L278JAO	281	L281JAO	284	L271LHH	286	L273LHH		

293	J263KRN	Leyland Swift ST2R44C97A4	Reeve Burgess Harrier	B39F	1991	Hyndburn 1996
294	J264KRN	Leyland Swift ST2R44C97A4	Reeve Burgess Harrier	B39F	1991	Hyndburn 1996

302-310

Volvo B6-9.9M — Alexander Dash — B40F — 1994 — Stagecoach Manchester, 1999

302	M742PRS	304	M744PRS	306	M746PRS	308	M748PRS	310	M750PRS
303	M743PRS	305	M745PRS	307	M847PRS	309	M749PRS		

311-321

Volvo B6-9.9M — Alexander Dash — B40F — 1994 — Stagecoach Manchester, 1999

311	M461VHE	314	M454VHE	316	M456VHE	318	M458VHE	320	M741PRS
313	M846HDF	315	M455VHE	317	M457VHE	319	M459VHE	321	M462VHE

333	FUH33V	Leyland National 2 NL116L11/1R	B49F	1980	Burnley & Pendle, 1997
339	BUH239V	Leyland National 2 NL106L11/1R	B44F	1980	Burnley & Pendle, 1997
340	BUH240V	Leyland National 2 NL106L11/1R	B44F	1980	Burnley & Pendle, 1997

344-349

Leyland National 2 NL116L11/1R — B52F — 1980 — Burnley & Pendle, 1997

344	XRN44V	345	XRN45V	347	XRN47V	348	XRN48V	349	XRN49V

357	KHH377W	Leyland National 2 NL116L11/1R	B52F	1980	Cumberland, 1993
385	RRM384X	Leyland National 2 NL116AL11/1R	BC52F	1982	Cumberland, 1993
386	RRM386X	Leyland National 2 NL116AL11/1R	B52F	1982	Cumberland, 1993
387	SHH387X	Leyland National 2 NL116AL11/1R	B52F	1982	Cumberland, 1993
390	SHH390X	Leyland National 2 NL116AL11/1R	B52F	1982	Cumberland, 1993
396	WAO396Y	Leyland National 2 NL116HLXB/1R	B52F	1982	Cumberland, 1993
397	SNS831W	Leyland National 2 NL116AL11/1R	B52F	1981	Cumberland, 1993
399	SHH388X	Leyland National 2 NL116AL11/1R	B52F	1982	Cumberland, 1993

401-406

Volvo B10M-55 — Alexander P — BC53F* — 1988 — Burnley & Pendle, 1997
*401 is B53F

401	E61JFV	403	E63JFV	404	E64JFV	405	E65JFV	406	E66JFV
402	E62JFV								

407	G67PFR	Volvo B10M-55	East Lancashire EL2000	B51F	1990	Burnley & Pendle, 1997
408	G68PFR	Volvo B10M-55	East Lancashire EL2000	B51F	1990	Burnley & Pendle, 1997

Opposite, top: **Ribble undertake several rosters for National Express. Two Jonckheere-bodied Volvo coaches joined the fleet in 1998 and carry National Express colours, though others in the fleet wear Flightlink livery. Pictured at Manchester International is Plaxton Expressliner 2 number 1164, M164SCK.** *Bill Potter*
Opposite, bottom: **An exchange of double-deck vehicles saw the former Burnley & Pendle bus version of Volvo Citybuses move to Bolton while Northern Counties-bodied Olympians arrived in Burnley. As we go to press the first of fifteen Olympians from Manchester has arrived, all expected to work from Burnley. Pictured in the town is 2228, P228VCK.** *Bill Potter*

Not all of Stagecoach's Volvo B10Ms are bodied by Alexander and Northern Counties. Four with East Lancashire bodywork were acquired with Burnley & Pendle. Still based in the town is 426, K26WBV, seen here on local service number 1. *Bill Potter*

417-423

						Volvo B10M-55		Alexander PS		B51F	1991	Burnley & Pendle, 1997

417	H617ACK	419	H619ACK	421	H621ACK	422	H622ACK	423	H623ACK
418	H618ACK	420	H620ACK						

424	J24MCW	Volvo B10M-50	East Lancashire EL2000	B45F	1992	Burnley & Pendle, 1997
425	J25MCW	Volvo B10M-50	East Lancashire EL2000	B45F	1992	Burnley & Pendle, 1997
426	K26WBV	Volvo B10M-50	East Lancashire EL2000	B45F	1993	Burnley & Pendle, 1997
427	K27WBV	Volvo B10M-50	East Lancashire EL2000	B45F	1993	Burnley & Pendle, 1997

428-442

		Volvo B10M-55		Alexander PS		BC48F	1994-95

428	M782PRS	431	M231TBV	434	M234TBV	437	M794PRS	440	M797PRS
429	M783PRS	432	M232TBV	435	M235TBV	438	M795PRS	441	M798PRS
430	M230TBV	433	M233TBV	436	M236TBV	439	M796PRS	442	M799PRS

451	M451VCW	Volvo B10M-55	Alexander PS	BC48F	1995	
452	M452VCW	Volvo B10M-55	Alexander PS	BC48F	1995	
453	M453VCW	Volvo B10M-55	Alexander PS	BC48F	1995	
454	M454VCW	Volvo B10M-55	Alexander PS	BC48F	1995	
464	K740DAO	Volvo B10M-55	Alexander PS	B48F	1993	Cumberland, 1996

465-472

		Volvo B10M-55		Alexander PS		B49F	1996

465	P127XCN	467	P129XCN	469	P131XCN	471	P133XCN	472	P134XCN
466	P128XCN	468	P130XCN	470	P132XCN				

473-482

		Volvo B10M-55		Alexander PS		B49F	1997

473	R473MCW	475	R475MCW	477	R477MCW	479	R479MCW	481	R481MCW
474	R474MCW	476	R476MCW	478	R478MCW	480	R480MCW	482	R482MCW

The days of Leyland Nationals with Ribble are now numbered as newer vehicles join the fleet. Four Nationals from the Greenway conversion programme joined the fleet from Hyndburn, however, non-Greenway examples total twenty-six, all of which are mark 2s. Pictured at Blackburn is 903, NOE595R, one of the Greenways. *Paul Wigan*

483	N801DNE	Volvo B10M-55		Alexander PS		B49F	1996	Manchester, 1998
484	N802DNE	Volvo B10M-55		Alexander PS		B49F	1996	Manchester, 1998

546	N648VSS	Mercedes-Benz 709D		Alexander Sprint		B25F	1996	Manchester, 1998
547	N647VSS	Mercedes-Benz 709D		Alexander Sprint		B25F	1996	Manchester, 1998

568-591   Mercedes-Benz 709D   Alexander Sprint   B23F*   1990   579/80 Magicbus, 1990

*568/9 is BC25F

568	G568PRM	**577**	G577PRM	**581**	G181PAO	**586**	G186PAO	**589**	G189PAO
569	G569PRM	**578**	G578PRM	**582**	G182PAO	**587**	G187PAO	**590**	G190PAO
573	G573PRM	**579**	G579PRM	**584**	G184PAO	**588**	G188PAO	**591**	G191PAO
574	G574PRM	**580**	G180PAO	**585**	G185PAO				

595-608   Mercedes-Benz 709D   Alexander Sprint   B25F   1993

595	K115XHG	**598**	K118XHG	**600**	K120XHG	**605**	L125DRN	**608**	L128DRN
596	K116XHG	**599**	L119DRN						

610-628   Mercedes-Benz 709D   Alexander Sprint   B23F   1992-93

610	K610UFR	**613**	K613UFR	**617**	K617UFR	**621**	K621UFR	**627**	K627UFR
611	K611UFR	**614**	K614UFR	**620**	K620UFR	**624**	K624UFR	**628**	K628UFR
612	K612UFR	**616**	K616UFR						

629-637   Mercedes-Benz 709D   Alexander Sprint   B25F   1993

629	L629BFV	**631**	L631BFV	**633**	L633BFV	**635**	L635BFV	**637**	K112XHG
630	L630BFV	**632**	L632BFV	**634**	L634BFV	**636**	L636BFV		

The arrival of larger buses has displaced some minibuses where greater capacity was needed. The last to arrive were five Vario O814 models. Initially based at Blackburn three are now at Preston, including 670, R670LFV shown here passing along Fishergate. *Paul Wigan*

638-644

				Mercedes-Benz 709D		Alexander Sprint		B25F	1996	
638	N519BJA	640	N451VOD	642	N453VOD	643	N454VOD	644	N455VOD	
639	N520BJA	641	N452VOD							

647-659

				Mercedes-Benz 709D		Alexander Sprint		B25F	1996	
647	N456VOD	650	N459VOD	653	N462VOD	656	N465VOD	658	N467VOD	
648	N457VOD	651	N460VOD	654	N463VOD	657	N466VOD	659	N468VOD	
649	N458VOD	652	N461VOD	655	N464VOD					

660-667

				Mercedes-Benz 709D		Alexander Sprint		B25F	1996	
660	N201LFV	662	N194LFV	664	N196LFV	666	N198LFV	667	N199LFV	
661	N202LFV	663	N195LFV	665	N197LFV					

668-672

				Mercedes-Benz Vario O814		Plaxton Beaver 2		B27F	1997	
668	R668LFV	669	R669LFV	670	R670LFV	671	R671LFV	672	R672LFV	

675	K75XCW	Optare MetroRider MR03	Optare	B29F	1993	Burnley & Pendle, 1997
678	L178KHG	Optare MetroRider MR17	Optare	B29F	1994	Burnley & Pendle, 1997
679	L179KHG	Optare MetroRider MR17	Optare	B29F	1994	Burnley & Pendle, 1997

778	H78CFV	Mercedes-Benz 811D	Alexander AM	B31F	1991	Burnley & Pendle, 1997
779	H79CFV	Mercedes-Benz 811D	Alexander AM	B31F	1991	Burnley & Pendle, 1997
784	E84HRN	Mercedes-Benz 709D	Robin Hood	B29F	1987	Burnley & Pendle, 1997
785	E85HRN	Mercedes-Benz 811D	Robin Hood	B29F	1987	Burnley & Pendle, 1997
789	E89HRN	Mercedes-Benz 811D	Robin Hood	B29F	1987	Burnley & Pendle, 1997
790	E90HRN	Mercedes-Benz 811D	Robin Hood	B29F	1987	Burnley & Pendle, 1997
797	G97MRN	Mercedes-Benz 811D	Reeve Burgess Beaver	B31F	1990	Burnley & Pendle, 1997
798	G98PCK	Mercedes-Benz 811D	Reeve Burgess Beaver	B31F	1990	Burnley & Pendle, 1997

829	DBV829W	Leyland National 2 NL106L11/1R		B44F	1980	
839	DBV839W	Leyland National 2 NL106L11/1R		B44F	1980	
877	LFR877X	Leyland National 2 NL106AL11/1R		B44F	1981	
889	ARN889Y	Leyland National 2 NL116HLXB/1R		B52F	1983	
890	ARN890Y	Leyland National 2 NL116HLXB/1R		B52F	1983	
895	CEO720W	Leyland National 2 NL116L11/1R		B45F	1980	Cumberland, 1993
901	AFM1W	Leyland National 2 NL116AL11/2R East Lancs Greenway(1992)	B48F	1981	Hyndburn, 1996
902	WPC316X	Leyland National 2 NL116AL11/2R East Lancs Greenway(1992)	BC49F	1981	Hyndburn, 1996
903	NOE595R	Leyland National 11351/1R	East Lancs Greenway(1992)	B52F	1976	Hyndburn, 1996
904	CWX669T	Leyland National 11351A/1R	East Lancs Greenway(1992)	B52F	1981	Hyndburn, 1996
905	MDS866V	Leyland National 2 NL116L11/1R		B48F	1980	Western Buses, 1996
906	MDS859V	Leyland National 2 NL116L11/1R		B48F	1980	Western Buses, 1996
907	MDS858V	Leyland National 2 NL116L11/1R		B52F	1980	Western Buses, 1996
909	RFS584V	Leyland National 2 NL116L11/1R		B52F	1980	Western Buses, 1996
1120	R120VFR	Volvo B10M-62	Jonckheere Mistral 50	C46FT	1998	
1121	S905JHG	Volvo B10M-62	Jonckheere Mistral 50	C46FT	1998	
1123	J123AHH	Volvo B10M-60	Plaxton Expressliner	C46FT	1992	Cumberland, 1995
1125	L125NAO	Volvo B10M-62	Plaxton Expressliner 2	C46FT	1994	Stagecoach Cumberland, 1998
1126	S906JHG	Volvo B10M-62	Jonckheere Mistral 50	C46FT	1998	
1164	M164SCK	Volvo B10M-62	Plaxton Expressliner 2	C46FT	1994	
1165	M165SCK	Volvo B10M-62	Plaxton Expressliner 2	C46FT	1994	
1201	SND432X	Leyland Atlantean AN68A/1R	Northern Counties	B43/32F	1981	Manchester, 1996
1203	A678HNB	Leyland Atlantean AN68D/1R	Northern Counties	B43/32F	1983	Stagecoach Manchester, 1998
1205	LFV205X	Leyland Atlantean AN68C/2R	East Lancashire	B50/36F	1981	Lancaster, 1993
1210	GBV110N	Leyland Atlantean AN68/2R	Alexander AL	B49/35F	1975	Hyndburn, 1996
1211	GBV101N	Leyland Atlantean AN68/2R	Alexander AL	B49/35F	1974	Hyndburn, 1996
1219	A679HNB	Leyland Atlantean AN68D/1R	Northern Counties	B43/32F	1983	Stagecoach Manchester, 1999
1235	RGV40W	Leyland Atlantean AN68C/1R	East Lancashire	B46/30F	1980	Hyndburn, 1996
1236	RGV36W	Leyland Atlantean AN68C/1R	East Lancashire	B46/30F	1980	Hyndburn, 1996
1237	RGV37W	Leyland Atlantean AN68C/1R	East Lancashire	B46/30F	1980	Hyndburn, 1996
1238	RGV38W	Leyland Atlantean AN68C/1R	East Lancashire	B46/30F	1980	Hyndburn, 1996
1301	E101JFV	Volvo Citybus B10M-50	Alexander RV	BC47/35F	1988	Burnley & Pendle, 1997
1302	E102JFV	Volvo Citybus B10M-50	Alexander RV	BC47/35F	1988	Burnley & Pendle, 1997

1303-1312

		Volvo Citybus B10M-50	Alexander RV	B47/37F	1989	Burnley & Pendle, 1997

1303	F103XCW	1305	F105XCW	1307	F107XCW	1309	F109XCW	1311	F111XCW
1304	F104XCW	1306	F106XCW	1308	F108XCW	1310	F110XCW	1312	F112XCW

1313	H113ABV	Volvo Citybus B10M-50	Alexander RV	B47/37F	1991	Burnley & Pendle, 1997
1314	H114ABV	Volvo Citybus B10M-50	Alexander RV	BC47/35F	1991	Burnley & Pendle, 1997
1315	H115ABV	Volvo Citybus B10M-50	Alexander RV	BC47/35F	1991	Burnley & Pendle, 1997
1481	TRN481V	Leyland Atlantean AN68A/1R	Eastern Coach Works	B43/31F	1980	Cumberland, 1993
2030	DBV30W	Bristol VRT/SL3/6LXB	Eastern Coach Works	B43/31F	1980	
2042	RRP858R	Bristol VRT/SL3/501	Eastern Coach Works	B43/31F	1977	United Counties, 1990
2043	FDV817V	Bristol VRT/SL3/6LXB	Eastern Coach Works	B43/31F	1980	Magicbus, 1990
2044	FDV833V	Bristol VRT/SL3/6LXB	Eastern Coach Works	B43/31F	1980	Magicbus, 1990
2045	FDV784V	Bristol VRT/SL3/6LXB	Eastern Coach Works	B43/31F	1980	Magicbus, 1990
2052	LFJ883W	Bristol VRT/SL3/6LXC	Eastern Coach Works	B43/31F	1980	United Counties, 1993
2053	LFJ858W	Bristol VRT/SL3/6LXB	Eastern Coach Works	B43/31F	1980	United Counties, 1993
2054	LFJ859W	Bristol VRT/SL3/6LXB	Eastern Coach Works	B43/31F	1980	United Counties, 1993
2055	LFJ885W	Bristol VRT/SL3/6LXC	Eastern Coach Works	B43/31F	1980	United Counties, 1993
2056	LFJ866W	Bristol VRT/SL3/6LXB	Eastern Coach Works	B43/31F	1980	United Counties, 1993
2057	LFJ861W	Bristol VRT/SL3/6LXB	Eastern Coach Works	B43/31F	1980	United Counties, 1993
2058	LFJ884W	Bristol VRT/SL3/6LXC	Eastern Coach Works	B43/31F	1980	United Counties, 1993
2066	FFR166S	Bristol VRT/SL3/6LXB	Eastern Coach Works	B43/31F	1978	Burnley & Pendle, 1997
2074	FFR174S	Bristol VRT/SL3/6LXB	Eastern Coach Works	B43/31F	1978	Burnley & Pendle, 1997
2095	OSR195R	Bristol VRT/LL3/6LXB	Alexander AL	B49/35F	1977	Burnley & Pendle, 1997
2097	OSR197R	Bristol VRT/LL3/6LXB	Alexander AL	B49/35F	1977	Burnley & Pendle, 1997

2101-2132

		Leyland Olympian ONLXB/1R*	Eastern Coach Works	B45/32F	1981-83	*2124-30 are ONLXBT/1R

2101	GFR101W	2108	JFR8W	2114	OFV14X	2122	OFV22X	2127	VRN827Y
2103	JFR3W	2109	JFR9W	2115	OFV15X	2123	OFV23X	2128	VRN828Y
2104	JFR4W	2110	JFR10W	2118	OFV18X	2124	SCK224X	2130	VRN830Y
2105	JFR5W	2111	JFR11W	2119	OFV19X	2125	SCK225X	2131	DBV131Y
2106	JFR6W	2112	JFR12W	2120	OFV20X	2126	SCK226X	2132	DBV132Y
2107	JFR7W	2113	JFR13W	2121	OFV21X				

2135	CWR525Y	Leyland Olympian ONLXB/1R	Eastern Coach Works	B45/32F	1983	Hyndburn, 1996			
2136	CWR526Y	Leyland Olympian ONLXB/1R	Eastern Coach Works	B45/32F	1983	Hyndburn, 1996			
2137	DBV137Y	Leyland Olympian ONLXB/1R	Eastern Coach Works	B45/32F	1983				
2142	A142MRN	Leyland Olympian ONLXB/1R	Eastern Coach Works	B45/32F	1984				
2143	A143MRN	Leyland Olympian ONLXB/1R	Eastern Coach Works	B45/32F	1984				
2145	A145OFR	Leyland Olympian ONLXB/1R	Eastern Coach Works	B45/32F	1984				
2147	ANA1Y	Leyland Olympian ONLXB/1R	Northern Counties	BC43/26F	1985	Stagecoach Manchester, 1998			
2149	ANA2Y	Leyland Olympian ONLXB/1R	Northern Counties	B43/30F	1985	Stagecoach Manchester, 1998			
2150	ANA3Y	Leyland Olympian ONLXB/1R	Northern Counties	B43/30F	1985	Stagecoach Manchester, 1998			
2152	B152TRN	Leyland Olympian ONLXB/1R	Eastern Coach Works	B45/32F	1984				

2156-2178

Leyland Olympian ONLXB/1R Eastern Coach Works BC41/26F* 1984-85 *Seating varies

2156	A156OFR	2158	A158OFR	2171	C171ECK	2173	C173ECK	2178	C178ECK
2157	A157OFR	2159	A159OFR	2172	C172ECK				

2187	G187JHG	Leyland Olympian ONLXB/2RZ	Alexander RL	BC51/31F	1989
2188	G188JHG	Leyland Olympian ONLXB/2RZ	Alexander RL	BC51/31F	1989
2193	H193WFR	Leyland Olympian ON2R56G16Z4 Alexander RL		B51/36F	1990
2195	H195WFR	Leyland Olympian ON2R56G16Z4 Alexander RL		B51/36F	1990
2196	H196WFR	Leyland Olympian ON2R56G16Z4 Alexander RL		B51/36F	1990
2197	H197WFR	Leyland Olympian ON2R56G16Z4 Alexander RL		B51/36F	1990
2198	J198HFR	Leyland Olympian ON2R56G13Z4 Alexander RL		BC43/27F	1991

2213-2222

Leyland Olympian ONLXB/1R Alexander RL B45/32F 1984-85 Highland Scottish, 1991

2213	A978OST	2215	B891UAS	2220	B896UAS	2221	B897UAS	2222	B898UAS
2214	A979OST	2218	B894UAS						

2224-2235

Volvo Olympian YN2RV18Z4 Northern Counties Palatine B49/33F 1996

2224	P224VCK	2227	P227VCK	2230	P230VCK	2232	P232VCK	2234	P234VCK
2225	P225VCK	2228	P228VCK	2231	P231VCK	2233	P233VCK	2235	P235VCK
2226	P226VCK	2229	P229VCK						

2236-2245

Volvo Olympian YN2RV18Z4 Alexander RL B45/27F 1996

2236	P260VPN	2238	P262VPN	2240	P270VPN	2242	P272VPN	2244	P274VPN
2237	P261VPN	2239	P263VPN	2241	P271VPN	2243	P273VPN	2245	P275VPN

2246-2268

Volvo Olympian Alexander RL B51/36F 1997

2246	R246NBV	2251	R251NBV	2256	R256NBV	2261	R261NBV	2265	R265NBV
2247	R247NBV	2252	R252NBV	2257	R257NBV	2262	R262NBV	2266	R266NBV
2248	R248NBV	2253	R253NBV	2258	R258NBV	2263	R263NBV	2267	R267NBV
2249	R249NBV	2254	R254NBV	2259	R259NBV	2264	R264NBV	2268	R268NBV
2250	R250NBV	2255	R255NBV	2260	R260NBV				

2269	S903JHG	Volvo Olympian	Alexander RL	BC43/27F	1998
2270	S904JHG	Volvo Olympian	Alexander RL	BC43/27F	1998

2271-2285

Volvo Olympian YN2RC16V3 Alexander RL B47/32F 1996 Stagecoach Manchester, 1999

2271	N325NPN	2274	N328NPN	2277	N331NPN	2280	N334NPN	2283	N337NPN
2272	N326NPN	2275	N329NPN	2278	N332NPN	2281	N335NPN	2284	N338NPN
2273	N327NPN	2276	N330NPN	2279	N333NPN	2282	N336NPN	2285	N339NPN

Ancilliary Vehicles

T251	SCS355M	Leyland Leopard PSU3/3R	Alexander AY	TV	1974	
T254	EGB53T	Leyland Leopard PSU3E/3R	Alexander AY	TV	1978	
T257	XSU906	Dodge Commando G13	Reeve Burgess	TV	1985	US Forces, 1998
T258	B358NAB	Dodge Commando G13	Reeve Burgess	TV	1985	US Forces, 1998
T259		Dodge Commando G13	Reeve Burgess	TV	1985	US Forces, 1998
T260		Dodge Commando G13	Reeve Burgess	TV	1985	US Forces, 1998

Bolton depot provides the vehicles for many of Ribble's services that work into Manchester from the north. Alternate vehicles on route M10 are advertised as low floor vehicles. For the contract Stagecoach purchased five Berkhof-bodied Dennis Lance buses similar to a batch delivered to Stagecoach South. Pictured in Manchester and illustrating the route branding carried by the type is 176, N176LCK. *David Heath*

Allocations:-

Blackburn (George Street) - Stagecoach Ribble

Mercedes-Benz	546	547	600	605	620	621	624	628
	630	631	666	667				
National	901	902	903	904				
Volvo B6	239	240	241	257	260	261	263	264
	284	285	286	287				
Atlantean	1210	1211						
Bristol VR	2045	2054	2095					
Olympian	2103	2106	2111	2114	2118	2127	2130	2142
	2143							

Bolton (Goodwin Street) - Stagecoach Ribble

Mercedes-Benz	577	579	581	582	584	585	586	587
	588	590	591	660	661	662	663	664
	668	669						
National	333	339	340	348	386	387	390	817
	839	905	906	909				
Lance	176	177	178	179	180	181	182	183
	184	185	186	187	188	189	190	191
	192	193	194	195	196			
Volvo PS	436	437	438	439	440	441	442	451
	452	467	468	469	470	471	472	483
	484							
Volvo Citybus	1303	1304	1305	1306	1307	1308	1309	1310
	1311	1312	1313					
Olympian	2108	2193	2196	2197	2218			

Burnley(Colne Road) - Stagecoach Burnley & Pendle

MetroRider	675	678	679				
Mercedes-Benz	778	779	789	790	798		
Swifts	293	294					
Volvo B6	209	214					
National	345	347	349				
Javelin	145	146	148	149	150	151	153	155
	156	157	158	159	162	165	166	
Volvo B10M SD	401	402	403	404	405	406	407	408
	417	418	419	420	421	422	423	424
	425	426	427	473	474	475	476	477
	478	479	480	481	482			
Bristol VRs	2030	2074						
Volvo B10M DD	1301	1302	1314	1315				
Olympian	2101	2104	2110	2113	2122	2136	2156	2171
	2172	2173	2178	2198	2221	2224	2225	2226
	2227	2228	2246	2247	2248	2249	2250	2251
	2252	2253	2254	2255	2269	2270	2271	

Chorley (Eaves Lane)- Stagecoach Ribble

Mercedes-Benz	573	580	598	629	633	634	636	665
	784							
National	357	385	396	831	895	907		
Atlantean	1235	1237	1238	1481				
Olympian	2105	2109	2120	2123	2124	2126	2128	2157
	2195	2213	2214	2215	2236	2237	2238	2239
	2256	2257	2258	2259	2260	2261	2262	2263
	2264	2265	2266	2267	2268			

Clitheroe (Pimlico Road) - Stagecoach Ribble

Mercedes-Benz	568	595	596	608	616		
Javelins	144	164					
National	829						
Volvo PS	430	431	432	433	434	435	453
Bristol VR	2042	2043	2044	2052	2053	2055	2056	2057
	2058	2066						
Olympian	2158	2159						

Ribble operate duties on route 478, the link between Bolton and Bury that passes through Radcliffe. Volvo Citybus 1307, F107XCW is seen undertaking the duty in July 1999.
Tony Wilson

National Express service 540 joins London with Bury, a service which Ribble currently operate as part of the network. Seen at the southern end is 1120, R120VFR, a Jonckheere-bodied Volvo B10M. The curved Mistral body style has been specified for all the coaches being delivered to the group during 1999. *Colin Lloyd*

Fleetwood (Sidings Road) - Stagecoach Ribble

Mercedes-Benz	574	610	611	612	613	614	632	637
	638	639	640					
Volvo B6	262	277	278	281	283			
Volvo PS	428	429	454	464				
Volvo Olympian	2112	2152	2220	2222				

Preston (Selbourne Street) - Stagecoach Ribble

Mercedes-Benz	569	617	627	641	642	643	644	647
	648	649	650	651	652	653	654	655
	656	657	658	659	670	671	672	797
Volvo B6	237	251	252	253	255	256	258	259
	265	279	307	308	319			
National	397	399	877	889	890			
Volvo B10M	465	466						
Javelin	138	139	140	141	142	163		
Volvo Interurban	105	106	107	108	109	110	112	113
	114	123	124					
Expressliner	1120	1121	1123	1125	1126	1164	1165	
Atlantean	1201	1203	1205	1236				
Bristol VR	2097							
Olympian	2107	2115	2119	2121	2125	2131	2132	2135
	2137	2145	2147	2149	2150	2187	2188	2229
	2230	2231	2232	2233	2234	2235	2240	2241
	2242	2243	2244	2245				

Unallocated

Mercedes-Benz	578	589	599	635	785
National	344				

Volvo B6 & Olympians transferring from Manchester are not yet allocated.

STAINTON

F W Stainton & Sons Ltd, Settlings Garage, 39 Burton Road, Kendal LA9 7LJ

LIB3626	Volvo B10M-61	Plaxton Paramount 3200	C53F	1983	Paul James, Ratcliffe, 1995
RJI2162	Volvo B10M-61	Plaxton Paramount 3200	C57F	1985	Brooks, Kendal, 1996
LIB3769	Volvo B10M-61	Van Hool Alizée H	C49FT	1988	
SIB2633	Volvo B10M-61	Van Hool Alizée H	C49FT	1989	Robinson's, Appleby, 1998
A5FWS	Volvo B10M-60	Van Hool Alizée	C49FT	1990	
H710BRG	Toyota Coaster HB31R	Caetano Optimo	C18FT	1990	Durham City, Brandon, 1994
CAZ6835	Kässbohrer Setra S215HD	Kässbohrer Tornado	C49FT	1992	Bebb, Llantwit Fardre, 1994
J35NLN	Kässbohrer Setra S215HD	Kässbohrer Tornado	C49FT	1992	Allied Coachlines, Uxbridge, 1999
LIB3768	Volvo B10M-60	Van Hool Alizée HE	C48FT	1993	Chambers, Bures, 1996
CAZ2051	Setra S215HD	Setra Tornado	C49FT	1995	
R2SOH	Setra S250	Setra Special	C48FT	1998	
T3FWS	Setra S315	Setra	C48FT	1999	

Previous registrations:

3179TR	G500CJT, XEL254, G307GJT	LIB3768	K815HUM
A5FWS	G789URY	LIB3769	E327OMG
CAZ2051	From new	RJI2162	B634OEC
CAZ6835	J74VTG	SIB2633	G501CJT, XEL606, G303GJT, 3927TR
J35NLN	J76VTG, WLU887		
LIB3626	FUA389Y, BWC800, UJN174Y, PJI7754, RJU565Y		

One of the first Setra S315 coaches for the UK market is Stainton's T3FWS. The vehicle carries contract livery for Leger, to whom the vehicle is contracted. While its visits to Cumbria are few during the season, the vehicle was seen when prepared for delivery. Stainton's vehicles carry a livery similar to that used here.
F W Stainton & Son

STOTTS

Stotts Tours (Oldham) Ltd, 144 Lees Road, Oldham OL4 1HT

ANA47T	Leyland Fleetline FE30AGR	Northern Counties	B43/32F	1979	Topp Line, Wavertree, 1995
CWG726V	Leyland Atlantean AN68A/1R	Alexander AL	B45/33F	1980	South Yorkshire's Transport, 1991
JKW281W	Leyland Atlantean AN68B/1R	Alexander AL	B45/33F	1981	South Yorkshire's Transport, 1991
JKW292W	Leyland Atlantean AN68B/1R	Alexander AL	B45/33F	1981	South Yorkshire's Transport, 1991
JKW298W	Leyland Atlantean AN68B/1R	Alexander AL	B45/33F	1981	South Yorkshire's Transport, 1991
JKW304W	Leyland Atlantean AN68B/1R	Alexander AL	B45/33F	1981	South Yorkshire's Transport, 1991
JKW315W	Leyland Atlantean AN68B/1R	Alexander AL	B45/33F	1981	Mainline, 1995
DWH700W	Leyland Fleetline FE30AGR	Northern Counties	B43/32F	1979	Village, Garston, 1995
A695HNB	Leyland Atlantean AN68D/1R	Northern Counties	B43/32F	1984	G M South, 1997
A704LNC	Leyland Atlantean AN68D/1R	Northern Counties	B43/32F	1984	G M South, 1997
A722LNC	Leyland Atlantean AN68D/1R	Northern Counties	B43/32F	1984	G M South, 1997
A735NNA	Leyland Atlantean AN68D/1R	Northern Counties	B43/32F	1984	G M South, 1997
A750NNA	Leyland Atlantean AN68D/1R	Northern Counties	B43/32F	1984	G M South, 1997
GIB1437	Leyland Tiger TRCTL11/3RZ	Plaxton Paramount 3200 II	C53F	1985	Hills, Tredegar, 1991
D171PYB	Leyland Tiger TRCTL11/3RZ	Plaxton Paramount 3200 II	C57F	1987	Denslow, Chard, 1990
F995HGE	Volvo B10M-60	Plaxton Paramount 3500 III	C53F	1988	Park's of Hamilton, 1990
E134SAT	Dennis Dominator DDA1014	East Lancashire	B45/31F	1987	Stagecoach Transit, 1999
E135SAT	Dennis Dominator DDA1014	East Lancashire	B45/31F	1987	Stagecoach Transit, 1999
E137SAT	Dennis Dominator DDA1014	East Lancashire	B45/31F	1987	Stagecoach Transit, 1999
E139SAT	Dennis Dominator DDA1014	East Lancashire	B45/31F	1987	Stagecoach Transit, 1999
E141SAT	Dennis Dominator DDA1014	East Lancashire	B45/31F	1987	Stagecoach Transit, 1999
F638BKD	Dennis Dominator DDA1025	East Lancashire	B45/31F	1989	North Western, 1997
F639BKD	Dennis Dominator DDA1025	East Lancashire	B45/31F	1989	North Western, 1997
G627EKA	Dennis Dominator DDA1031	East Lancashire	BC43/25F	1990	North Western, 1997

Previous registration
GIB1437   B614CKG

Livery:- Cream, red and black

Stotts provide school transport services from the Oldham area. Three Dennis Dominators arrived from North Western in 1997, including G627EKA seen here. These have recently been joined by five similar vehicles from the Hull operation of Stagecoach Transit.
Keith Grimes

TIMELINE

Timeline Travel, 31 Moor Lane, Bolton BL1 4TA

901	R207JSF	Iveco EuroRider 391.12.35	Beulas Stergo E	C49FT	1998	Barry Rayould, Walsall, 1999
902	V	Volvo B7R	Plaxton Prima	C53F	1999	
903	V	Volvo B7R	Plaxton Prima	C53F	1999	
908	M908OVR	Dennis Javelin GX	Neoplan Transliner	C53F	1995	
915	L360YNR	Dennis Javelin	Plaxton Premiere 320	C49FT	1994	Barry Rayboild, Walsall, 1999
916	M916OVR	Dennis Javelin GX	Neoplan Transliner	C49FT	1995	
917	M917OVR	Dennis Javelin GX	Neoplan Transliner	C49FT	1995	
918	P918HNA	Dennis Javelin	Neoplan Transliner	C53F	1996	
919	P919HNA	Dennis Javelin	Neoplan Transliner	C49FT	1996	
920	P920HNA	Dennis Javelin	Neoplan Transliner	C49FT	1996	
921	F621OHD	Toyota Coaster HB31R	Caetano Optimo	C21F	1988	Barry Raybould, Walsall, 1999
959	J259NNC	Volvo B10M-60	Plaxton Premiere 350	C49FT	1992	Shearings, 1999
966	J266NNC	Volvo B10M-60	Plaxton Premiere 350	C49FT	1992	Shearings, 1999
973	H173DVM	Volvo B10M-60	Van Hool Alizée H	C49FT	1991	Shearings, 1995
974	H174DVM	Volvo B10M-60	Van Hool Alizée H	C49FT	1991	Shearings, 1995

Depot: Moss Industrial Estate, Leigh and Birchills Street, Walsall.

TITTERINGTONS

G S I P & C Titterington, The Garage, Blencow, Penrith, Cumbria, CA11 0DG

KUM537L	Leyland Leopard PSU3B/4R	Plaxton Panorama Elite III	C49F	1973	Yeowarts, Whitehaven, 1980
TAO154R	Leyland Leopard PSU3C/4R	Plaxton Supreme III	C53F	1976	Holmeswood, Rufford, 1987
368SHX	Leyland Leopard PSU3E/4R	Plaxton Supreme IV Express	C53F	1979	Brainwood High School, 1996
188TAE	Volvo B58-61	Plaxton Supreme IV	C57F	1979	Clayton, Pudsey, 1996
XAP956	Leyland Leopard PSU3E/4R	Plaxton Supreme IV Express	C53F	1979	West Sussex, Chichester, 1997
890TTE	Leyland Leopard PSU3F/4R	Plaxton Supreme IV	C49F	1981	Johnson, Hodthorpe, 1987
212VPF	Leyland Tiger TRCTL11/3R	Duple Laser	C51F	1984	
C196OHH	Volkwagen Caravelle	Volkswagen	M8	1986	
OZ4688	Volvo B10M-61	Plaxton Paramount 3500 III	C53F	1986	Clarkes of London, 1992
CUI925	Volvo B10M-61	Plaxton Paramount 3500 III	C49FT	1986	National Travel East, 1987
TYT653	LAG G355Z	LAG Panoramic	C49FT	1989	
G906RHH	LAG G355Z	LAG Panoramic	C49FT	1990	
XOU692	Volvo B10M-60	Jonckheere Deauville P599	C51FT	1990	Tellings-Golden Miller, Byfleet, 1993
J711CWT	Volvo B10M-62	Plaxton Excalibur	C50FT	1994	Bakers, Biddulph, 1999
M949RHH	Volvo B10M-62	Van Hool Alizée H	C49FT	1995	
M950RHH	Volvo B10M-62	Van Hool Alizée H	C49FT	1995	
M439ECS	Volvo B10M-62	Jonckheere Deauville 45	C53F	1995	Park's of Hamilton, 1997
M131UWY	Volvo B10M-62	Plaxton Première 350	C50F	1995	Wallace Arnold Coaches, 1997
N214HWX	Volvo B10M-62	Plaxton Première 350	C48FT	1996	Wallace Arnold Coaches, 1998
N354TTH	Volkswagen Transporter	Volkswagen	M7	1996	?, 1999
T789JAO	Iveco EuroRider 391.12.35	Beulas Stergo E	C49FT	1999	

Previous registrations:

188TAE	AFB233V	CUI925	C450CWR	TAO154R	LOT779R, XAP956
212VPF	B342GRM	G906RHH	G39ORM, 3685HX	TYT653	F432GHH
368SHX	AWJ 292T	M439ECS	LSK555, KSK978	XAP956	YBN629V
890TTE	PNW342W	OZ4688	C178LWB	XOU692	G647ONH

Timeline sold its bus interests during 1998-99 though it has retained coaching businesses in Bolton and the West Midlands. Pictured at Hawes in the Yorkshire Dales is 917, M917OVR, a Neoplan Transliner. Two Plaxton Prema-bodied Volvo B7 coaches will join the fleet later in 1999. *Ralph Stevens*

Titterington Holidays are based near the M6 motorway at Penrith. Two Van Hool Alizèe coaches new to the company arrived in 1995. One of these, M949RHH, is seen here. The latest arrival is an Iveco coach with Spanish-built Beulas coachwork.

TRAVELLERS CHOICE

J Shaw & Son (Silverdale) Ltd, The Coach & Travel Centre, Scotland Road, Carnforth, Lancashire, LA5 9RQ

Reg	Chassis	Body	Code	Year	History
HSC164X	Leyland Cub CU435	Duple Dominant	B33F	1981	Munro, Uddington, 1995
UCW 315X	Volvo B58-61	Plaxton Supreme VI	C57F	1982	Mountain Goat, Windermere, 1994
6267UA	Volvo B10M-61	Jonckheere Jubilee P50	C51FT	1983	
899CAN	Volvo B10M-61	Jonckheere Jubilee P50	C52FT	1983	
KBZ5749	Volvo B10M-61	Duple Dominant IV	C57F	1984	Brown's, Ambleside, 1994
HIL8917	Leyland Tiger TRCTL11/3RH	Plaxton Paramount 3500	C53F	1984	Lancaster, 1993
HIL8433	Volvo B10M-61	Van Hool Astral	C50/7FT	1984	Homer, Upton Warren, 1998
LSU939	Volvo B10M-53	Jonckheere Jubilee P90	C54/13DT	1985	Hiltons, Newton-le-Willows, 1999
C963END	Ford Transit 190	Steedrive	M16L	1986	Gwynedd CC, 1993
BYP985	Neoplan N122/3	Neoplan Skyliner	C57/20CT	1986	Swallow, Rainham, 1998
IIL3198	Leyland Tiger TRCTL11/3RH	Duple 320	C57F	1986	Lancaster, 1993
HIL8915	Leyland Tiger TRCTL11/3RZ	Plaxton Paramount 3500 III	C53F	1987	Lancaster, 1993
JIB3515	Volvo B10M-61	Plaxton Paramount 3200 III	C57F	1987	Express Travel, 1995
509EBL	Volvo B10M-61	Plaxton Paramount 3200 III	C49FT	1987	Express Travel, 1995
XJF386	Volvo B10M-61	Plaxton Paramount 3500 III	C50FT	1988	Wallace Arnold, 1992
5129UA	Volvo B10M-61	Plaxton Paramount 3500 III	C49FT	1988	Wallace Arnold, 1992
E775WEC	Mercedes-Benz L307D	Mercedes-Benz	M8	1988	Barrow Travel, 1991
F371JTN	Mercedes-Benz 407D	Reeve Burgess	M15	1988	Target, Cramlington, 1993
NIL9932	Mercedes-Benz 609D	Whitaker Europa	C24F	1988	
NIL9581	Mercedes-Benz 609D	Reeve Burgess Beaver	B25F	1988	Go-Ahead (OK), 1997
NIL7914	Mercedes-Benz 609D	Reeve Burgess Beaver	B25F	1988	Go-Ahead (OK), 1997
F258DAG	Volkswagen LT35	Kirkham	M12L	1988	Bullock, Cheadle, 1998
4150RU	Volvo B10M-60	Duple 340	C57F	1989	Baker, Biddulph, 1995
F953KMA	Ford Transit VE6	Ford	M14	1989	Carr, Maghull, 1996
G581PVU	Ford Transit VE6	Ford	M8L	1990	Tarmac Construction, 1993
G607JUG	Ford Transit VE6	Dormobile	B12FL	1990	Wakefield MBC, 1998
G112TND	Mercedes-Benz 811D	Carlyle C16	B31F	1990	Arriva Manchester, 1998
H176ANE	Ford Transit VE6	Deansgate	M14	1990	
H251ANE	Ford Transit VE6	Deansgate	M14	1990	
NIL6258	Mercedes-Benz 811D	Made-to-Measure	C28F	1990	
XDL521	Volvo B10M-60	Plaxton Paramount 3500 III	C46FT	1991	
YFG333	Volvo B10M-60	Plaxton Paramount 3500 III	C46FT	1991	
824HAO	Volvo B10M-60	Van Hool Alizée H	C53F	1993	
6137RU	Volvo B10M-60	Plaxton Première 350	C49FT	1993	Go Whittle, Kidderminster, 1995
6SVK	Volvo B10M-60	Jonckheere Deauville 45	C49FT	1993	Stagecoach Oxford, 1998
XDO32	Volvo B10M-60	Jonckheere Deauville 45	C49FT	1993	Stagecoach Oxford, 1998
6682WY	Volvo B10M-60	Jonckheere Deauville 45	C49FT	1993	Stagecoach Oxford, 1998
M208SCK	Volvo B10M-62	Plaxton Première 320	C53FT	1994	
M209SCK	Volvo B10M-62	Plaxton Première 320	C53FT	1994	
M338EEC	Volvo B10M-62	Plaxton Première 350	C49FT	1995	
M339EEC	Volvo B10M-62	Plaxton Première 350	C51FT	1995	
N160GRN	Volvo B10M-62	Plaxton Première 350	C49FT	1995	
N481REC	Volvo B10M-62	Plaxton Première 350	C49FT	1996	
N610REC	Volvo B10M-62	Plaxton Première 350	C49FT	1996	
N781PEC	Volvo B10M-62	Plaxton Première 350	C53F	1996	
N398CNB	Ford Transit VE6	Deansgate	M14	1996	
N281OYE	Volvo B10M-62	Plaxton Première 350	C53F	1996	Redwing, Camberwell, 1999
N282OYE	Volvo B10M-62	Plaxton Première 350	C53F	1996	Redwing, Camberwell, 1999
R171SUT	Volvo B10M-62	Jonckheere Mistral 50	C51FT	1998	
R791NEC	Volvo B10M-62	Jonckheere Mistral 50	C51FT	1998	
R512BUA	Mercedes-Benz Sprinter 312D	Mercedes-Benz	M16	1998	
S989EEC	Volkswagen	Volkswagen	M8	1999	

Opposite: **In the last edition of this book the fleet was known as Shaw Hadwin. Since then the Travellers Choice name has been adopted with vehicles for the main fleet being painted in livery. Shown here are two Plaxton coaches in contract liveries. The upper picture shows Paramount XDL521 with new insignia above the windscreen while in the lower picture N610REC is seen on National Express duplication work in** *interski* **colours.** *David Heath/Colin Lloyd*

Plaxton Première 350 bodywork is fitted to Volvo N781PEC, seen here in all-over white livery with Travellers Choice names applied to the windscreen. The latest vehicles to join the fleet are also Volvo based but with Jonckheere Mistral 50 bodystyling. The vehicle maintenance base lies next to the main West Coast rail line with the M6 access just a short distance to the north. *Bill Potter*

T61LEC	Volvo B10M-62	Jonckheere Mistral 50	C51FT	1999	
T62LEC	Volvo B10M-62	Jonckheere Mistral 50	C51FT	1999	
T63LEC	Volvo B10M-62	Jonckheere Mistral 50	C51FT	1999	
T64LEC	Volvo B10M-62	Jonckheere Mistral 50	C51FT	1999	

Special event vehicles

| FAP9 | Bedford OB | Duple Vista | C29F | 1949 | Hurst & Leek, Wigan, 1995 |
| LTF346 | Bedford OB | Duple Vista | C29F | 1950 | Topp Line, Liverpool, 1995 |

Previous registrations:

6SVK	L210GJO	6682WY	L213GJO	NIL6258	H493BND
509EBL	D443CNR	BYP985	C174KET	NIL7914	F266KTN
824HAO	K615EEO	HIL8433	A853TDS	NIL9581	F265KTN
899CAN	A539BEC	HIL8915	D120GWS	NIL9932	F485CKU
4150RU	F477WFX, 9530RU, F515WFA	HIL8917	A203OCW	UCW315X	TRB25X, LSU939
5129UA	E902UNW, RIB5093	IIL3198	D98SCW	XDL521	H538SEO
6137RU	K36OUY	JIB3515	D446CNR, NXI900?, D997UKA	XJF386	E901UNW, RIB5092
6267UA	A538BEC, XDO32	KBZ5749	A287FEC	XDO32	L211GJO
		LSU939	B710EOF	YFG333	H539SEO

Livery: White with graduated cream to orange skirt

UK NORTH

UK North Enterprises Ltd, Gorton Lane, Gorton, Manchester M18 8DA

MNC507W	Leyland Atlantean AN68A/1R	Northern Counties	B43/32F	1980	Forrest, Bootle, 1997
MNC512W	Leyland Atlantean AN68A/1R	Northern Counties	B43/32F	1980	Forrest, Bootle, 1997
ORJ371W	Leyland Atlantean AN68A/1R	Northern Counties	B43/32F	1981	GM Buses South, 1996
SND449X	Leyland Atlantean AN68B/1R	Northern Counties	B43/32F	1981	Forrest, Bootle, 1997
SND473X	Leyland Atlantean AN68A/1R	Northern Counties	B43/32F	1982	Forrest, Bootle, 1997
SND506X	Leyland Atlantean AN68B/1R	Northern Counties	B43/32F	1982	Castle, Speke, 1990
A680HNB	Leyland Atlantean AN68D/1R	Northern Counties	B43/32F	1983	Forrest, Aintree, 1999
A711LNC	Leyland Atlantean AN68D/1R	Northern Counties	B43/32F	1984	Stagecoach Manchester, 1998
P902PWW	DAF SB220LT550	Northern Counties Paladin	B49F	1996	Speedlink, 1999
P909PWW	DAF SB220LT550	Northern Counties Paladin	B49F	1996	Speedlink, 1999
R396XDA	DAF DE02GSSB220	Plaxton Prestige	N42F	1997	Arriva Bus & Coach, 1999
R397XDA	DAF DE02GSSB220	Plaxton Prestige	N42F	1997	Arriva Bus & Coach, 1999
V651LWT	DAF DE02RSDB250	Alexander ALX400	N45/23F	1999	
V652LWT	DAF DE02RSDB250	Alexander ALX400	N45/23F	1999	

Livery: Red and dark blue, grey and yellow is being added to new vehicles.

UK North commenced operation with a fleet of Leyland Atlanteans on several routes in the Manchester area. The vehicles were all new to Greater Manchester Transport, though have been sourced from various fleets. Recent arrivals have been modern DAF buses, the latest with low-floor Alexander ALX400 bodywork. Pictured in Piccadilly is Atlantean SND449X which was working route 86 when seen. *Paul Wigan*

UNIVERSAL

Universal Buses Ltd, Ward Street, Chadderton, Oldham OL9 9EX

801	KDZ5801	Dennis Dart 9SDL3011	Wright Handybus	B32F	1991	Travel West Midlands (YB), 1999
802	KDZ5802	Dennis Dart 9SDL3011	Wright Handybus	B32F	1991	Travel West Midlands (YB), 1999
803	KDZ5803	Dennis Dart 9SDL3011	Wright Handybus	B32F	1991	Travel West Midlands (YB), 1999
804	KDZ5804	Dennis Dart 9SDL3011	Wright Handybus	B32F	1991	Travel West Midlands (YB), 1999
805	KDZ5805	Dennis Dart 9SDL3011	Wright Handybus	B32F	1991	Travel West Midlands (YB), 1999
807	R807WJA	Dennis Dart SLF	UVG UrbanStar	N31F	1997	
808	R808WJA	Dennis Dart SLF	UVG UrbanStar	N31F	1997	
809	R809WJA	Dennis Dart SLF	UVG UrbanStar	N31F	1997	
810	R810WJA	Dennis Dart SLF	UVG UrbanStar	N31F	1997	
811	R811WJA	Dennis Dart SLF	UVG UrbanStar	N31F	1997	
812	R812WJA	Dennis Dart SLF	UVG UrbanStar	N31F	1997	
813	R813WJA	Mercedes-Benz Vario O810	Plaxton Beaver 2	B31F	1998	
814	R814WJA	Mercedes-Benz Vario O810	Plaxton Beaver 2	B27F	1998	
815	R815WJA	Mercedes-Benz Vario O810	Plaxton Beaver 2	B27F	1998	
816	R816WJA	Mercedes-Benz Vario O810	Plaxton Beaver 2	B31F	1998	
817	R817WJA	Optare L1150	Optare Excel	N42F	1997	
818	R818WJA	Optare L1150	Optare Excel	N42F	1997	
819	R819WJA	Optare L1150	Optare Excel	N42F	1997	
920	S920SVM	Dennis Dart SLF	Plaxton Pointer SPD	N42F	1999	
925	S925SVM	Mercedes-Benz Vario O814	Plaxton Beaver 2	B31F	1998	

Livery:- White

VALE of MANCHESTER

Vales Coaches (Manchester) Ltd, 49 Broughton Street, Manchester M8 8AN

F623YCW	Iveco Daily 49.10	Northern Counties	BC22F	1989	
H406BVR	Mercedes-Benz 709D	Carlyle	B27F	1990	Timeline, Leigh, 1997
H522FSB	Mercedes-Benz 709D	Reeve Burgess Beaver	B23F	1990	Timeline, Leigh, 1997
H564OOK	Mercedes-Benz 709D	Carlyle	B27F	1991	Timeline, Leigh, 1997
H415BVR	Mercedes-Benz 709D	Carlyle	B27F	1991	Timeline, Leigh, 1996
K881UDB	Mercedes-Benz 709D	Plaxton Beaver	B27F	1993	Derwent, Swalwell, 1997
K883UDB	Mercedes-Benz 709D	Plaxton Beaver	B27F	1993	G M North, 1997
L644DNA	Mercedes-Benz 709D	Plaxton Beaver	B27F	1993	Cooper, Dukinfield, 1996
L645DNA	Mercedes-Benz 709D	Plaxton Beaver	B27F	1993	Cooper, Dukinfield, 1996
N416CBU	Mercedes-Benz 709D	Plaxton Beaver	B27F	1996	
N417CBU	Mercedes-Benz 709D	Plaxton Beaver	B27F	1996	
P418HNF	Mercedes-Benz 709D	Alexander Sprint	B23F	1996	
P419HNF	Mercedes-Benz 709D	Alexander Sprint	B23F	1996	
S738RNE	Mercedes-Benz Vario O814	Plaxton Beaver 2	B27F	1998	
S739RNE	Mercedes-Benz Vario O814	Plaxton Beaver 2	B27F	1998	

Livery: Cream and blue

Opposite, top: **Universal is a new operation for the region, complete with new buses. Initially the work comprised tendered services with linking journeys over established routes, though the company has expanded with new registrations. Pictured near Manchester Arndale is R811WJA, a Dennis Dart with UVG bodywork.** *Cliff Beeton*
Opposite, bottom:- **The all-minibus fleet of Vale of Manchester has recently reduced the number of non-Mercedes-Benz minis to just one. Representing the fleet is H415BVR, one of three with Carlyle bodywork. Vale of Manchester use the Wayfarer 2 ticket system.** *Phillip Stephenson*

WRIGHT BROS

Wright Brothers (Coaches) Ltd, Central Garage Nenthead, Alston, Cumbria, CA9 3NP

FUN319	Crossley SD42/7	Burlingham	C33F	1949	Patterson, Beadnell, 1959
RRM915M	Bedford YRQ	Plaxton Panorama Elite III Exp	C45F	1974	
VRM73S	Bedford YLQ	Plaxton Supreme III Express	C45F	1978	
JAO400V	Bedford YMT	Plaxton Supreme IV Express	C45F	1980	
UGE807W	Volvo B10M-61	Plaxton Supreme IV	C57F	1981	McPhail, Newarthill, 1992
LTG271X	Volvo B58-56	Plaxton Supreme IV	C53F	1981	Capital, Cwmbran, 1994
SAO466X	Bedford YNT	Plaxton Supreme V Express	C53F	1982	
SAO467X	Bedford YMP	Plaxton Supreme V Express	C45F	1982	
MJI6406	Volvo B10M-56	Plaxton Viewmaster IV	C51F	1982	Thandi S, Rowley Regis, 1998
A431ESO	Volvo B10M-56	Plaxton Paramount 3200	C53F	1983	Dereham, East Dereham, 1998
TSU613	Kässbohrer Setra S228DT	Kässbohrer Imperial	C16/12CT	1984	Vector, Bishops Waltham, 1998
CIW290	Volvo B10M-56	Van Hool Alizée H	C49F	1984	Park's of Hamilton, 1988
UDX921	Volvo B10M-53	Jonckheere Jubilee P90	C52/6FT	1986	Team Travel, Horsforth, 1992
SJI8113	Scania K112CRB	Jonckheere Jubilee P599	C12FT	1988	Buddens, Romsey , 1996
TSV807	Scania K113TRB	Van Hool Astrobel	C--/16DT	1990	Busways, 1994
H917PTG	Volvo B10M-60	Ikarus Blue Danube 358	C53FT	1991	Thames Transit, 1995
J499MOD	Volvo B10M-60	Ikarus Blue Danube 358	C49FT	1991	Thames Transit, 1997

Previous registrations:

CIW290	A604UGD	SJI8113	E517KNV	TSV807	G31WTY,813VPU, G852NUP
MJI6406	KNP5X	TSU613	A411GPY	UDX921	C363SVV

Livery: Cream, gold, sky blue and black

Nenthead is located to the east of Penrith. A depot in the latter town was replaced some time ago. Representing the fleet is SAO467X, a Bedford with Plaxton Supreme V bodywork to express specification. It had just completed service to the village when pictured. *Bill Potter*

Index to Vehicles

Reg	Operator	Reg	Operator	Reg	Operator	Reg	Operator
5AAX	Holmeswood	A247GAU	Stagecoach Cumberland	A736LNC	First Manchester	ANA538Y	Finglands
6RED	Redline Coaches	A280ROW	R Bullocks	A738NNA	First Manchester	ANA539Y	First Manchester
6SVK	Travellers	A355HHG	Blackpool	A739NNA	First Manchester	ANA540Y	First Manchester
10RU	Finglands	A356HHG	Blackpool	A740NNA	First Manchester	ANA541Y	First Manchester
12RED	Redline Coaches	A357HHG	Blackpool	A741NNA	Rossendale	ANA542Y	First Manchester
15RED	Redline Coaches	A358HHG	Blackpool	A745DRM	Robinson's	ANA543Y	Finglands
16RED	Redline Coaches	A359HHG	Blackpool	A746NNA	First Manchester	ANA547Y	First Manchester
109DRM	Stagecoach Cumberland	A360HHG	Blackpool	A747NNA	Stagecoach Manchester	ANA548Y	First Manchester
188TAE	Titterington	A361HHG	Blackpool	A749NNA	Stagecoach Manchester	ANA549Y	First Manchester
201SC	Holmeswood	A362HHG	Blackpool	A750NNA	Stotts Tours	ANA551Y	First Manchester
212VPF	Titterington	A431ESO	Wright Bros	A752NNA	Rossendale	ANA554Y	First Manchester
213ONU	Blackburn	A462LFV	Fishwick	A753LWY	First Manchester	ANA555Y	First Manchester
219DLV	Sim's Travel	A499MHG	Jim Stones	A753NNA	First Manchester	ANA558Y	First Manchester
368SHX	Titterington	A541KUM	First Manchester	A755LWY	First Manchester	ANA561Y	First Manchester
403BGO	Mayne	A546KUM	First Manchester	A755NNA	First Manchester	ANA562Y	First Manchester
4150RU	Travellers	A547HBV	Abbotts	A756NNA	First Manchester	ANA563Y	First Manchester
4360WF	Battersby	A547KUM	First Manchester	A757NNA	Stagecoach Manchester	ANA564Y	Finglands
466YMG	Holmeswood	A576HDB	First Manchester	A758NNA	First Manchester	ANA566Y	First Manchester
509EBL	Travellers	A577HDB	First Manchester	A760NNA	First Manchester	ANA567Y	First Manchester
515VTB	Hulme Hall	A578HDB	First Manchester	A761NNA	Stagecoach Manchester	ANA570Y	First Manchester
563UM	Brownrigg's	A579HDB	First Manchester	A763NNA	First Manchester	ANA571Y	First Manchester
647JOE	Finglands	A580HDB	First Manchester	A764NNA	Stagecoach Manchester	ANA573Y	First Manchester
824HAO	Travellers	A581HDB	Stagecoach Manchester	A765NNA	First Manchester	ANA575Y	First Manchester
890TTE	Titterington	A582HDB	Stagecoach Manchester	A777RBV	Abbotts	ANA576Y	First Manchester
899CAN	Travellers	A583HDB	Stagecoach Manchester	A914RRN	Holmeswood	ANA578Y	First Manchester
990ENR	Robinson's	A584HDB	Stagecoach Manchester	A975OST	Stagecoach Cumberland	ANA580Y	First Manchester
1359UP	Battersby	A585HDB	Stagecoach Manchester	A978OST	Stagecoach Ribble	ANA581Y	First Manchester
3182NF	Battersby	A618FCD	Lancaster Bus	A979OST	Stagecoach Ribble	ANA583Y	First Manchester
3267HX	Battersby	A656HNB	First Manchester	AAP651T	Fishwick	ANA584Y	First Manchester
3927TR	Robinson's	A658HNB	First Manchester	AAX300A	Holmeswood	ANA587Y	First Manchester
4761TR	Robinson's	A659HNB	First Manchester	AAX488A	Border	ANA588Y	First Manchester
5108VX	Battersby	A662HNB	First Manchester	ABN721T	Border	ANA590Y	First Manchester
5129UA	Travellers	A663HNB	First Manchester	ABV43B	Blackburn	ANA591Y	First Manchester
6137RU	Travellers	A664KUM	Blue Bus	ABV939Y	First Manchester	ANA594Y	First Manchester
6267UA	Travellers	A666KUM	Blue Bus	AFB597V	South Lancs Travel	ANA595Y	First Manchester
6682WY	Travellers	A667HNB	First Manchester	AFM1W	Stagecoach Ribble	ANA599Y	First Manchester
7017UN	Battersby	A667KUM	Blue Bus	AFM5W	Blackburn	ANA603Y	First Manchester
7121RU	Battersby	A670HNB	First Manchester	AHG331V	Blackpool	ANA606Y	First Manchester
7144FN	Battersby	A671HNB	Finglands	AHG332V	Blackpool	ANA607Y	First Manchester
7622UK	Battersby	A672HNB	First Manchester	AHG333V	Blackpool	ANA610Y	First Manchester
7845UG	Battersby	A673HNB	First Manchester	AHG334V	Blackpool	ANA611Y	First Manchester
8850WU	Battersby	A676HNB	First Manchester	AHG336V	Blackpool	ANA615Y	First Manchester
9884TR	Robinson's	A677HNB	First Manchester	AHG337V	Blackpool	ANA616Y	First Manchester
A4HWD	Holmeswood	A678HNB	Stagecoach Ribble	AHG338V	Blackpool	ANA617Y	First Manchester
A5FWS	Stainton	A679HNB	Stagecoach Ribble	AHG339V	Blackpool	ANA621Y	First Manchester
A15TVL	Sim's Travel	A680HNB	UK North	AHG340V	Blackpool	ANA622Y	First Manchester
A19HWD	Holmeswood	A681HNB	First Manchester	ANA1Y	Stagecoach Ribble	ANA623Y	First Manchester
A20HWD	Holmeswood	A682HNB	First Manchester	ANA2Y	Stagecoach Ribble	ANA626Y	First Manchester
A20JDA	Archway	A686HNB	First Manchester	ANA3Y	Stagecoach Ribble	ANA629Y	First Manchester
A21HNC	Stagecoach Manchester	A689HNB	First Manchester	ANA4Y	Stagecoach Manchester	ANA633Y	First Manchester
A22HNC	Stagecoach Manchester	A691HNB	First Manchester	ANA6Y	Stagecoach Manchester	ANA635Y	First Manchester
A23HNC	Stagecoach Manchester	A692HNB	First Manchester	ANA7Y	Stagecoach Manchester	ANA636Y	First Manchester
A23JBV	Blackburn	A695HNB	Stotts Tours	ANA8Y	Stagecoach Manchester	ANA637Y	Finglands
A24HNC	Stagecoach Manchester	A697HNB	First Manchester	ANA9Y	Stagecoach Manchester	ANA638Y	First Manchester
A25HNC	Stagecoach Manchester	A701LNC	First Manchester	ANA10Y	Stagecoach Manchester	ANA639Y	Finglands
A26JBV	Blackburn	A703LNC	First Manchester	ANA47T	Stotts Tours	ANA640Y	First Manchester
A26ORJ	Stagecoach Manchester	A704LNC	Stotts Tours	ANA151Y	First Manchester	ANA641Y	First Manchester
A27ORJ	Stagecoach Manchester	A707DAU	Blackpool	ANA152Y	First Manchester	ANA642Y	First Manchester
A28JBV	Blackburn	A708DAU	Blackpool	ANA158Y	Stagecoach Manchester	ANA645Y	First Manchester
A28ORJ	Stagecoach Manchester	A709DAU	Blackpool	ANA159Y	Holmeswood	ANA648Y	First Manchester
A29JBV	Blackburn	A709LNC	First Manchester	ANA166Y	First Manchester	ANA649Y	First Manchester
A29ORJ	Stagecoach Manchester	A710DAU	Blackpool	ANA167Y	First Manchester	ANA650Y	First Manchester
A30ORJ	Stagecoach Manchester	A710LNC	Finglands	ANA168Y	First Manchester	ANA652Y	First Manchester
A31ORJ	Stagecoach Manchester	A711LNC	UK North	ANA169Y	First Manchester	ANA654Y	First Manchester
A32ORJ	Stagecoach Manchester	A712LNC	First Manchester	ANA171Y	First Manchester	ANA655Y	First Manchester
A33MRN	Preston	A713LNC	First Manchester	ANA172Y	First Manchester	ARC669T	Holmeswood
A33ORJ	Stagecoach Manchester	A716LNC	First Manchester	ANA173Y	Stagecoach Manchester	ARH304K	Blackpool
A101DPB	Mayne	A717LNC	First Manchester	ANA174Y	First Manchester	ARH309K	Blackpool
A102DAO	Stagecoach Cumberland	A718LNC	First Manchester	ANA175Y	First Manchester	ARN888Y	Stagecoach Cumberland
A129MFL	East Lancashire	A720LNC	First Manchester	ANA176Y	First Manchester	AYR324T	Blackpool
A138MRN	Stagecoach Cumberland	A721LNC	First Manchester	ANA178Y	First Manchester	B1BUS	Jim Stones
A142MRN	Stagecoach Ribble	A722LNC	Stotts Tours	ANA181Y	First Manchester	B10JYM	Jim Stones
A143MRN	Stagecoach Ribble	A727LNC	First Manchester	ANA184Y	First Manchester	B11JYM	Jim Stones
A145OFR	Stagecoach Ribble	A728ANH	East Lancashire	ANA186Y	First Manchester	B16TYG	Jim Stones
A156OFR	Stagecoach Ribble	A728LNC	First Manchester	ANA187Y	First Manchester	B21TVU	Stagecoach Manchester
A157OFR	Stagecoach Ribble	A729ANH	East Lancashire	ANA188Y	First Manchester	B22TVU	Stagecoach Manchester
A158OFR	Stagecoach Ribble	A729LNC	First Manchester	ANA531Y	First Manchester	B23TVU	Stagecoach Manchester
A159OFR	Stagecoach Ribble	A732LNC	First Manchester	ANA532Y	First Manchester	B24TVU	Stagecoach Manchester
A196WGE	Rossendale	A733LNC	First Manchester	ANA535Y	First Manchester	B25ADW	Blue Bus
A213SAE	Border	A735NNA	Stotts Tours			B25TVU	Stagecoach Manchester

Reg	Operator	Reg	Operator	Reg	Operator	Reg	Operator
B26ADW	South Lancs Travel	B105SJA	First Manchester	B903TVR	Stagecoach Manchester	C177ECK	Stagecoach Cumberland
B26TVU	Stagecoach Manchester	B106HAO	Stagecoach Cumberland	B904TVR	Stagecoach Manchester	C177YBA	First Manchester
B27ADW	South Lancs Travel	B106SJA	First Manchester	B905TVR	Stagecoach Manchester	C178ECK	Stagecoach Ribble
B27TVU	Stagecoach Manchester	B107SJA	First Manchester	B906TVR	Stagecoach Manchester	C178YBA	Stagecoach Manchester
B28TVU	Stagecoach Manchester	B108SJA	First Manchester	B907TVR	Stagecoach Manchester	C179ECK	Stagecoach Cumberland
B29TVU	Stagecoach Manchester	B109SJA	First Manchester	B908TVR	Stagecoach Manchester	C179YBA	Stagecoach Manchester
B30TVU	Stagecoach Manchester	B110SJA	Stagecoach Manchester	B909BGA	Kirby Lonsdale	C180YBA	First Manchester
B34PJA	Stagecoach Manchester	B111SJA	First Manchester	B909TVR	Stagecoach Manchester	C181YBA	Stagecoach Manchester
B35PJA	Stagecoach Manchester	B112SJA	First Manchester	B910TVR	Stagecoach Manchester	C182YBA	First Manchester
B36PJA	Stagecoach Manchester	B113SJA	First Manchester	B911TVR	Stagecoach Manchester	C183YBA	First Manchester
B37PJA	First Manchester	B114SJA	Stagecoach Manchester	B912TVR	Stagecoach Manchester	C184YBA	Stagecoach Manchester
B38PJA	First Manchester	B115SJA	First Manchester	B913TVR	Stagecoach Manchester	C185YBA	Stagecoach Manchester
B39PJA	Stagecoach Manchester	B116TVU	First Manchester	B914TVR	Stagecoach Manchester	C186YBA	First Manchester
B40PJA	First Manchester	B117TVU	First Manchester	B915TVR	Stagecoach Manchester	C187YBA	First Manchester
B41PJA	First Manchester	B117TVU	Stagecoach Cumberland	B916TVR	Stagecoach Manchester	C188YBA	First Manchester
B42PJA	First Manchester	B118TVU	Stagecoach Cumberland	B917TVR	Stagecoach Manchester	C189YBA	First Manchester
B43MAO	Stagecoach Cumberland	B119TVU	Stagecoach Manchester	B918TVR	Stagecoach Manchester	C190YBA	First Manchester
B43PJA	First Manchester	B120TVU	First Manchester	B919TVR	Stagecoach Manchester	C191YBA	Stagecoach Manchester
B43UCK	Blue Bus	B121TVU	Stagecoach Manchester	B920TVR	Stagecoach Manchester	C192YBA	First Manchester
B44PJA	First Manchester	B122TVU	Stagecoach Manchester	B930CDT	R Bullocks	C193YBA	Stagecoach Manchester
B45PJA	First Manchester	B123TVU	First Manchester	B931YCW	Darwen Coach	C194YBA	First Manchester
B46PJA	First Manchester	B124TVU	Stagecoach Manchester	B944FET	R Bullocks	C195YBA	Stagecoach Manchester
B47PJA	First Manchester	B125TVU	Stagecoach Manchester	B946FET	R Bullocks	C196OHH	Titterington
B48PJA	First Manchester	B126WNB	Stagecoach Manchester	B957LHN	Blue Bus	C196YBA	Stagecoach Manchester
B49PJA	Stagecoach Manchester	B127WNB	First Manchester	BFV861R	Blackburn	C197YBA	Stagecoach Manchester
B51XFV	Pilkington	B128WNB	First Manchester	BHF291A	Holmeswood	C198YBA	Stagecoach Manchester
B52PJA	First Manchester	B129WNB	First Manchester	BNC947T	Archway	C199YBA	Stagecoach Manchester
B53PJA	Stagecoach Manchester	B130WNB	First Manchester	BOM7V	Border	C200WGV	Lancaster Bus
B54PJA	First Manchester	B131WNB	First Manchester	BUH239V	Stagecoach Ribble	C200YBA	First Manchester
B55PJA	Stagecoach Manchester	B132WNB	Stagecoach Manchester	BUH240V	Stagecoach Ribble	C201CBU	First Manchester
B56AOP	Lancaster Bus	B133WNB	First Manchester	BUI1133	R Bullocks	C201FVU	First Manchester
B56PJA	Stagecoach Manchester	B134WNB	First Manchester	BUI1424	R Bullocks	C202CBU	First Manchester
B57PJA	Stagecoach Manchester	B135WNB	Stagecoach Manchester	BUI1484	R Bullocks	C202FVU	First Manchester
B58PJA	Stagecoach Manchester	B136WNB	First Manchester	BUI1610	R Bullocks	C203CBU	First Manchester
B59PJA	First Manchester	B137WNB	Stagecoach Manchester	BUI1675	R Bullocks	C203FVU	First Manchester
B60PJA	Stagecoach Manchester	B138WNB	Stagecoach Manchester	BUS1N	Jim Stones	C204CBU	First Manchester
B61PJA	First Manchester	B140WNB	First Manchester	BUS1T	Jim Stones	C204FVU	First Manchester
B62PJA	First Manchester	B141WNB	First Manchester	BVP807V	Blackburn	C205CBU	Stagecoach Manchester
B63PJA	First Manchester	B142WNB	First Manchester	BVR100T	Mayne	C205FVU	First Manchester
B64PJA	First Manchester	B143WNB	Stagecoach Manchester	BYP985	Travellers	C206CBU	First Manchester
B65PJA	Stagecoach Manchester	B144WNB	First Manchester	BYW361V	Blackburn	C206FVU	First Manchester
B66PJA	First Manchester	B145WNB	Stagecoach Manchester	BYW379V	R Bullocks	C207CBU	Stagecoach Manchester
B67PJA	Stagecoach Manchester	B146XNA	Stagecoach Manchester	BYW402V	Pilkington	C207FVU	First Manchester
B68PJA	First Manchester	B147XNA	Stagecoach Manchester	C34CHM	Rossendale	C208CBU	Stagecoach Manchester
B69PJA	Stagecoach Manchester	B148XNA	First Manchester	C39CHM	Rossendale	C208FVU	First Manchester
B70PJA	Stagecoach Manchester	B149XNA	Stagecoach Manchester	C40CHM	Rossendale	C209CBU	First Manchester
B71PJA	First Manchester	B150XNA	Stagecoach Manchester	C76UHN	Blue Bus	C209FVU	First Manchester
B72PJA	Stagecoach Manchester	B151WRN	Stagecoach Cumberland	C84CHM	Rossendale	C210CBU	Stagecoach Manchester
B73PJA	First Manchester	B151XNA	First Manchester	C85CHM	Rossendale	C210FVU	First Manchester
B74PJA	First Manchester	B152TRN	Stagecoach Ribble	C88CHM	Rossendale	C211CBU	First Manchester
B75PJA	First Manchester	B152XNA	First Manchester	C89CHM	Rossendale	C212CBU	Stagecoach Manchester
B76PJA	First Manchester	B153WRN	Stagecoach Cumberland	C90CHM	Rossendale	C213CBU	Stagecoach Manchester
B77PJA	Stagecoach Manchester	B153XNA	Stagecoach Cumberland	C93CHM	Rossendale	C214CBU	Stagecoach Manchester
B78PJA	First Manchester	B154WRN	Stagecoach Cumberland	C96CHM	Rossendale	C215CBU	Stagecoach Manchester
B79PJA	First Manchester	B154XNA	Stagecoach Manchester	C100HSJ	The Coachmasters	C216CDU	Stagecoach Manchester
B80PJA	Stagecoach Manchester	B155XNA	Stagecoach Manchester	C150LWA	Springfield Coachways	C217CBU	First Manchester
B81PJA	First Manchester	B162WRN	Stagecoach Cumberland	C156YBA	Stagecoach Manchester	C218CBU	First Manchester
B82PJA	Stagecoach Manchester	B183FDM	Rossendale	C157YBA	First Manchester	C219CBU	First Manchester
B83PJA	First Manchester	B350PJA	First Manchester	C158YBA	Stagecoach Manchester	C220CBU	First Manchester
B84PJA	Stagecoach Manchester	B351PJA	First Manchester	C159YBA	First Manchester	C221CBU	Stagecoach Manchester
B85PJA	First Manchester	B357UCW	Abbotts	C160YBA	First Manchester	C222CBU	First Manchester
B86SJA	Stagecoach Manchester	B363UBV	Blackpool	C161YBA	First Manchester	C223CBU	First Manchester
B87SJA	Stagecoach Manchester	B364UBV	Blackpool	C162YBA	First Manchester	C224CBU	Stagecoach Manchester
B88SJA	Stagecoach Manchester	B500MPY	Jim Stones	C163YBA	First Manchester	C225CBU	First Manchester
B89SJA	Stagecoach Manchester	B562RWY	First Manchester	C164YBA	Stagecoach Manchester	C226ENE	Stagecoach Manchester
B90SJA	First Manchester	B564RWY	First Manchester	C165YBA	Stagecoach Manchester	C227ENE	First Manchester
B91SJA	Stagecoach Manchester	B565RWY	First Manchester	C166YBA	Stagecoach Manchester	C228ENE	First Manchester
B92SJA	First Manchester	B568RWY	First Manchester	C167YBA	Stagecoach Manchester	C229ENE	First Manchester
B93SJA	First Manchester	B569RWY	First Manchester	C168YBA	First Manchester	C230ENE	Stagecoach Manchester
B94SJA	Stagecoach Manchester	B571RWY	First Manchester	C169YBA	Stagecoach Manchester	C231ENE	First Manchester
B95SJA	Stagecoach Manchester	B572RWY	First Manchester	C170ECK	Stagecoach Cumberland	C232ENE	First Manchester
B96SJA	First Manchester	B579RWY	First Manchester	C170YBA	Stagecoach Manchester	C233ENE	First Manchester
B97SJA	First Manchester	B891UAS	Stagecoach Ribble	C171ECK	Stagecoach Ribble	C234ENE	Stagecoach Manchester
B98SJA	First Manchester	B892UAS	Stagecoach Cumberland	C171YBA	First Manchester	C235ENE	First Manchester
B99SJA	First Manchester	B893UAS	Stagecoach Cumberland	C172ECK	Stagecoach Ribble	C236EVU	Stagecoach Manchester
B100SJA	First Manchester	B894UAS	Stagecoach Ribble	C172YBA	Stagecoach Manchester	C237EVU	First Manchester
B101PHC	Rossendale	B895UAS	Stagecoach Cumberland	C173ECK	Stagecoach Ribble	C238EVU	First Manchester
B101SJA	First Manchester	B896UAS	Stagecoach Ribble	C173YBA	Stagecoach Manchester	C239EVU	First Manchester
B102PHC	Rossendale	B897UAS	Stagecoach Ribble	C174ECK	Stagecoach Cumberland	C240EVU	First Manchester
B102SJA	First Manchester	B898UAS	Stagecoach Ribble	C174YBA	Stagecoach Manchester	C241EVU	First Manchester
B103HAO	Stagecoach Cumberland	B899UAS	Stagecoach Cumberland	C175ECK	Stagecoach Cumberland	C242EVU	First Manchester
B103SJA	First Manchester	B900WRN	Stagecoach Cumberland	C175YBA	Stagecoach Manchester	C243EVU	First Manchester
B104SJA	First Manchester	B901TVR	Stagecoach Manchester	C176ECK	Stagecoach Cumberland	C244EVU	First Manchester
B105HAO	Stagecoach Cumberland	B902TVR	Stagecoach Manchester	C176YBA	Stagecoach Manchester	C245EVU	First Manchester

Reg	Operator	Reg	Operator	Reg	Operator	Reg	Operator
C246FRJ	First Manchester	D261FUL	Holmeswood	DBV144W	Blackburn	E570OCW	Blackpool
C247FRJ	First Manchester	D261JVR	First Manchester	DBV145W	Blackburn	E674DCU	Rossendale
C248FRJ	First Manchester	D262JVR	First Manchester	DBV146W	Blackburn	E675KDG	First Manchester
C249FRJ	First Manchester	D263JVR	First Manchester	DBV147W	Blackburn	E754CHH	Brownrigg's
C250FRJ	First Manchester	D264JVR	First Manchester	DBV829W	Stagecoach Ribble	E755VJO	Brownrigg's
C251FRJ	First Manchester	D265JVR	First Manchester	DBV831W	Stagecoach Ribble	E764KJX	Rossendale
C252FRJ	First Manchester	D266JVR	First Manchester	DBV832W	Stagecoach Ribble	E76MHG	Kirby Lonsdale
C253FRJ	First Manchester	D267JVR	First Manchester	DBV835W	Pilkington	E775WEC	Travellers
C254FRJ	First Manchester	D268JVR	Stagecoach Manchester	DBV839W	Stagecoach Ribble	E902JBB	Blue Bus
C255FRJ	Stagecoach Manchester	D269JVR	Stagecoach Manchester	DEM760Y	Border	E968CVM	Stagecoach Manchester
C281BBP	R Bullocks	D270JVR	First Manchester	DRN1Y	Preston	E979DNK	Lancaster Bus
C282BBP	R Bullocks	D271JVR	First Manchester	DRN2Y	Preston	ECK865E	Holmeswood
C283BBP	R Bullocks	D272JVR	Stagecoach Manchester	DRN173Y	Preston	EFR97W	Abbotts
C284BBP	R Bullocks	D273JVR	First Manchester	DRN174Y	Preston	EFR107W	Abbotts
C285BBP	R Bullocks	D274JVR	First Manchester	DRN175Y	Preston	EGB52T	Stagecoach Cumberland
C293PDC	Stagecoach Manchester	D275JVR	First Manchester	DRN176Y	Preston	ENF555Y	Sim's Travel
C310ENA	Stagecoach Manchester	D276JVR	First Manchester	DRN177Y	Preston	ESU913	Brownrigg's
C336SFL	Brownrigg's	D277JVR	Stagecoach Manchester	DSA253T	First Manchester	ESU920	Brownrigg's
C382SAO	Stagecoach Cumberland	D301JVR	First Manchester	DSA254T	First Manchester	ESU926	Lakeland
C383SAO	Stagecoach Cumberland	D302JVR	First Manchester	DSV943	Stagecoach Cumberland	ETC310W	Stagecoach Manchester
C410VVN	Darwen Coach	D303JVR	First Manchester	DWH700W	Stotts Tours	EUK978	Mayne
C419VVN	Darwen Coach	D304JVR	First Manchester	DWU295T	Fishwick	EXI2455	Blackburn
C481CBU	First Manchester	D305JVR	First Manchester	E45HBV	Fishwick	F30CWY	South Lancs Travel
C482CBU	First Manchester	D306JVR	First Manchester	E45HFE	Brownrigg's	F32AHG	Preston
C483CBU	First Manchester	D307JVR	First Manchester	E46HBV	Fishwick	F42CWY	South Lancs Travel
C718NCD	R Bullocks	D308JVR	First Manchester	E46HFE	Brownrigg's	F88UHG	Preston
C719NCD	R Bullocks	D309JVR	First Manchester	E47CHH	Stagecoach Cumberland	F89UHG	Preston
C720NCD	R Bullocks	D310JVR	First Manchester	E47HBV	Fishwick	F90UHG	Preston
C721NCD	R Bullocks	D311LNB	First Manchester	E48CHH	Stagecoach Cumberland	F91AHG	Preston
C950LWJ	Border	D312LNB	First Manchester	E49CHH	Stagecoach Cumberland	F91CWG	Rossendale
C952LWJ	Border	D313LNB	First Manchester	E50CHH	Stagecoach Cumberland	F92AHG	Rossendale
C954LWJ	Border	D314LNB	First Manchester	E56HFE	Brownrigg's	F92CWG	Rossendale
C959LWJ	R Bullocks	D315LNB	First Manchester	E57HFE	Brownrigg's	F92XBV	Rossendale
C963END	Travellers	D316LNB	First Manchester	E61JFV	Stagecoach Ribble	F93CWG	Rossendale
CAU113T	Border	D317LNB	First Manchester	E62JFV	Stagecoach Ribble	F93XBV	Rossendale
CAZ2051	Stainton	D318LNB	First Manchester	E63JFV	Stagecoach Ribble	F94CWG	Rossendale
CAZ6835	Stainton	D319LNB	First Manchester	E64JFV	Stagecoach Ribble	F94XBV	Rossendale
CEO720W	Stagecoach Ribble	D320LNB	First Manchester	E65JFV	Stagecoach Ribble	F95XBV	Rossendale
CHA460K	Robinson's	D327VVV	Abbotts	E66JFV	Stagecoach Ribble	F100BPW	East Lancashire
CIW290	Wright Bros	D331VVV	Archway	E77LFR	Preston	F100UNV	Archway
CLZ8353	Mayne	D337VBB	J P Travel	E84HRN	Stagecoach Ribble	F101BPW	East Lancashire
CRN80	Cumbria Classic Coaches	D359JUM	Springfield Coachways	E85HRN	Stagecoach Ribble	F102VFV	Battersby
CSF160W	Blue Bus	D380XRS	Stagecoach Cumberland	E88HRN	Stagecoach Ribble	F103XCW	Stagecoach Ribble
CUB532Y	First Manchester	D381XRS	Stagecoach Cumberland	E89HRN	Stagecoach Ribble	F104XCW	Stagecoach Ribble
CUI925	Titterington	D384XAO	Stagecoach Cumberland	E90JHG	Stagecoach Ribble	F105XCW	Stagecoach Ribble
CWG286	Cumbria Classic Coaches	D429NNA	Pilkington	E92LHG	Border	F106XCW	Stagecoach Ribble
CWG726V	Stotts Tours	D501LNA	First Manchester	E94LHG	Border	F107XCW	Stagecoach Ribble
CWR525Y	Stagecoach Ribble	D502LNA	First Manchester	E100MFV	Fishwick	F108XCW	Stagecoach Ribble
CWR526Y	Stagecoach Ribble	D503LNA	First Manchester	E101EVM	Darwen Coach	F109XCW	Stagecoach Ribble
CWX669T	Stagecoach Ribble	D504LNA	First Manchester	E101JFV	Stagecoach Ribble	F110XCW	Stagecoach Ribble
D30VCW	Fishwick	D513VAO	Stagecoach Cumberland	E102EVM	Darwen Coach	F111XCW	Stagecoach Ribble
D32YCW	Fishwick	D528RCK	Stagecoach Cumberland	E102JFV	Stagecoach Ribble	F112HNC	Mayne
D33YCW	Fishwick	D529RCK	Stagecoach Cumberland	E129KYW	J P Travel	F112XCW	Stagecoach Ribble
D35UAO	Stagecoach Manchester	D533RCK	Stagecoach Cumberland	E134SAT	Stotts Tours	F113HNC	Mayne
D36UAO	Stagecoach Cumberland	D559RCK	Stagecoach Cumberland	E135SAT	Stotts Tours	F115YWO	Rossendale
D41SNE	Stagecoach Manchester	D560RCK	Stagecoach Cumberland	E137SAT	Stotts Tours	F130AEL	Sim's Travel
D43AFV	Preston	D641MDB	Lancaster Bus	E139SAT	Stotts Tours	F135SPX	Stagecoach Cumberland
D44UAO	Stagecoach Cumberland	D646NOE	Lancaster Bus	E141SAT	Stotts Tours	F136SPX	Stagecoach Cumberland
D45UAO	Stagecoach Cumberland	D672SEM	Darwen Coach	E144RAX	Darwen Coach	F137SPX	Stagecoach Cumberland
D56SNE	Stagecoach Manchester	D676MHS	Bluebird	E156XHS	Blue Bus	F140HNC	First Manchester
D700KG	Lancaster Bus	D678MHS	Bluebird	E177UWF	Darwen Coach	F145UFR	J P Travel
D72AFV	Preston	D680MHS	Bluebird	E181CNE	Bu-val	F152HAT	The Coachmasters
D73AFV	Preston	D682MHS	Bluebird	E183GRG	Redline Coaches	F153HAT	The Coachmasters
D74AFV	Preston	D682SEM	Darwen Coach	E185CNE	Vale of Manchester	F154HAT	The Coachmasters
D84BLF	Fishwick	D683MHS	Bluebird	E186CNE	Bu-val	F155HAT	The Coachmasters
D102VRP	Border	D683SEM	Darwen Coach	E238UWR	Bu-val	F156HAT	The Coachmasters
D108VRP	Border	D685SEM	Darwen Coach	E245UWR	Bu-val	F157HAT	The Coachmasters
D121HML	Redline Coaches	D689SEM	Darwen Coach	E248UWR	Rossendale	F164DET	Rossendale
D122NON	Archway	D751YCW	Preston	E254UWR	Bu-val	F165DET	Rossendale
D130NON	Lancaster Bus	D754YCW	Preston	E357KPO	J P Travel	F169DET	Rossendale
D137NUS	Battersby	D759YCW	East Lancashire	E402TBS	Darwen Coach	F201FHH	Stagecoach Cumberland
D171PYB	Stotts Tours	D761YCW	Preston	E473SON	Finglands	F202FHH	Stagecoach Cumberland
D177VRP	Border	D762YCW	Preston	E474SON	Finglands	F210YHG	Preston
D210OKY	Redline Coaches	D764YCW	Preston	E476SON	Finglands	F211YHG	Preston
D238PPU	First Manchester	D857XBV	Abbotts	E477SON	Finglands	F212YHG	Preston
D239NCS	Darwen Coach	DBV30W	Stagecoach Cumberland	E480UOF	Finglands	F213YHG	Preston
D240SNC	Stagecoach Manchester	DBV30W	Stagecoach Ribble	E510PVV	Stagecoach Cumberland	F220RSE	Battersby
D241PPU	First Manchester	DBV32W	Stagecoach Ribble	E511PVV	Stagecoach Cumberland	F226FNE	Bu-val
D256JVR	First Manchester	DBV100W	Stagecoach Cumberland	E512PVV	Stagecoach Cumberland	F241FNE	Bu-val
D257JVR	First Manchester	DBV131Y	Stagecoach Ribble	E559GFR	Blackpool	F242MBA	Finglands
D258JVR	First Manchester	DBV132Y	Stagecoach Ribble	E567GFR	Blackpool	F243FNE	Bu-val
D259JVR	First Manchester	DBV134Y	Stagecoach Ribble	E568GFR	Blackpool	F258DAG	Travellers
D25VCW	Fishwick	DBV137Y	Stagecoach Ribble	E569OCW	Blackpool	F278DRJ	First Manchester
D260JVR	Stagecoach Manchester	DBV143W	Blackburn	E570MAC	Lancaster Bus	F279DRJ	First Manchester

Reg	Operator	Reg	Operator	Reg	Operator	Reg	Operator
F280DRJ	First Manchester	F806FAO	Stagecoach Cumberland	G116SBA	Mayne	G906RHH	Titterington
F281DRJ	First Manchester	F807FAO	Stagecoach Cumberland	G117SBA	Mayne	G911RPN	South Lancs Travel
F282DRJ	Stagecoach Manchester	F808FAO	Stagecoach Cumberland	G121PGT	South Lancs Travel	G914RPN	South Lancs Travel
F283DRJ	Stagecoach Manchester	F809FAO	Stagecoach Cumberland	G178PAO	Stagecoach Cumberland	G918DVX	R Bullocks
F284DRJ	First Manchester	F810FAO	Stagecoach Cumberland	G180JHG	Stagecoach Cumberland	G996RKN	Blackburn
F285DRJ	Stagecoach Manchester	F811FAO	Stagecoach Cumberland	G180PAO	Stagecoach Ribble	G999RKN	Blackburn
F286DRJ	First Manchester	F820FWE	J P Travel	G181JHG	Stagecoach Cumberland	GBU12V	First Manchester
F287DRJ	First Manchester	F842EHH	Robinson's	G181PAO	Stagecoach Ribble	GBU13V	First Manchester
F288DRJ	First Manchester	F865LCU	Border	G182JHG	Stagecoach Cumberland	GBU14V	First Manchester
F289DRJ	Stagecoach Manchester	F893XOE	J P Travel	G182PAO	Stagecoach Ribble	GBU15V	First Manchester
F290DRJ	First Manchester	F905YWY	Darwen Coach	G183JHG	Stagecoach Cumberland	GBV101N	Stagecoach Ribble
F291DRJ	Stagecoach Manchester	F914XWY	South Lancs Travel	G184JHG	Stagecoach Cumberland	GBV110N	Stagecoach Ribble
F292DRJ	First Manchester	F915YWY	Darwen Coach	G184PAO	Stagecoach Ribble	GBV152W	Preston
F293DRJ	First Manchester	F919YWY	South Lancs Travel	G185JHG	Stagecoach Cumberland	GBV156W	Preston
F294DRJ	Stagecoach Manchester	F934AWW	Blackpool	G185PAO	Stagecoach Ribble	GCK428W	Fishwick
F295DRJ	Stagecoach Manchester	F953KMA	Travellers	G186JHG	Stagecoach Cumberland	GCK429W	Fishwick
F296DRJ	Stagecoach Manchester	F984HGE	Blackburn	G186PAO	Stagecoach Ribble	GCK430W	Fishwick
F297DRJ	Stagecoach Manchester	F995HGE	Stotts Tours	G187JHG	Stagecoach Cumberland	GDZ3841	Mayne
F298DRJ	Stagecoach Manchester	F998SBC	Archway	G187PAO	Stagecoach Ribble	GFR101W	Stagecoach Ribble
F299DRJ	First Manchester	FAO420V	Stagecoach Cumberland	G188JHG	Stagecoach Cumberland	GHG341W	Blackpool
F300DRJ	Stagecoach Manchester	FAO421V	Stagecoach Cumberland	G188PAO	Stagecoach Ribble	GHG343W	Blackpool
F301DRJ	Stagecoach Manchester	FAO422V	Stagecoach Cumberland	G189JHG	Stagecoach Cumberland	GHG344W	Blackpool
F301JNC	Finglands	FAO423V	Stagecoach Cumberland	G189PAO	Stagecoach Ribble	GHG345W	Blackpool
F302DRJ	First Manchester	FAO424V	Stagecoach Cumberland	G190PAO	Stagecoach Ribble	GHG346W	Blackpool
F302JNC	Finglands	FAO425V	Stagecoach Cumberland	G191PAO	Stagecoach Ribble	GHG347W	Blackpool
F303DRJ	First Manchester	FAO426V	Stagecoach Cumberland	G192PAO	Stagecoach Cumberland	GHG348W	Blackpool
F304DRJ	Stagecoach Manchester	FAO427V	Stagecoach Cumberland	G214KRN	Preston	GHG349W	Blackpool
F305DRJ	First Manchester	FAO428V	Stagecoach Cumberland	G215KRN	Preston	GHG350W	Blackpool
F338VSD	Rossendale	FAP9	Travellers	G216KRN	Preston	GIB1437	Stotts Tours
F339VSD	Rossendale	FBV524S	Fishwick	G217KRN	Preston	GIL2160	Mayne
F359FNB	Vale of Manchester	FCK24Y	Blackburn	G218KRN	Preston	GIL3112	East Lancashire
F368AFR	Blackburn	FCK25Y	Blackburn	G263TSL	Stagecoach Cumberland	GLJ490N	Stagecoach Manchester
F369AFR	Blackburn	FCK27Y	Blackburn	G264TSL	Stagecoach Cumberland	GLJ682N	Pilkington
F370AFR	Blackburn	FDV784V	Stagecoach Ribble	G265TSL	Stagecoach Cumberland	GMB379T	Pilkington
F371AFR	Blackburn	FDV799V	Stagecoach Cumberland	G266TSL	Stagecoach Cumberland	GMS299S	Blue Bus
F371JTN	Travellers	FDV817V	Stagecoach Ribble	G267TSL	Stagecoach Cumberland	GND505N	Mayne
F372AFR	Blackburn	FDV833V	Stagecoach Ribble	G268TSL	Stagecoach Cumberland	GOG226W	Border
F373AFR	Blackburn	FDZ362	Lakeland	G269TSL	Stagecoach Cumberland	GOG231W	Border
F452FDB	R Bullocks	FFR166S	Stagecoach Cumberland	G275MWU	Bu-val	GOG236W	Border
F571RCW	Blackburn	FFR174S	Stagecoach Cumberland	G276MWU	Bu-val	GOG241W	Border
F572RCW	Blackburn	FIL4988	Archway	G293TSL	Stagecoach Cumberland	GOG275W	Border
F573RCW	Blackburn	FUH33V	Stagecoach Ribble	G294TSL	Stagecoach Cumberland	GRM623V	Brownrigg's
F574RCW	Blackburn	FUN319	Wright Bros	G295TSL	Stagecoach Cumberland	GRM625V	Stagecoach Cumberland
F575RCW	Blackburn	FVR257V	Border	G296TSL	Stagecoach Cumberland	GRN895W	Fishwick
F576RCW	Blackburn	FVR259V	Rossendale	G297TSL	Stagecoach Cumberland	GSU554	Border
F577RCW	Blackburn	FVR269V	First Manchester	G298TSL	Stagecoach Cumberland	GSU859T	Stagecoach Manchester
F578RCW	Blackburn	G25HDW	South Lancs Travel	G299TSL	Stagecoach Cumberland	H1FBT	Blackpool
F579WCW	Blackburn	G34OCK	Preston	G300TSL	Stagecoach Cumberland	H2FBT	Blackpool
F580WCW	Blackburn	G35OCK	Preston	G423SNF	R Bullocks	H2HWD	Holmeswood
F581WCW	Blackburn	G36OCK	Preston	G449LKW	Bu-val	H3FBT	Blackpool
F582WCW	Blackburn	G37OCK	Preston	G492XWS	South Lancs Travel	H23YBV	Preston
F597FAM	First Manchester	G57RND	First Manchester	G520LWU	Stagecoach Cumberland	H24YBV	Preston
F616UBV	Bluebird	G58RND	First Manchester	G566PRM	Stagecoach Cumberland	H26YBV	Preston
F617UBV	Blackburn	G59RND	South Lancs Travel	G567PRM	Stagecoach Cumberland	H27YBV	Preston
F618UBV	Blackburn	G60RND	First Manchester	G568PRM	Stagecoach Ribble	H28YBV	Preston
F619UBV	Blackburn	G61RND	South Lancs Travel	G570PRM	Stagecoach Cumberland	H29YBV	Preston
F620UBV	Blackburn	G62RND	First Manchester	G571PRM	Stagecoach Cumberland	H38YCW	Stagecoach Ribble
F621OHD	Timeline	G63RND	First Manchester	G572PRM	Stagecoach Cumberland	H64CCK	Fishwick
F621UBV	Blackburn	G64RND	First Manchester	G573PRM	Stagecoach Ribble	H65CCK	Fishwick
F622UBV	Blackburn	G65RND	First Manchester	G574PRM	Stagecoach Cumberland	H78CFV	Stagecoach Ribble
F623UBV	Blackburn	G66RND	First Manchester	G575PRM	Border	H79CFV	Stagecoach Ribble
F623YCW	Vale of Manchester	G67PFR	Stagecoach Ribble	G576PRM	Border	H81PTG	Kirby Lonsdale
F624UBV	Blackburn	G67RND	First Manchester	G577PRM	Stagecoach Cumberland	H85PTG	Kirby Lonsdale
F625UBV	Blackburn	G68PFR	Stagecoach Ribble	G578PRM	Stagecoach Ribble	H94MOB	Border
F626UBV	Blackburn	G68RND	First Manchester	G579PRM	Stagecoach Ribble	H98MOB	Border
F636XMS	First Manchester	G69RND	First Manchester	G581PVU	Travellers	H101BFR	Preston
F638BKD	Stotts Tours	G70RND	First Manchester	G607JUG	Travellers	H101EKR	South Lancs Travel
F638HVU	East Lancashire	G71RND	First Manchester	G613OTV	Finglands	H101MOB	Border
F639BKD	Stotts Tours	G72RND	First Manchester	G616OTV	Finglands	H101VFV	Rossendale
F639HVU	J P Travel	G97MRN	Stagecoach Ribble	G617OTV	Finglands	H102BFR	Preston
F640XMS	First Manchester	G98NBD	Border	G618OTV	Finglands	H102MOB	Rossendale
F642XMS	First Manchester	G98PCK	Stagecoach Cumberland	G621CPS	South Lancs Travel	H102VFV	Rossendale
F644UVT	Redline Coaches	G99NBD	Border	G627EKA	Stotts Tours	H103BFR	Preston
F672XMS	First Manchester	G101NBV	Blackpool	G665PHH	Stagecoach Cumberland	H103VFV	Rossendale
F682SRN	R Bullocks	G102NBV	Blackpool	G744WEE	Battersby	H104BFR	Preston
F701ENE	Blue Bus	G103NBV	Blackpool	G801JRH	The Coachmasters	H104CHG	Rossendale
F705WFV	Fishwick	G104NBV	Blackpool	G802JRH	The Coachmasters	H104MOB	Rossendale
F706WFV	Fishwick	G105NBV	Blackpool	G803JRH	The Coachmasters	H105CHG	Rossendale
F727VAC	Abbotts	G106NBV	Blackpool	G804JRH	The Coachmasters	H105MOB	Border
F744FDV	Redline Coaches	G107NBV	Blackpool	G805JRH	The Coachmasters	H106MOB	Border
F787EBV	Abbotts	G108NBV	Blackpool	G813RNC	Bluebird	H108MOB	Rossendale
F803FAO	Stagecoach Cumberland	G112TND	Travellers	G874DSC	Vale of Manchester	H109MOB	Rossendale
F804FAO	Stagecoach Cumberland	G114PGT	Border	G888TJA	J P Travel	H109YHG	Blackpool
F805FAO	Stagecoach Cumberland	G115SBA	Mayne	G889TJA	J P Travel	H110MOB	Rossendale

Reg	Operator	Reg	Operator	Reg	Operator	Reg	Operator
H110MOB	Rossendale	H564OOK	Vale of Manchester	HPF313N	Blackburn	J259NNC	Timeline
H110YHG	Blackpool	H611CGG	Phoenix	HRN98N	Blackburn	J263KRN	Stagecoach Ribble
H112MOB	Rossendale	H611MOM	**Rossendale**	HRN99N	Blackburn	J264KRN	Stagecoach Ribble
H112SAO	Stagecoach Cumberland	H612CGG	Phoenix	HRN100N	Blackburn	J266NNC	Timeline
H112YHG	Blackpool	H613CGG	Phoenix	HRN101N	Blackburn	J289NNC	Holmeswood
H113ABV	Stagecoach Ribble	H617ACK	Stagecoach Ribble	HRN102N	Blackburn	J294NNC	Holmeswood
H113MOB	Rossendale	H618ACK	Stagecoach Ribble	HRN103N	Blackburn	J297NNC	Holmeswood
H113SAO	Stagecoach Cumberland	H619ACK	Stagecoach Ribble	HSC164X	Travellers	J298NNC	Holmeswood
H113YHG	Blackpool	H620ACK	Stagecoach Ribble	HSO284V	First Manchester	J299NNC	Holmeswood
H114ABV	Stagecoach Ribble	H620MOM	Rossendale	HWT54N	First Manchester	J400BUL	R Bullocks
H114MOB	Rossendale	H621ACK	Stagecoach Ribble	HXI311	Border	J411WSC	Stagecoach Ribble
H114SAO	Stagecoach Cumberland	H621MOM	Rossendale	IAZ4775	Mayne	J421JBV	Blackburn
H114YHG	Blackpool	H622ACK	Stagecoach Ribble	IAZ4776	Mayne	J422JBV	Blackburn
H115ABV	Stagecoach Ribble	H623ACK	Stagecoach Ribble	IIL3198	Travellers	J423JBV	Blackburn
H115MOB	Rossendale	H627UWR	Vale of Manchester	J7JFS	Fishwick	J424JBV	Blackburn
H115SAO	Stagecoach Cumberland	H628UWR	Vale of Manchester	J14JFS	Fishwick	J425JBV	Blackburn
H115YHG	Blackpool	H629UWR	Vale of Manchester	J20JPT	J P Travel	J461OVU	First Manchester
H116MOB	Rossendale	H649UWR	Brownrigg's	J24MCW	Stagecoach Ribble	J499MOD	Wright Bros
H116SAO	Stagecoach Cumberland	H652UWR	Brownrigg's	J25MCW	Stagecoach Ribble	J505DBE	Battersby
H116YHG	Blackpool	H653UWR	Brownrigg's	J32KLR	First Manchester	J584CUB	Rossendale
H117MOB	Rossendale	H687XBV	Abbotts	J34KLR	First Manchester	J585CUB	Rossendale
H117SAO	Stagecoach Cumberland	H691FNB	J P Travel	J35KLR	First Manchester	J587CUB	Rossendale
H117YHG	Blackpool	H703GVM	First Manchester	J35NLN	Stainton	J588CUB	Rossendale
H118CHG	Blackpool	H705GVM	First Manchester	J36KLR	First Manchester	J603HMF	First Manchester
H118MOB	Rossendale	H708GVM	First Manchester	J101WSC	Stagecoach Ribble	J604HMF	First Manchester
H118SAO	Stagecoach Cumberland	H710BRG	Stainton	J102WSC	Stagecoach Ribble	J606HMF	First Manchester
H119CHG	Blackpool	H724VWU	Blackburn	J103WSC	Stagecoach Ribble	J607HMF	First Manchester
H119MOB	Rossendale	H726LOL	Manchester Airport	J104WSC	Stagecoach Ribble	J608HMF	First Manchester
H119SAO	Stagecoach Cumberland	H804SFP	Phoenix	J105WSC	Stagecoach Ribble	J608KGB	Phoenix
H120CHG	Blackpool	H809WKH	The Coachmasters	J106WSC	Stagecoach Ribble	J609HMF	First Manchester
H122CHG	Blackpool	H810WKH	The Coachmasters	J107KCW	Preston	J614HMF	First Manchester
H127MOB	Rossendale	H812WKH	The Coachmasters	J107WSC	Stagecoach Ribble	J619HMF	First Manchester
H128MOB	Rossendale	H813WKH	The Coachmasters	J108KCW	Preston	J694CGK	Blackburn
H129MOB	Rossendale	H814WKH	The Coachmasters	J108WSC	Stagecoach Ribble	J701CGK	Blackburn
H129YGG	Springfield Coachways	H815WKH	The Coachmasters	J109KCW	Preston	J703CGK	Blackburn
H130MOB	Rossendale	H816WKH	The Coachmasters	J109WSC	Stagecoach Ribble	J704CGK	Blackburn
H131GVM	Stagecoach Manchester	H858NOC	Border	J110KCW	Preston	J708CGK	Blackburn
H131MOB	Rossendale	H881NFS	Stagecoach Manchester	J110WSC	Stagecoach Ribble	J709ONF	First Manchester
H132GVM	Stagecoach Manchester	H917PTG	Wright Bros	J112KCW	Preston	J710CGK	Blackburn
H133GVM	Stagecoach Manchester	H918XUA	Bu-val	J112WSC	Stagecoach Ribble	J710ONF	First Manchester
H134GVM	Stagecoach Manchester	H927DRJ	Holmeswood	J113KCW	Preston	J711CWT	Titterington
H135GVM	Stagecoach Manchester	HBZ4680	Battersby	J113WSC	Stagecoach Ribble	J712BAO	Ken Routledge
H136GVM	Stagecoach Manchester	HCK847S	Abbotts	J114KCW	Preston	J967CGK	Blackburn
H137GVM	Stagecoach Manchester	HDZ5404	First Manchester	J114WSC	Stagecoach Ribble	J969CGK	Blackburn
H137MOB	Border	HDZ5405	First Manchester	J115WSC	Stagecoach Ribble	J976PRW	Preston
H138GVM	Stagecoach Manchester	HDZ5406	First Manchester	J116WSC	Stagecoach Ribble	JAO400V	Wright Bros
H139GVM	Stagecoach Manchester	HDZ5408	First Manchester	J118LKO	South Lancs Travel	JCW517S	Abbotts
H140GVM	Stagecoach Manchester	HDZ5409	First Manchester	J120AAO	Stagecoach Cumberland	JDT432N	Blackburn
H147CBU	J P Travel	HDZ5419	First Manchester	J120AHH	Stagecoach Cumberland	JFR2W	Stagecoach Cumberland
H149SAO	Brownrigg's	HDZ5420	First Manchester	J121AAO	Stagecoach Cumberland	JFR3W	Stagecoach Ribble
H163DJU	Blue Bus	HDZ5422	First Manchester	J121AHH	Stagecoach Cumberland	JFR4W	Stagecoach Ribble
H169WWT	Lancaster Bus	HDZ5423	First Manchester	J122AAO	Stagecoach Cumberland	JFR5W	Stagecoach Ribble
H173DVM	Timeline	HDZ5424	First Manchester	J123AHH	Stagecoach Cumberland	JFR6W	Stagecoach Ribble
H174DVM	Timeline	HDZ5425	First Manchester	J123GRN	Blackpool	JFR7W	Stagecoach Ribble
H174EJU	Blackburn	HDZ5426	First Manchester	J123XHH	Stagecoach Cumberland	JFR8W	Stagecoach Ribble
H176ANE	Travellers	HDZ5429	First Manchester	J124GRN	Blackpool	JFR9W	Stagecoach Ribble
H191WFR	Stagecoach Cumberland	HDZ5431	First Manchester	J124XHH	Stagecoach Cumberland	JFR10W	Stagecoach Ribble
H192WFR	Stagecoach Cumberland	HDZ5433	First Manchester	J125GRN	Blackpool	JFR11W	Stagecoach Ribble
H193WFR	Stagecoach Cumberland	HDZ5435	First Manchester	J125XHH	Stagecoach Cumberland	JFR12W	Stagecoach Ribble
H194WFR	Stagecoach Cumberland	HDZ5437	First Manchester	J126GRN	Blackpool	JFR13W	Stagecoach Ribble
H195WFR	Stagecoach Ribble	HDZ5438	First Manchester	J126XHH	Stagecoach Cumberland	JIB3515	Travellers
H196WFR	Stagecoach Ribble	HDZ5439	First Manchester	J127XHH	Stagecoach Cumberland	JIL6526	J P Travel
H197WFR	Stagecoach Ribble	HDZ5443	First Manchester	J198HFR	Stagecoach Ribble	JIL7608	Stagecoach Manchester
H199ENC	Manchester Airport	HDZ5445	First Manchester	J199HFR	Stagecoach Cumberland	JIL8204	R Bullocks
H201ENC	Manchester Airport	HDZ5448	First Manchester	J200BUL	R Bullocks	JIL8205	R Bullocks
H237AFV	Robinsons	HDZ5449	First Manchester	J201HFR	Stagecoach Cumberland	JIL8206	R Bullocks
H238AFV	Robinsons	HDZ5450	First Manchester	J202HFR	Stagecoach Cumberland	JIL8208	R Bullocks
H239AFV	Robinsons	HDZ5451	First Manchester	J203HFR	Stagecoach Cumberland	JIL8209	R Bullocks
H240AFV	Robinsons	HHH373V	Stagecoach Cumberland	J204HFR	Stagecoach Cumberland	JIL8211	R Bullocks
H241AFV	Robinsons	HIL5341	Blackpool	J205HFR	Stagecoach Cumberland	JIL8212	R Bullocks
H242AFV	Robinsons	HIL5342	Blackpool	J206HFR	Stagecoach Cumberland	JIL8214	R Bullocks
H251ANE	Travellers	HIL5943	Blackpool	J207HFR	Stagecoach Cumberland	JIL8215	R Bullocks
H372OHK	First Manchester	HIL6956	Springfield Coachways	J208HFR	Stagecoach Cumberland	JIL8216	R Bullocks
H373OHK	First Manchester	HIL7467	South Lancs Travel	J209HFR	Stagecoach Cumberland	JIL8217	R Bullocks
H374OHK	First Manchester	HIL7745	Finglands	J210HFR	Stagecoach Cumberland	JJG907P	Blackburn
H406BVR	Vale of Manchester	HIL7746	Finglands	J220XKY	Holmeswood	JKW281W	Stotts Tours
H415BVR	Vale of Manchester	HIL7747	Finglands	J227HDS	Phoenix	JKW292W	Stotts Tours
H463GVM	Stagecoach Manchester	HIL8433	Travellers	J229JJR	South Lancs Travel	JKW298W	Stotts Tours
H464GVM	Stagecoach Manchester	HIL8915	Travellers	J230JJR	South Lancs Travel	JKW304W	Stotts Tours
H465GVM	Stagecoach Manchester	HIL8917	Travellers	J243LFR	Robinsons	JKW315W	Stotts Tours
H466GVM	Stagecoach Manchester	HIL9152	Blue Bus	J244LFR	Robinsons	JND264V	Brownrigg's
H467GVM	Stagecoach Manchester	HJB461W	Fishwick	J245LFR	Robinsons	JPU817	Stagecoach Cumberland
H522FSB	Vale of Manchester	HNE253V	Stagecoach Cumberland	J246LFR	Robinsons	JSJ429W	Lancaster Bus
H538EVM	Sim's Travel	HNL157N	Pilkington	J247LFR	Robinsons	JTY404X	Finglands

Reg	Operator	Reg	Operator	Reg	Operator	Reg	Operator
JWG191P	Blackburn	K614UFR	Stagecoach Ribble	K767DAO	Stagecoach Cumberland	L127DRN	Stagecoach Cumberland
K1BLU	Blue Bus	K615UFR	Stagecoach Cumberland	K768DAO	Stagecoach Cumberland	L127NAO	Stagecoach Cumberland
K4HWD	Holmeswood	K616UFR	Stagecoach Ribble	K769DAO	Stagecoach Cumberland	L128DRN	Stagecoach Ribble
K5JFS	Fishwick	K617SBV	Abbotts	K770DAO	Stagecoach Cumberland	L138BFV	Stagecoach Ribble
K26WBV	Stagecoach Ribble	K617UFR	Stagecoach Ribble	K771DAO	Stagecoach Cumberland	L138XDS	Phoenix
K27WBV	Stagecoach Ribble	K618UFR	Stagecoach Cumberland	K772DAO	Stagecoach Cumberland	L139BFV	Stagecoach Ribble
K28XBA	Rossendale	K619UFR	Stagecoach Cumberland	K773DAO	Stagecoach Cumberland	L140BFV	Stagecoach Ribble
K29XBA	Rossendale	K620UFR	Stagecoach Ribble	K774DAO	Stagecoach Cumberland	L141BFV	Stagecoach Ribble
K75XCW	Stagecoach Ribble	K621UFR	Stagecoach Ribble	K775DAO	Stagecoach Cumberland	L142BFV	Stagecoach Ribble
K84UND	J P Travel	K622UFR	Stagecoach Cumberland	K776DAO	Stagecoach Cumberland	L143BFV	Stagecoach Cumberland
K100BLU	Blue Bus	K623UFR	Stagecoach Ribble	K777DAO	Stagecoach Cumberland	L144BFV	Stagecoach Ribble
K106RNS	Phoenix	K624UFR	Stagecoach Ribble	K778DAO	Stagecoach Cumberland	L145BFV	Stagecoach Ribble
K112XHG	Stagecoach Ribble	K625UFR	Stagecoach Cumberland	K779DAO	Stagecoach Cumberland	L146BFV	Stagecoach Ribble
K113XHG	Stagecoach Cumberland	K626UFR	Stagecoach Cumberland	K780DAO	Stagecoach Cumberland	L148BFV	Stagecoach Ribble
K114XHG	Stagecoach Cumberland	K627UFR	Stagecoach Ribble	K781DAO	Stagecoach Cumberland	L149BFV	Stagecoach Ribble
K115XHG	Stagecoach Ribble	K628UFR	Stagecoach Ribble	K783DAO	Stagecoach Cumberland	L150BFV	Stagecoach Ribble
K116XHG	Stagecoach Ribble	K699ERM	Stagecoach Cumberland	K784DAO	Stagecoach Cumberland	L151BFV	Stagecoach Ribble
K117XHG	Stagecoach Cumberland	K700DAO	Stagecoach Cumberland	K785DAO	Stagecoach Cumberland	L152BFV	Stagecoach Cumberland
K118XHG	Stagecoach Ribble	K701DAO	Stagecoach Cumberland	K786DAO	Stagecoach Cumberland	L153BFV	Stagecoach Ribble
K120XHG	Stagecoach Ribble	K702DAO	Stagecoach Cumberland	K787DAO	Stagecoach Cumberland	L154BFV	Stagecoach Cumberland
K121XHG	Stagecoach Cumberland	K703DAO	Stagecoach Cumberland	K788DAO	Stagecoach Cumberland	L155BFV	Stagecoach Ribble
K123AJA	J P Travel	K704ERM	Stagecoach Cumberland	K833HUM	Lakeland	L156BFV	Stagecoach Ribble
K124XHG	Stagecoach Cumberland	K705DAO	Stagecoach Cumberland	K834HUM	Lakeland	L157BFV	Stagecoach Ribble
K125TCP	Manchester Airport	K706DAO	Stagecoach Cumberland	K871GHH	Stagecoach Cumberland	L158BFV	Stagecoach Ribble
K126TCP	Manchester Airport	K707DAO	Stagecoach Cumberland	K872GHH	Stagecoach Cumberland	L159CCW	Stagecoach Ribble
K127TCP	Manchester Airport	K708DAO	Stagecoach Cumberland	K873GHH	Stagecoach Cumberland	L160CCW	Stagecoach Cumberland
K127UFV	Blackpool	K709DAO	Stagecoach Cumberland	K874GHH	Stagecoach Cumberland	L161CCW	Stagecoach Cumberland
K128DAO	Stagecoach Cumberland	K710DAO	Stagecoach Cumberland	K875GHH	Stagecoach Cumberland	L178KHG	Stagecoach Ribble
K128UFV	Blackpool	K711DAO	Stagecoach Cumberland	K876GHH	Stagecoach Cumberland	L179KHG	Stagecoach Ribble
K129DAO	Stagecoach Cumberland	K712DAO	Stagecoach Cumberland	K877GHH	Stagecoach Cumberland	L196DVM	J P Travel
K129UFV	Blackpool	K713DAO	Stagecoach Cumberland	K878GHH	Stagecoach Cumberland	L237CCW	Stagecoach Ribble
K130DAO	Stagecoach Cumberland	K714DAO	Stagecoach Cumberland	K881UDB	Vale of Manchester	L239CCW	Stagecoach Ribble
K130UFV	Blackpool	K715DAO	Stagecoach Cumberland	K883UDB	Vale of Manchester	L240CCW	Stagecoach Ribble
K131DAO	Stagecoach Cumberland	K716DAO	Stagecoach Cumberland	K977JWW	Manchester Airport	L241CCK	Stagecoach Ribble
K132DAO	Stagecoach Cumberland	K717DAO	Stagecoach Cumberland	K978JWW	Manchester Airport	L248JBV	Robinsons
K133DAO	Stagecoach Cumberland	K718DAO	Stagecoach Cumberland	KAZ1363	Finglands	L249JBV	Robinsons
K134DAO	Stagecoach Cumberland	K719DAO	Stagecoach Cumberland	KAZ4127	Kirby Lonsdale	L250JBV	Robinsons
K135DAO	Stagecoach Cumberland	K720DAO	Stagecoach Cumberland	KBD21V	Robinson's	L251CCK	Stagecoach Ribble
K223MGT	Blackburn	K721DAO	Stagecoach Cumberland	KBZ5749	Travellers	L252CCK	Stagecoach Ribble
K449YCW	Stagecoach Cumberland	K722DAO	Stagecoach Cumberland	KDB137V	Mayne	L253CCK	Stagecoach Ribble
K450YCW	Stagecoach Cumberland	K723DAO	Stagecoach Cumberland	KDZ5801	Universal	L255CCK	Stagecoach Ribble
K451VVR	Shearings	K724DAO	Stagecoach Cumberland	KDZ5802	Universal	L256CCK	Stagecoach Ribble
K452VVR	Shearings	K725DAO	Stagecoach Cumberland	KDZ5803	Universal	L257VSU	Phoenix
K453VVR	Shearings	K726DAO	Stagecoach Cumberland	KDZ5804	Universal	L266VUS	The Coachmasters
K454VVR	Shearings	K727DAO	Stagecoach Cumberland	KDZ5805	Universal	L270LHH	Stagecoach Cumberland
K455VVR	Shearings	K728DAO	Stagecoach Cumberland	KHH377W	Stagecoach Ribble	L271LHH	Stagecoach Ribble
K456VVR	Shearings	K729DAO	Stagecoach Cumberland	KPJ286W	Finglands	L272LHH	Stagecoach Ribble
K457VVR	Shearings	K730DAO	Stagecoach Cumberland	KRM431W	Stagecoach Cumberland	L273LHH	Stagecoach Ribble
K458VVR	Shearings	K731DAO	Stagecoach Cumberland	KRM432W	Stagecoach Cumberland	L274LHH	Stagecoach Ribble
K459VVR	Shearings	K732DAO	Stagecoach Cumberland	KRM433W	Stagecoach Cumberland	L275JAO	Stagecoach Cumberland
K460VVR	Shearings	K733DAO	Stagecoach Cumberland	KRM434W	Stagecoach Cumberland	L276JAO	Stagecoach Cumberland
K461VVR	Shearings	K734DAO	Stagecoach Cumberland	KRM435W	Stagecoach Cumberland	L277JAO	Stagecoach Ribble
K462VVR	Shearings	K735DAO	Stagecoach Cumberland	KRM436W	Stagecoach Cumberland	L278JAO	Stagecoach Ribble
K463VVR	Shearings	K736DAO	Stagecoach Cumberland	KRM437W	Stagecoach Cumberland	L279JAO	Stagecoach Ribble
K464VVR	Shearings	K737DAO	Stagecoach Cumberland	KRN103T	Stagecoach Cumberland	L281JAO	Stagecoach Ribble
K465VVR	Shearings	K738DAO	Stagecoach Cumberland	KRN105T	Stagecoach Cumberland	L282JAO	Stagecoach Cumberland
K466VVR	Shearings	K739DAO	Stagecoach Cumberland	KRN113T	Stagecoach Cumberland	L283JAO	Stagecoach Ribble
K467VVR	Shearings	K740DAO	Stagecoach Ribble	KRN119T	Stagecoach Cumberland	L345ERU	Blackburn
K468VVR	Shearings	K741DAO	Stagecoach Cumberland	KSU857P	Border	L360YNR	Timeline
K469VVR	Shearings	K742DAO	Stagecoach Cumberland	KUM537L	Titterington	L435KHH	Ken Routledge
K470VVR	Shearings	K743DAO	Stagecoach Cumberland	L4BLU	Bluebird	L502FVU	J P Travel
K471VVR	Brownrigg's	K744DAO	Stagecoach Cumberland	L5BUS	J P Travel	L506MAO	Brownrigg's
K472VVR	Shearings	K745DAO	Stagecoach Cumberland	L8SLT	R Bullocks	L510JND	Dennis's
K473VVR	Shearings	K746DAO	Stagecoach Cumberland	L10BUL	R Bullocks	L510MAO	Brownrigg's
K474VVR	Shearings	K748DAO	Stagecoach Cumberland	L18HWD	Holmeswood	L547KRE	Brownrigg's
K475VVR	Shearings	K749DAO	Stagecoach Cumberland	L20BUL	R Bullocks	L561FND	Shearings
K476VVR	Shearings	K750DAO	Stagecoach Cumberland	L26FNE	Rossendale	L562FND	Shearings
K486VVR	Shearings	K751DAO	Stagecoach Cumberland	L27FNE	Rossendale	L563FND	Shearings
K487VVR	Shearings	K752DAO	Stagecoach Cumberland	L42DBC	R Bullocks	L564FND	Shearings
K488VVR	Shearings	K753DAO	Stagecoach Cumberland	L101SDY	Stagecoach Ribble	L565FND	Shearings
K489VVR	Shearings	K754DAO	Stagecoach Cumberland	L102SDY	Stagecoach Ribble	L566FND	Shearings
K490VVR	Shearings	K755DAO	Stagecoach Cumberland	L103SDY	Stagecoach Ribble	L567FND	Shearings
K491VVR	Shearings	K756DAO	Stagecoach Cumberland	L104SDY	Stagecoach Ribble	L568FND	Shearings
K492VVR	Shearings	K757DAO	Stagecoach Cumberland	L105SDY	Stagecoach Manchester	L569FND	Shearings
K493VVR	Shearings	K757PUT	J P Travel	L106SDY	Stagecoach Ribble	L570FND	Shearings
K494VVR	Shearings	K758DAO	Stagecoach Cumberland	L107SDY	Stagecoach Manchester	L629BFV	Stagecoach Ribble
K495VVR	Shearings	K759DAO	Stagecoach Cumberland	L114DNA	Mayne	L630BFV	Stagecoach Ribble
K496VVR	Shearings	K760DAO	Stagecoach Cumberland	L119DRN	Stagecoach Ribble	L631BFV	Stagecoach Ribble
K529EFL	Bu-val	K761DAO	Stagecoach Cumberland	L122DRN	Stagecoach Ribble	L632BFV	Stagecoach Ribble
K600BUL	R Bullocks	K762DAO	Stagecoach Cumberland	L123DRN	Stagecoach Cumberland	L633BFV	Stagecoach Ribble
K610UFR	Stagecoach Ribble	K763DAO	Stagecoach Cumberland	L125DRN	Stagecoach Ribble	L634BFV	Stagecoach Ribble
K611UFR	Stagecoach Cumberland	K764DAO	Stagecoach Cumberland	L125NAO	Stagecoach Cumberland	L635BFV	Stagecoach Ribble
K612UFR	Stagecoach Cumberland	K765DAO	Stagecoach Cumberland	L126DRN	Stagecoach Ribble	L636BFV	Stagecoach Ribble
K613UFR	Stagecoach Ribble	K766DAO	Stagecoach Cumberland	L126NAO	Stagecoach Cumberland	L644DNA	Vale of Manchester

Reg	Operator	Reg	Operator	Reg	Operator	Reg	Operator
L645DNA	Vale of Manchester	M10MGH	Mountain Goat	M348MCY	Rossendale	M609SBA	First Manchester
L660HKS	Stagecoach Ribble	M12BLU	Bluebird	M351MRU	Blackburn	M610SBA	First Manchester
L661MSF	Stagecoach Ribble	M20MGH	Mountain Goat	M359OBU	Manchester Airport	M611SBA	First Manchester
L662MSF	Stagecoach Ribble	M42ONF	Mayne	M360OBU	Manchester Airport	M612SBA	First Manchester
L663MSF	Stagecoach Ribble	M55BUS	Jim Stones	M361OBU	Manchester Airport	M613SBA	First Manchester
L664MSF	Stagecoach Ribble	M101RRJ	First Manchester	M362OBU	Manchester Airport	M614SBA	First Manchester
L665MSF	Stagecoach Ribble	M102RRJ	First Manchester	M374SCK	Blackpool	M617SBA	First Manchester
L667MSF	Stagecoach Ribble	M103RRJ	First Manchester	M375SCK	Blackpool	M618SBA	First Manchester
L668MSF	Stagecoach Ribble	M104RRJ	First Manchester	M376SCK	Blackpool	M627WBV	Blackburn
L669MSF	Stagecoach Ribble	M105RRJ	First Manchester	M377SCK	Blackpool	M628WBV	Blackburn
L680GNA	Dennis's	M106RRJ	First Manchester	M378SCK	Blackpool	M629WBV	Blackburn
L681GNA	Dennis's	M113RNK	Mayne	M379SCK	Blackpool	M630WFR	Blackburn
L682GNA	Dennis's	M131UWY	Titterington	M401TCK	Preston	M631KVU	Shearings
L683GNA	Dennis's	M152LPL	Phoenix	M402TCK	Preston	M631WFR	Blackburn
L707LKY	J P Travel	M158LNC	First Manchester	M403TCK	Preston	M632KVU	Shearings
L708LKY	J P Travel	M159LNC	First Manchester	M404TCK	Preston	M632WFR	Blackburn
L741NFS	Battersby	M160LNC	First Manchester	M405TCK	Preston	M633KVU	Shearings
L743MAO	Ken Routledge	M161LNC	First Manchester	M406TCK	Preston	M634FJF	Stagecoach Manchester
L800BUL	R Bullocks	M164SCK	Stagecoach Ribble	M407TCK	Preston	M634KVU	Shearings
L803FBA	Bu-val	M165SCK	Stagecoach Ribble	M408TCK	Preston	M635KVU	Shearings
L804FBA	Bu-val	M201LNC	First Manchester	M409TCK	Preston	M636KVU	Shearings
L805YBC	Phoenix	M202LNC	First Manchester	M410RND	First Manchester	M637KVU	Shearings
L806YBC	Phoenix	M203LNC	First Manchester	M410TCK	Preston	M638KVU	Shearings
L808YBC	Phoenix	M204VWF	Brownrigg's	M412RND	First Manchester	M639KVU	Shearings
L813KCW	Rossendale	M206LNC	First Manchester	M415RND	First Manchester	M640KVU	Shearings
L814KCW	Rossendale	M207VWU	First Manchester	M416RND	First Manchester	M641KVU	Shearings
L848WDS	Phoenix	M208SCK	Travellers	M422RRN	Finglands	M642KVU	Shearings
L911ECW	Rossendale	M209SCK	Travellers	M423RRN	Finglands	M643KVU	Shearings
L912ECW	Rossendale	M209VWU	First Manchester	M424RRN	Finglands	M644KVU	Shearings
LBZ4071	Blue Bus	M210NDB	Mayne	M425RRN	Finglands	M645KVU	Shearings
LCW411W	Holmeswood	M211NDB	Mayne	M426RRN	Finglands	M646KVU	Shearings
LDZ2951	Blue Bus	M211VWU	First Manchester	M427RRN	Finglands	M646RCP	Blue Bus
LFJ854W	Redline Coaches	M212VWU	First Manchester	M439ECS	Titterington	M647KVU	Shearings
LFJ858W	Stagecoach Ribble	M213VWU	First Manchester	M451VCW	Stagecoach Ribble	M647RCP	Blue Bus
LFJ859W	Stagecoach Ribble	M214VWU	First Manchester	M452VCW	Stagecoach Ribble	M648KVU	Shearings
LFJ861W	Stagecoach Ribble	M215VWU	First Manchester	M453VCW	Stagecoach Ribble	M649KVU	Shearings
LFJ866W	Stagecoach Ribble	M218VWU	First Manchester	M454VCW	Stagecoach Ribble	M650KVU	Shearings
LFJ868W	Redline Coaches	M223VWU	First Manchester	M454VHE	Stagecoach Ribble	M651KVU	Shearings
LFJ883W	Stagecoach Ribble	M224VWU	First Manchester	M455VCW	Stagecoach Cumberland	M652KVU	Shearings
LFJ884W	Stagecoach Ribble	M225VWU	First Manchester	M455VHE	Stagecoach Ribble	M653KVU	Shearings
LFJ885W	Stagecoach Ribble	M226VWU	First Manchester	M456VCW	Stagecoach Cumberland	M654KVU	Shearings
LFR399W	Redline Coaches	M230TBV	Stagecoach Ribble	M456VHE	Stagecoach Ribble	M655KVU	Shearings
LFV205X	Stagecoach Ribble	M231TBV	Stagecoach Ribble	M457VCW	Stagecoach Cumberland	M656KVU	Shearings
LIB1180	Rossendale	M232TBV	Stagecoach Ribble	M457VHE	Stagecoach Ribble	M657KVU	Shearings
LIB1181	Rossendale	M233TBV	Stagecoach Ribble	M458VCW	Stagecoach Cumberland	M658KVU	Shearings
LIB1182	Stagecoach Manchester	M234TBV	Stagecoach Ribble	M458VHE	Stagecoach Ribble	M659KVU	Shearings
LIB283	J P Travel	M234VWU	First Manchester	M459VCW	Stagecoach Cumberland	M660KVU	Shearings
LIB3626	Stainton	M235TBV	Stagecoach Ribble	M459VHE	Stagecoach Ribble	M661KVU	Shearings
LIB3768	Stainton	M236TBV	Stagecoach Ribble	M460VCW	Stagecoach Cumberland	M662KVU	Shearings
LIB3769	Stainton	M236VWU	First Manchester	M460VHE	Stagecoach Ribble	M663KVU	Shearings
LIB6437	Mayne	M237VWU	First Manchester	M461VCW	Stagecoach Cumberland	M664KVU	Shearings
LIB6439	Mayne	M238VWU	First Manchester	M461VHE	Stagecoach Ribble	M664WCK	Fishwick
LIJ749	Blackburn	M239VWU	First Manchester	M462VCW	Stagecoach Cumberland	M665KVU	Shearings
LIL2830	J P Travel	M244VWU	First Manchester	M462VHE	Stagecoach Ribble	M665WCK	Fishwick
LIL2831	J P Travel	M245VWU	First Manchester	M463VCW	Stagecoach Cumberland	M667KVU	Shearings
LIL3317	Stagecoach Manchester	M247VWU	First Manchester	M465RVO	Kirby Lonsdale	M668KVU	Shearings
LIL4492	Redline Coaches	M248VWU	First Manchester	M501PNA	First Manchester	M669KVU	Shearings
LIL4612	Stagecoach Manchester	M249VWU	First Manchester	M502PNA	First Manchester	M670KVU	Shearings
LIW4289	Rossendale	M251NVM	First Manchester	M503PNA	First Manchester	M671KVU	Shearings
LJY145	Stagecoach Cumberland	M252NVM	First Manchester	M504PNA	First Manchester	M672KVU	Shearings
LRN552N	Blackburn	M253NVM	First Manchester	M505PNA	First Manchester	M672RAJ	South Lancs Travel
LRN695N	Redline Coaches	M254NVM	First Manchester	M506PNA	First Manchester	M673KVU	Shearings
LSU939	Travellers	M255NVM	First Manchester	M507PNA	First Manchester	M674KVU	Shearings
LTF346	Travellers	M256NVM	First Manchester	M508PNA	First Manchester	M675KVU	Shearings
LTG271X	Wright Bros	M257NVM	First Manchester	M509PNA	First Manchester	M676KVU	Shearings
LUA273V	Stagecoach Cumberland	M258NVM	First Manchester	M510PNA	First Manchester	M677KVU	Shearings
LUA275V	Stagecoach Cumberland	M259NVM	First Manchester	M511PNA	First Manchester	M678KVU	Shearings
LUA714V	Fishwick	M260KWK	First Manchester	M512PNA	First Manchester	M679KVU	Shearings
LUF549	Blackburn	M261SVU	First Manchester	M513PNA	First Manchester	M680KVU	Shearings
LVS424V	Brownrigg's	M262SVU	First Manchester	M514PNA	First Manchester	M680TDB	Stagecoach Manchester
M1BUS	Jim Stones	M263SVU	First Manchester	M515PNA	First Manchester	M681KVU	Shearings
M1JPT	J P Travel	M264SVU	First Manchester	M516PNA	First Manchester	M681TDB	Stagecoach Manchester
M2BLU	Blue Bus	M265SVU	First Manchester	M517PNA	First Manchester	M682KVU	Shearings
M2JPT	J P Travel	M266SVU	First Manchester	M518PNA	First Manchester	M682TDB	Stagecoach Manchester
M5BLU	Bluebird	M267SVU	First Manchester	M519PNA	First Manchester	M683KVU	Shearings
M6BLU	Bluebird	M268SVU	First Manchester	M520PNA	First Manchester	M683TDB	Stagecoach Manchester
M6HWD	Holmeswood	M269SVU	First Manchester	M529RHG	Rossendale	M684KVU	Shearings
M6MGH	Mountain Goat	M270SVU	First Manchester	M530RHG	Rossendale	M684TDB	Stagecoach Manchester
M6OAT	Mountain Goat	M307KRY	Abbotts	M533RCW	Blackburn	M685KVU	Shearings
M7JPT	J P Travel	M337KRY	Abbotts	M534RCW	Blackburn	M685TDB	Stagecoach Manchester
M8BLU	Bluebird	M338EEC	Travellers	M535RCW	Blackburn	M686KVU	Shearings
M8JPT	J P Travel	M339EEC	Travellers	M536RCW	Blackburn	M686TDB	Stagecoach Manchester
M9BLU	Bluebird	M347MCY	Rossendale	M596WCW	Shearings	M687KVU	Shearings
M10BLU	Bluebird			M608SBA	First Manchester	M687TDB	Stagecoach Manchester

Reg	Operator	Reg	Operator	Reg	Operator	Reg	Operator
M688KVU	Shearings	MRJ48W	Stagecoach Manchester	N207UHH	Stagecoach Cumberland	N407WVR	Stagecoach Manchester
M688TDB	Stagecoach Manchester	MRJ50W	First Manchester	N207WBA	First Manchester	N408WVR	Stagecoach Manchester
M689TDB	Stagecoach Manchester	MRJ55W	Stagecoach Manchester	N208UHH	Stagecoach Cumberland	N409WVR	Stagecoach Manchester
M690TDB	Stagecoach Manchester	MRJ56W	First Manchester	N208WBA	First Manchester	N410WVR	Stagecoach Manchester
M691TDB	Stagecoach Manchester	MRJ58W	First Manchester	N209UHH	Stagecoach Cumberland	N411WVR	Stagecoach Manchester
M692TDB	Stagecoach Manchester	MRJ60W	First Manchester	N209WBA	First Manchester	N412WVR	Stagecoach Manchester
M693TDB	Stagecoach Manchester	MRJ61W	First Manchester	N210LCK	Rossendale	N413WVR	Stagecoach Manchester
M694TDB	Stagecoach Manchester	MRJ62W	First Manchester	N210UHH	Stagecoach Cumberland	N414WVR	Stagecoach Manchester
M695TDB	Stagecoach Manchester	MRJ64W	First Manchester	N210WBA	First Manchester	N415WVR	Stagecoach Manchester
M696TDB	Stagecoach Manchester	MRJ68W	First Manchester	N211UHH	Stagecoach Cumberland	N416CBU	Vale of Manchester
M697TDB	Stagecoach Manchester	MRJ70W	First Manchester	N211WBA	First Manchester	N416WVR	Stagecoach Manchester
M698TDB	Stagecoach Manchester	MRJ275W	Stagecoach Cumberland	N212UHH	Stagecoach Cumberland	N417CBU	Vale of Manchester
M699TDB	Stagecoach Manchester	MRJ401W	First Manchester	N212WBA	First Manchester	N417WVR	Stagecoach Manchester
M728MBU	Dennis's	MRJ407W	First Manchester	N213UHH	Stagecoach Cumberland	N418WVR	Stagecoach Manchester
M729MBU	Dennis's	MSU611Y	Abbotts	N214HWX	Titterington	N419WVR	Stagecoach Manchester
M730MBU	Dennis's	N3BLU	Blue Bus	N214UHH	Stagecoach Cumberland	N420GBV	Preston
M741PRS	Stagecoach Ribble	N4BLU	Blue Bus	N215UHH	Stagecoach Cumberland	N420WVR	Stagecoach Manchester
M742PRS	Stagecoach Ribble	N5BLU	Blue Bus	N224THO	Blackburn	N421GBV	Preston
M743PRS	Stagecoach Ribble	N7BLU	Bluebird	N251KFR	Robinsons	N421WVR	Stagecoach Manchester
M744PRS	Stagecoach Ribble	N13BLU	Bluebird	N252KFR	Robinsons	N422GBV	Preston
M745PRS	Stagecoach Ribble	N14BLU	Bluebird	N253KFR	Robinsons	N422WVR	Stagecoach Manchester
M746PRS	Stagecoach Ribble	N17BLU	Bluebird	N254KFR	Robinsons	N423GBV	Preston
M748PRS	Stagecoach Ribble	N47ANE	Finglands	N256THO	Sim's Travel	N423WVR	Stagecoach Manchester
M749PRS	Stagecoach Ribble	N56CNF	Mayne	N258DUR	South Lancs Travel	N424GBV	Preston
M750PRS	Stagecoach Ribble	N67YVR	Mayne	N281OYE	Travellers	N424WVR	Stagecoach Manchester
M771VCW	Shearings	N68YVR	Mayne	N282OYE	Travellers	N425GBV	Preston
M772VCW	Shearings	N71YNF	First Manchester	N298VRM	Sim's Travel	N425WVR	Stagecoach Manchester
M773VCW	Shearings	N91WVC	Holmeswood	N300EST	Rossendale	N426GBV	Preston
M774VCW	Shearings	N94BNF	Blue Bus	N301WNF	First Manchester	N426WVR	Stagecoach Manchester
M776VCW	Shearings	N95BNF	Blue Bus	N302WNF	First Manchester	N427GBV	Preston
M782PRS	Stagecoach Ribble	N103YHH	Mountain Goat	N303WNF	First Manchester	N427WVR	Stagecoach Manchester
M783PRS	Stagecoach Ribble	N106LCK	Rossendale	N304WNF	First Manchester	N428GBV	Preston
M785PAO	Robinson's	N107LCK	Rossendale	N305WNF	First Manchester	N428WVR	Stagecoach Manchester
M786NBA	R Bullocks	N108LCK	Rossendale	N306WNF	First Manchester	N429GBV	Preston
M788NBA	R Bullocks	N109LCK	Rossendale	N320YNC	Dennis's	N429WVR	Stagecoach Manchester
M789NBA	R Bullocks	N116YHH	Stagecoach Cumberland	N321YNC	Dennis's	N430GBV	Preston
M790NBA	R Bullocks	N117YHH	Stagecoach Cumberland	N322YNC	Dennis's	N430WVR	Stagecoach Manchester
M794PRS	Stagecoach Ribble	N118YHH	Stagecoach Cumberland	N325NPN	Stagecoach Ribble	N431GBV	Preston
M795PRS	Stagecoach Ribble	N119YHH	Stagecoach Cumberland	N326NPN	Stagecoach Ribble	N451VOD	Stagecoach Ribble
M796PRS	Stagecoach Ribble	N120YHH	Stagecoach Cumberland	N327NPN	Stagecoach Ribble	N452VOD	Stagecoach Ribble
M797PRS	Stagecoach Ribble	N121YHH	Stagecoach Cumberland	N327XRP	Stagecoach Cumberland	N453VOD	Stagecoach Ribble
M798PRS	Stagecoach Ribble	N122YHH	Stagecoach Cumberland	N328NPN	Stagecoach Ribble	N454VOD	Stagecoach Ribble
M799PRS	Stagecoach Ribble	N123YHH	Stagecoach Cumberland	N328XRP	Stagecoach Cumberland	N455VOD	Stagecoach Ribble
M832HVC	Finglands	N124YHH	Stagecoach Cumberland	N329NPN	Stagecoach Ribble	N456VOD	Stagecoach Ribble
M844LFP	Holmeswood	N125YHH	Stagecoach Cumberland	N329XRP	Stagecoach Cumberland	N457VOD	Stagecoach Ribble
M846HDF	Stagecoach Ribble	N126YRM	Stagecoach Cumberland	N330NPN	Stagecoach Ribble	N458VOD	Stagecoach Ribble
M847PRS	Stagecoach Ribble	N127YRM	Stagecoach Cumberland	N331NPN	Stagecoach Ribble	N459VOD	Stagecoach Ribble
M8MGH	Mountain Goat	N128VAO	Stagecoach Cumberland	N332NPN	Stagecoach Ribble	N460VOD	Stagecoach Ribble
M907OVR	Border	N128YRM	Stagecoach Cumberland	N333EST	Rossendale	N461VOD	Stagecoach Ribble
M908OVR	Timeline	N129VAO	Stagecoach Cumberland	N333NPN	Stagecoach Ribble	N462VOD	Stagecoach Ribble
M916OVR	Timeline	N129YRM	Stagecoach Cumberland	N334NPN	Stagecoach Ribble	N463VOD	Stagecoach Ribble
M917OVR	Timeline	N130VAO	Stagecoach Cumberland	N335NPN	Stagecoach Ribble	N464VOD	Stagecoach Ribble
M924TYG	Blackpool	N130YRM	Stagecoach Cumberland	N336NPN	Stagecoach Ribble	N465VOD	Stagecoach Ribble
M947OVC	First Manchester	N131VAO	Stagecoach Cumberland	N337NPN	Stagecoach Ribble	N466VOD	Stagecoach Ribble
M949RHH	Titterington	N131YRM	Stagecoach Cumberland	N338NPN	Stagecoach Ribble	N467VOD	Stagecoach Ribble
M950RHH	Titterington	N132VAO	Stagecoach Cumberland	N339NPN	Stagecoach Ribble	N468VOD	Stagecoach Ribble
M958VWY	Manchester Airport	N132YRM	Stagecoach Cumberland	N343CJA	First Manchester	N481REC	Travellers
MAZ4969	Bluebird	N133YRM	Stagecoach Cumberland	N344CJA	First Manchester	N519BJA	Stagecoach Ribble
MAZ4970	Bluebird	N160GRN	Travellers	N347CJA	First Manchester	N520BJA	Stagecoach Ribble
MBZ6454	South Lancs Travel	N173WNF	First Manchester	N348CJA	First Manchester	N521WVR	First Manchester
MDS858V	Stagecoach Ribble	N174WNF	First Manchester	N354TTH	Titterington	N522WVR	First Manchester
MDS859V	Stagecoach Ribble	N175WNF	First Manchester	N365BNF	Finglands	N523WVR	First Manchester
MDS866V	Stagecoach Ribble	N176LCK	Stagecoach Ribble	N372CJA	First Manchester	N524WVR	First Manchester
MEF823W	Hulme Hall	N176WNF	First Manchester	N373CJA	First Manchester	N525WVR	First Manchester
MFR420T	Springfield Coachways	N177LCK	Stagecoach Ribble	N374CJA	First Manchester	N526PYS	Border
MIB920	Blackburn	N177WNF	First Manchester	N375CJA	First Manchester	N526WVR	First Manchester
MIL5581	Pilkington	N178LCK	Stagecoach Ribble	N376CJA	First Manchester	N527WVR	First Manchester
MIW8187	Blackpool	N179LCK	Stagecoach Ribble	N377CJA	First Manchester	N528WVR	First Manchester
MJI5764	Mayne	N180LCK	Stagecoach Ribble	N378CJA	First Manchester	N529WVR	First Manchester
MJI5765	Mayne	N194LFV	Stagecoach Ribble	N379CJA	First Manchester	N530WVR	First Manchester
MJI5766	Mayne	N195LFV	Stagecoach Ribble	N380CJA	First Manchester	N531WVR	First Manchester
MJI6406	Wright Bros	N196LFV	Stagecoach Ribble	N381CJA	First Manchester	N532WVR	First Manchester
MNC504W	UK North	N197LFV	Stagecoach Ribble	N382CJA	First Manchester	N533WVR	First Manchester
MNC507W	UK North	N198LFV	Stagecoach Ribble	N383CJA	First Manchester	N534WVR	First Manchester
MNC512W	UK North	N199LFV	Stagecoach Ribble	N384CJA	First Manchester	N535WVR	First Manchester
MNC521W	Rossendale	N200BLU	Blue Bus	N385CRJ	First Manchester	N536WVR	First Manchester
MNC528W	UK North	N201LFV	Stagecoach Ribble	N386CRJ	First Manchester	N537WVR	First Manchester
MNC529W	Border	N201UHH	Stagecoach Cumberland	N398CNB	Travellers	N538WVR	First Manchester
MRJ32W	First Manchester	N202LFV	Stagecoach Ribble	N401WVR	Stagecoach Manchester	N539WVR	First Manchester
MRJ33W	First Manchester	N202UHH	Stagecoach Cumberland	N402WVR	Stagecoach Manchester	N540WVR	First Manchester
MRJ34W	First Manchester	N203UHH	Stagecoach Cumberland	N403WVR	Stagecoach Manchester	N541WVR	First Manchester
MRJ35W	First Manchester	N204UHH	Stagecoach Cumberland	N404WVR	Stagecoach Manchester	N542WVR	First Manchester
MRJ39W	First Manchester	N205UHH	Stagecoach Cumberland	N405WVR	Stagecoach Manchester	N543WVR	First Manchester
MRJ40W	Stagecoach Manchester	N206UHH	Stagecoach Cumberland	N406WVR	Stagecoach Manchester	N544WVR	First Manchester

Reg	Operator	Reg	Operator	Reg	Operator	Reg	Operator
N545WVR	First Manchester	N649CDB	First Manchester	N883AVV	Stagecoach Manchester	OIJ2645	Springfield Coachways
N546WVR	First Manchester	N649VSS	Stagecoach Cumberland	N884AVV	Stagecoach Manchester	OJD163R	Mayne
N547WVR	First Manchester	N650CDB	First Manchester	N885AVV	Stagecoach Cumberland	OJ4371	Blackpool
N548WVR	First Manchester	N650VSS	Stagecoach Cumberland	N955DWJ	Lakeland	OJ4372	Blackpool
N549WVR	First Manchester	N651CDB	First Manchester	N962WJA	Manchester Airport	OJ4373	Blackpool
N550WVR	First Manchester	N651VSS	Stagecoach Cumberland	N963WJA	Manchester Airport	OJ4374	Blackpool
N551WVR	First Manchester	N652CDB	First Manchester	N964WJA	Manchester Airport	ONF660R	Blackpool
N552WVR	First Manchester	N652VSS	Stagecoach Cumberland	N967ENA	Jim Stones	ONF669R	Blackpool
N553WVR	First Manchester	N653CDB	First Manchester	N973JFR	Shearings	ONF673R	Blackpool
N554SOA	Mountain Goat	N653VSS	Stagecoach Manchester	N974JFR	Shearings	ONF698R	Archway
N554WVR	First Manchester	N654VSS	Stagecoach Manchester	N975JFR	Shearings	OOX807R	Pilkington
N556WVR	First Manchester	N655VSS	Stagecoach Manchester	N976LWR	Brownrigg's	ORJ82W	First Manchester
N557BNF	First Manchester	N656VSS	Stagecoach Manchester	N985FWT	Fishwick	ORJ84W	First Manchester
N558BNF	First Manchester	N657AEO	Kirby Lonsdale	NCW747T	Abbotts	ORJ85W	First Manchester
N559BNF	First Manchester	N657VSS	Stagecoach Manchester	NDE916R	R Bullocks	ORJ86W	First Manchester
N561BNF	First Manchester	N658VSS	Stagecoach Manchester	NFR487M	Abbotts	ORJ89W	First Manchester
N562BNF	First Manchester	N659VSS	Stagecoach Manchester	NFR497M	Abbotts	ORJ96W	First Manchester
N585GRN	Blackpool	N660VSS	Stagecoach Manchester	NFR559T	Fishwick	ORJ97W	First Manchester
N586GRN	Blackpool	N661VSS	Stagecoach Manchester	NFR560T	Fishwick	ORJ353W	Border
N587GRN	Blackpool	N662KCW	Fishwick	NHH358W	Manchester Airport	ORJ357W	First Manchester
N588GRN	Blackpool	N662VSS	Stagecoach Manchester	NHH359W	Manchester Airport	ORJ371W	UK North
N589GRN	Blackpool	N663VSS	Stagecoach Manchester	NIB3261	Mayne	OSR195R	Stagecoach Ribble
N590GRN	Blackpool	N664VSS	Stagecoach Manchester	NIB4162	Mayne	OSR197R	Stagecoach Ribble
N591GRN	Blackpool	N665VSS	Stagecoach Manchester	NIL6108	Brownrigg's	OTK802	Hulme Hall
N592GRN	Blackpool	N701UVR	Shearings	NIL6258	Travellers	OZ4688	Titterington
N593LFV	Blackpool	N702UVR	Shearings	NIL7914	Travellers	P1JPT	J P Travel
N594LFV	Blackpool	N703UVR	Shearings	NIL8254	Mayne	P2HWD	Holmeswood
N595LFV	Blackpool	N704UVR	Shearings	NIL8255	Mayne	P2JPT	J P Travel
N596LFV	Blackpool	N705UVR	Shearings	NIL8256	Mayne	P3JPT	J P Travel
N599XRJ	Manchester Airport	N706UVR	Shearings	NIL8257	Mayne	P4HWD	Holmeswood
N601XRJ	Manchester Airport	N707UVR	Shearings	NIL8258	Mayne	P5HWD	Holmeswood
N602XRJ	Manchester Airport	N708UVR	Shearings	NIL8259	Mayne	P6JPT	J P Travel
N610REC	Travellers	N709UVR	Shearings	NIL8663	Brownrigg's	P8JPT	J P Travel
N613VSS	Stagecoach Cumberland	N710UVR	Shearings	NIL9581	Travellers	P20BLU	Bluebird
N614VSS	Stagecoach Cumberland	N711UVR	Shearings	NIL9773	Mayne	P30BLU	Bluebird
N615VSS	Stagecoach Cumberland	N712UVR	Shearings	NIL9774	Mayne	P40BLU	Bluebird
N616VSS	Stagecoach Cumberland	N713UVR	Shearings	NIL9932	Travellers	P50BLU	Bluebird
N617VSS	Stagecoach Cumberland	N714UVR	Shearings	NIW2399	Springfield Coachways	P50HWD	Holmeswood
N619CDB	First Manchester	N715UVR	Shearings	NIW6492	Blackpool	P75JND	Mayne
N619VSS	Stagecoach Cumberland	N716UVR	Shearings	NIW6514	East Lancashire	P76JND	Mayne
N620CDB	First Manchester	N717UVR	Shearings	NIW6515	East Lancashire	P101HNC	Mayne
N620XBU	R Bullocks	N718UVR	Shearings	NJI5504	Blackpool	P102HNC	Mayne
N621CDB	First Manchester	N719UVR	Shearings	NJI5505	Blackpool	P103HNC	Mayne
N621XBU	R Bullocks	N720UVR	Shearings	NMX643	Mayne	P104HNC	Mayne
N622CDB	First Manchester	N721UVR	Shearings	NOE595R	Stagecoach Ribble	P108DCW	Stagecoach Ribble
N623CDB	First Manchester	N722UVR	Shearings	NRG161M	Border	P109DCW	Stagecoach Ribble
N624CDB	First Manchester	N723UVR	Shearings	NRG165M	Border	P110DCW	Stagecoach Ribble
N625CDB	First Manchester	N724UVR	Shearings	NRG167M	Border	P112DCW	Stagecoach Ribble
N626CDB	First Manchester	N725UVR	Shearings	NSU181	Rossendale	P112OJA	Dennis's
N627CDB	First Manchester	N726UVR	Shearings	NUS333Y	Robinson's	P113DCW	Stagecoach Ribble
N628CDB	First Manchester	N727UVR	Shearings	OAZ9330	Holmeswood	P113OJA	Dennis's
N629CDB	First Manchester	N728UVR	Shearings	OBV158X	Preston	P114DCW	Stagecoach Ribble
N630CDB	First Manchester	N729UVR	Shearings	OBV159X	Preston	P121JNF	Mayne
N630XBU	R Bullocks	N730UVR	Shearings	OBV161X	Preston	P122JNF	Mayne
N631CDB	First Manchester	N731UVR	Shearings	OBV162X	Preston	P127XCN	Stagecoach Ribble
N631XBU	R Bullocks	N732UVR	Shearings	OBV163X	Preston	P128XCN	Stagecoach Ribble
N632CDB	First Manchester	N733UVR	Shearings	OBV164X	Preston	P129XCN	Stagecoach Ribble
N632XBU	R Bullocks	N734UVR	Shearings	OBV165X	Preston	P130XCN	Stagecoach Ribble
N633CDB	First Manchester	N735UVR	Shearings	OCW7X	Blackburn	P131XCN	Stagecoach Ribble
N633LFR	Blackburn	N740VBA	Finglands	OCW8X	Blackburn	P132XCN	Stagecoach Ribble
N633XBU	R Bullocks	N741VBA	Finglands	OCW9X	Blackburn	P133XCN	Stagecoach Ribble
N634CDB	First Manchester	N742GKH	First Manchester	OCW10X	Blackburn	P134XCN	Stagecoach Ribble
N634LFR	Blackburn	N742VBA	Finglands	OCW11X	Blackburn	P211DCK	Rossendale
N634XBU	R Bullocks	N743VBA	Finglands	OCW12X	Blackburn	P212DCK	Rossendale
N635CDB	First Manchester	N744ANE	Finglands	OCW13X	Blackburn	P213DCK	Rossendale
N635LFR	Blackburn	N745ANE	Finglands	OCW14X	Blackburn	P213HRJ	First Manchester
N636CDB	First Manchester	N746ANE	Finglands	OCW15X	Blackburn	P224VCK	Stagecoach Ribble
N636LFR	Blackburn	N746YVR	Stagecoach Manchester	ODM680V	Pilkington	P225VCK	Stagecoach Ribble
N637CDB	First Manchester	N748ANE	Finglands	OED201	Mayne	P226VCK	Stagecoach Ribble
N638CDB	First Manchester	N748YVR	Stagecoach Manchester	OFV14X	Stagecoach Ribble	P227VCK	Stagecoach Ribble
N640CDB	First Manchester	N781PEC	Travellers	OFV15X	Stagecoach Ribble	P228VCK	Stagecoach Ribble
N641CDB	First Manchester	N784URY	Holmeswood	OFV16X	Stagecoach Cumberland	P229VCK	Stagecoach Ribble
N641VSS	Stagecoach Cumberland	N789VRM	Stagecoach Cumberland	OFV17X	Stagecoach Cumberland	P230VCK	Stagecoach Ribble
N642CDB	First Manchester	N790VRM	Stagecoach Cumberland	OFV18X	Stagecoach Ribble	P231VCK	Stagecoach Ribble
N643CDB	First Manchester	N796CVU	Dennis's	OFV19X	Stagecoach Ribble	P232VCK	Stagecoach Ribble
N644CDB	First Manchester	N796XRA	South Lancs Travel	OFV20X	Stagecoach Ribble	P233VCK	Stagecoach Ribble
N645CDB	First Manchester	N801DNE	Stagecoach Ribble	OFV21X	Stagecoach Ribble	P234VCK	Stagecoach Ribble
N645VSS	Stagecoach Cumberland	N802DNE	Stagecoach Ribble	OFV22X	Stagecoach Ribble	P235VCK	Stagecoach Ribble
N646CDB	First Manchester	N829REC	Mountain Goat	OFV23X	Stagecoach Ribble	P248KND	South Lancs Travel
N646VSS	Stagecoach Cumberland	N839AOV	Holmeswood	OFV620X	Fishwick	P255YFR	Robinsons
N647CDB	First Manchester	N879AVV	Stagecoach Manchester	OFV621X	Fishwick	P256YFR	Robinsons
N647VSS	Stagecoach Ribble	N880AVV	Stagecoach Manchester	OIB1287	Rossendale	P257YFR	Robinsons
N648CDB	First Manchester	N881AVV	Stagecoach Manchester	OIB3604	Rossendale	P260VPN	Stagecoach Ribble
N648VSS	Stagecoach Ribble	N882AVV	Stagecoach Manchester	OIB5403	Rossendale	P261VPN	Stagecoach Ribble

Reg	Operator	Reg	Operator	Reg	Operator	Reg	Operator
P262VPN	Stagecoach Ribble	P514LND	First Manchester	P808GBA	Shearings	P885MNE	Stagecoach Manchester
P263VPN	Stagecoach Ribble	P515LND	First Manchester	P809GBA	Shearings	P886MNE	Stagecoach Manchester
P270VPN	Stagecoach Ribble	P516LND	First Manchester	P810GBA	Shearings	P887MNE	Stagecoach Manchester
P271VPN	Stagecoach Ribble	P517LND	First Manchester	P811GBA	Shearings	P889MNE	Stagecoach Manchester
P272VPN	Stagecoach Ribble	P518LND	First Manchester	P812GBA	Shearings	P890MNE	Stagecoach Manchester
P273VPN	Stagecoach Ribble	P519LND	First Manchester	P813GBA	Shearings	P891MNE	Stagecoach Manchester
P274VPN	Stagecoach Ribble	P520LND	First Manchester	P814GBA	Shearings	P892MNE	Stagecoach Manchester
P275VPN	Stagecoach Ribble	P521LND	First Manchester	P815GBA	Shearings	P893MNE	Stagecoach Manchester
P301LND	First Manchester	P522LND	First Manchester	P816GBA	Shearings	P894MNE	Stagecoach Manchester
P302LND	First Manchester	P523LND	First Manchester	P817GBA	Shearings	P894TCK	Battersby
P303LND	First Manchester	P524LND	First Manchester	P818GBA	Shearings	P895EEC	Battersby
P304LND	First Manchester	P525LND	First Manchester	P819GBA	Shearings	P896EEC	Battersby
P305LND	First Manchester	P526BLJ	Blackburn	P820GBA	Shearings	P897EEC	Battersby
P306LND	First Manchester	P526LND	First Manchester	P821GBA	Shearings	P915XUG	Rossendale
P307LND	First Manchester	P527LND	First Manchester	P822GBA	Shearings	P916XUG	Rossendale
P308LND	First Manchester	P528LND	First Manchester	P823GBA	Shearings	P918HNA	Timeline
P309LND	First Manchester	P529LND	First Manchester	P824GBA	Shearings	P919HNA	Timeline
P310LND	First Manchester	P530LND	First Manchester	P825GBA	Shearings	P920HNA	Timeline
P310XCW	Springfield Coachways	P530PNE	Stagecoach Manchester	P826GBA	Shearings	P962SFR	Lakeland
P311LND	First Manchester	P531PNE	Stagecoach Manchester	P827GBA	Shearings	P977UBV	Stagecoach Ribble
P312LND	First Manchester	P532PNE	Stagecoach Manchester	P828GBA	Shearings	P978LNB	Dennis's
P313LND	First Manchester	P533CLJ	Finglands	P829GBA	Shearings	P978UBV	Stagecoach Ribble
P314LND	First Manchester	P533PNE	Stagecoach Manchester	P830GBA	Shearings	P979LNB	Dennis's
P315LND	First Manchester	P534PNE	Stagecoach Manchester	P831GBA	Shearings	P979UBV	Stagecoach Ribble
P316LND	First Manchester	P535PNE	Stagecoach Manchester	P832GBA	Shearings	P980LNB	Dennis's
P317LND	First Manchester	P536PNE	Stagecoach Manchester	P833GBA	Shearings	PBV637P	Abbotts
P318LND	First Manchester	P537PNE	Stagecoach Manchester	P834GBA	Shearings	PCK335	Stagecoach Cumberland
P319LND	First Manchester	P538PNE	Stagecoach Manchester	P835GBA	Shearings	PFC514W	Hulme Hall
P320LND	First Manchester	P539PNE	Stagecoach Manchester	P837GND	Stagecoach Manchester	PFC515W	Hulme Hall
P321LND	First Manchester	P540PNE	Stagecoach Manchester	P838GND	Stagecoach Manchester	PIB1125	Pilkington
P322LND	First Manchester	P541PNE	Stagecoach Manchester	P839GND	Stagecoach Manchester	PIB1433	Pilkington
P323LND	First Manchester	P542PNE	Stagecoach Manchester	P839RBX	Holmeswood	PIB3488	Pilkington
P324LND	First Manchester	P543PNE	Stagecoach Manchester	P840GND	Stagecoach Manchester	PIB3705	Pilkington
P325LND	First Manchester	P544PNE	Stagecoach Manchester	P841GND	Stagecoach Manchester	PIB4033	Pilkington
P335JND	Stagecoach Ribble	P545PNE	Stagecoach Manchester	P842GND	Stagecoach Manchester	PIB4290	Pilkington
P336JND	Stagecoach Ribble	P546PNE	Stagecoach Manchester	P843GND	Stagecoach Manchester	PIB5144	Blue Bus
P337JND	Stagecoach Ribble	P547HVM	Dennis's	P844GND	Stagecoach Manchester	PIB5507	Pilkington
P338JND	Stagecoach Ribble	P547PNE	Stagecoach Manchester	P845GND	Stagecoach Manchester	PIB5823	Pilkington
P339JND	Stagecoach Ribble	P548PNE	Stagecoach Manchester	P846GND	Stagecoach Manchester	PIB5952	Pilkington
P340JND	Stagecoach Ribble	P549PNE	Stagecoach Manchester	P847GND	Stagecoach Manchester	PIB6434	Pilkington
P341JND	Stagecoach Ribble	P550PNE	Stagecoach Manchester	P848GND	Stagecoach Manchester	PIB6485	Pilkington
P342JND	Stagecoach Ribble	P551PNE	Stagecoach Manchester	P849GND	Stagecoach Manchester	PIB6667	Pilkington
P343JND	Stagecoach Ribble	P552PNE	Stagecoach Manchester	P850GND	Stagecoach Manchester	PIB6945	Pilkington
P344JND	Stagecoach Ribble	P553PNE	Stagecoach Manchester	P851GND	Stagecoach Manchester	PIB7014	Pilkington
P345JND	Stagecoach Ribble	P554PNE	Stagecoach Manchester	P852GND	Stagecoach Manchester	PIB7256	Pilkington
P346JND	Stagecoach Ribble	P556PNE	Stagecoach Manchester	P853GND	Stagecoach Manchester	PIB8076	Pilkington
P347JND	Stagecoach Ribble	P557PNE	Stagecoach Manchester	P854GND	Stagecoach Manchester	PIB8225	Pilkington
P348JND	Stagecoach Ribble	P558PNE	Stagecoach Manchester	P855GND	Stagecoach Manchester	PIB8301	Pilkington
P349JND	Stagecoach Ribble	P559PNE	Stagecoach Manchester	P856GND	Stagecoach Manchester	PIB8991	Pilkington
P405MDT	Lakeland	P561PNE	Stagecoach Manchester	P857GND	Stagecoach Manchester	PIB9051	Pilkington
P411TFR	Preston	P562PNE	Stagecoach Manchester	P858GND	Stagecoach Manchester	PIB9062	Pilkington
P412TFR	Preston	P563PNE	Stagecoach Manchester	P859GND	Stagecoach Manchester	PIB9482	Pilkington
P413TFR	Preston	P564PNE	Stagecoach Manchester	P860GND	Stagecoach Manchester	PIL2083	Pilkington
P414TFR	Preston	P565PNE	Stagecoach Manchester	P861GND	Stagecoach Manchester	PIL2086	Pilkington
P415TFR	Preston	P566PNE	Stagecoach Manchester	P862GND	Stagecoach Manchester	PIL2108	Pilkington
P416TFR	Preston	P637ARN	Blackburn	P863GND	Stagecoach Manchester	PIL5258	Archway
P417HVR	South Lancs Travel	P638ARN	Blackburn	P864GND	Stagecoach Manchester	PIL5941	Pilkington
P418HNF	Vale of Manchester	P639ARN	Blackburn	P865GND	Stagecoach Manchester	PIL6617	Pilkington
P419HNF	Vale of Manchester	P640ARN	Blackburn	P866GND	Stagecoach Manchester	PIL7012	Pilkington
P480HBA	R Bullocks	P652VBV	Shearings	P866PWW	Fishwick	PIL7013	Pilkington
P481HBA	R Bullocks	P653VBV	Shearings	P867GND	Stagecoach Manchester	PIL7237	Kirby Lonsdale
P482HBA	R Bullocks	P716GND	Stagecoach Manchester	P867PWW	Fishwick	PIL7752	Mayne
P483HBA	R Bullocks	P717GND	Stagecoach Manchester	P868GND	Stagecoach Manchester	PIL8560	Pilkington
P484HBA	R Bullocks	P718GND	Stagecoach Manchester	P869MNE	Stagecoach Manchester	PIL9546	Pilkington
P485HBA	R Bullocks	P719GND	Stagecoach Manchester	P870MNE	Stagecoach Manchester	PJI4317	Brownrigg's
P486HBA	R Bullocks	P720GND	Stagecoach Manchester	P871MNE	Stagecoach Manchester	PJI9170	Rossendale
P501LND	First Manchester	P721GND	Stagecoach Manchester	P871TAV	First Manchester	PJI9171	Rossendale
P501UFR	Blackpool	P722GND	Stagecoach Manchester	P872MNE	Stagecoach Manchester	PJI9172	Rossendale
P502LND	First Manchester	P723GND	Stagecoach Manchester	P872TAV	First Manchester	PJI9173	Rossendale
P502UFR	Blackpool	P724GND	Stagecoach Manchester	P873MNE	Stagecoach Manchester	PJI9174	Rossendale
P503LND	First Manchester	P725GND	Stagecoach Manchester	P874MNE	Stagecoach Manchester	PJI9175	Rossendale
P503UFR	Blackpool	P726GND	Stagecoach Manchester	P875MNE	Stagecoach Manchester	PJI9176	Rossendale
P504LND	First Manchester	P727GND	Stagecoach Manchester	P876MNE	Stagecoach Manchester	PJI9177	Rossendale
P504UFR	Blackpool	P728GND	Stagecoach Manchester	P876PWW	J P Travel	PJI9178	Rossendale
P505GHH	Sim's Travel	P729GND	Stagecoach Manchester	P877MNE	Stagecoach Manchester	PJI9179	Rossendale
P505LND	First Manchester	P730GND	Stagecoach Manchester	P878MNE	Stagecoach Manchester	PJT267R	Blackburn
P506LND	First Manchester	P741YCK	Springfield Coachways	P879MNE	Stagecoach Manchester	PSO32W	Lancaster Bus
P507LND	First Manchester	P801GBA	Shearings	P880MNE	Stagecoach Manchester	PSU787	Stagecoach Cumberland
P508LND	First Manchester	P802GBA	Shearings	P881MNE	Stagecoach Manchester	PSU788	Stagecoach Cumberland
P509LND	First Manchester	P803GBA	Shearings	P882CHH	Ken Routledge	PUS158W	Blackburn
P510LND	First Manchester	P804GBA	Shearings	P882MNE	Stagecoach Manchester	PWK7W	Brownrigg's
P511LND	First Manchester	P805GBA	Shearings	P883MNE	Stagecoach Manchester	Q580GRJ	Manchester Airport
P512LND	First Manchester	P806GBA	Shearings	P884CHH	Ken Routledge	R2JPT	J P Travel
P513LND	First Manchester	P807GBA	Shearings	P884MNE	Stagecoach Manchester	R2SOH	Stainton

Brownrigg's livery of white with purple relief and fleet names is seen on Mercedes-Benz N976LWR. Bodywork on this vehicle is by Mellor, a builder based in the North West at Rochdale. For a while the body styles were introduced, the dual-doored Duo being the first. Seen here is a Solo, the version with only one door. The vehicle is mostly used on school duties as indicated by the appropriate sign. *Bill Potter*

Reg	Operator	Reg	Operator	Reg	Operator	Reg	Operator
R3HWD	Holmeswood	R207JSF	Timeline	R254SBA	First Manchester	R277SBA	First Manchester
R3JPT	J P Travel	R214SBA	First Manchester	R255NBV	Stagecoach Ribble	R278SBA	First Manchester
R4HWD	Holmeswood	R215SBA	First Manchester	R255SBA	First Manchester	R279SBA	First Manchester
R5HWD	Holmeswood	R216SBA	First Manchester	R256NBV	Stagecoach Ribble	R280SBA	First Manchester
R6BLU	Blue Bus	R217SBA	First Manchester	R256SBA	First Manchester	R290CVM	R Bullocks
R6HWD	Holmeswood	R218SBA	First Manchester	R257NBV	Stagecoach Ribble	R291CVM	R Bullocks
R7BLU	Blue Bus	R219SBA	First Manchester	R257SBA	First Manchester	R292CVM	R Bullocks
R8BLU	Blue Bus	R220SBA	First Manchester	R258NBV	Stagecoach Ribble	R293CVM	R Bullocks
R15BLU	Bluebird	R221SBA	First Manchester	R258SBA	First Manchester	R300BLU	Blue Bus
R16BLU	Bluebird	R223SBA	First Manchester	R259NBV	Stagecoach Ribble	R357URM	Robinson's
R18BLU	Bluebird	R234SBA	First Manchester	R259SBA	First Manchester	R367WNC	Finglands
R18RED	Redline Coaches	R235SBA	First Manchester	R260NBV	Stagecoach Ribble	R399CVR	South Lancs Travel
R19BLU	Bluebird	R236SBA	First Manchester	R260SBA	First Manchester	R417RCW	Preston
R1BLU	Bluebird	R237SBA	First Manchester	R261NBV	Stagecoach Ribble	R418RCW	Preston
R22RED	Redline Coaches	R238SBA	First Manchester	R261SBA	First Manchester	R419RCW	Preston
R24YNC	Mayne	R239SBA	First Manchester	R262NBV	Stagecoach Ribble	R432NFR	Preston
R44BLU	Blue Bus	R240SBA	First Manchester	R262SBA	First Manchester	R433NFR	Preston
R45CDB	Mayne	R241SBA	First Manchester	R263NBV	Stagecoach Ribble	R434NFR	Preston
R46CDB	Mayne	R242SBA	First Manchester	R263SBA	First Manchester	R435NFR	Preston
R47CDB	Mayne	R243SBA	First Manchester	R264NBV	Stagecoach Ribble	R436NFR	Preston
R48CDB	Mayne	R244SBA	First Manchester	R264SBA	First Manchester	R437NFR	Preston
R49CDB	Mayne	R245SBA	First Manchester	R265NBV	Stagecoach Ribble	R438RCW	Preston
R60RED	Redline Coaches	R246NBV	Stagecoach Ribble	R265SBA	First Manchester	R439RCW	Preston
R61GNW	Fishwick	R246SBA	First Manchester	R266NBV	Stagecoach Ribble	R440RCW	Preston
R62GNW	Fishwick	R247NBV	Stagecoach Ribble	R266SBA	First Manchester	R446YNF	Stagecoach Manchester
R103BDB	Dennis's	R247SBA	First Manchester	R267NBV	Stagecoach Ribble	R447YNF	Stagecoach Manchester
R107GNW	Phoenix	R248NBV	Stagecoach Ribble	R267SBA	First Manchester	R473MCW	Stagecoach Ribble
R108GNW	Phoenix	R248SBA	First Manchester	R268NBV	Stagecoach Ribble	R474MCW	Stagecoach Ribble
R108YBA	Mayne	R249NBV	Stagecoach Ribble	R268SBA	First Manchester	R475MCW	Stagecoach Ribble
R109YBA	Mayne	R249SBA	First Manchester	R269SBA	First Manchester	R476MCW	Stagecoach Ribble
R119CNE	Mayne	R250NBV	Stagecoach Ribble	R270SBA	First Manchester	R477MCW	Stagecoach Ribble
R120CNE	Mayne	R250SBA	First Manchester	R271SBA	First Manchester	R478MCW	Stagecoach Ribble
R120VFR	Stagecoach Ribble	R251NBV	Stagecoach Ribble	R272SBA	First Manchester	R479MCW	Stagecoach Ribble
R165ESG	South Lancs Travel	R251SBA	First Manchester	R273SBA	First Manchester	R480MCW	Stagecoach Ribble
R166ESG	South Lancs Travel	R252NBV	Stagecoach Ribble	R274SBA	First Manchester	R481MCW	Stagecoach Ribble
R171SUT	Travellers	R252SBA	First Manchester	R275SBA	First Manchester	R482MCW	Stagecoach Ribble
R183OCW	Springfield Coachways	R253NBV	Stagecoach Ribble	R276CBU	Stagecoach Manchester	R484YVV	Ken Routledge
R184OCW	Springfield Coachways	R253SBA	First Manchester	R276SBA	First Manchester	R501UWL	Stagecoach Manchester
R185OCW	Springfield Coachways	R254NBV	Stagecoach Ribble	R277CBU	Stagecoach Manchester	R502UWL	Stagecoach Manchester

Reg	Operator	Reg	Operator	Reg	Operator	Reg	Operator
R503UWL	Stagecoach Manchester	R672LFV	Stagecoach Ribble	R913XVM	Stagecoach Manchester	R954XVM	Stagecoach Manchester
R504UWL	Stagecoach Manchester	R672NFR	Lakeland	R913YBA	Shearings	R954YNF	Shearings
R505UWL	Stagecoach Manchester	R744DRJ	Stagecoach Manchester	R914XVM	Stagecoach Manchester	R955XVM	Stagecoach Manchester
R506UWL	Stagecoach Manchester	R745DRJ	Stagecoach Manchester	R914YBA	Shearings	R956XVM	Stagecoach Manchester
R507UWL	Stagecoach Manchester	R746DRJ	Stagecoach Manchester	R915XVM	Stagecoach Manchester	R957XVM	Stagecoach Manchester
R508UWL	Stagecoach Manchester	R747DRJ	Stagecoach Manchester	R915YBA	Shearings	R958XVM	Stagecoach Manchester
R509UWL	Stagecoach Manchester	R748DRJ	Stagecoach Manchester	R916XVM	Stagecoach Manchester	R959XVM	Stagecoach Manchester
R510UWL	Stagecoach Manchester	R749DRJ	Stagecoach Manchester	R916YBA	Shearings	R960XVM	Stagecoach Manchester
R511UWL	Stagecoach Manchester	R751DRJ	Stagecoach Manchester	R917XVM	Stagecoach Manchester	R961XVM	Stagecoach Manchester
R512BUA	Travellers	R752DRJ	Stagecoach Manchester	R917YBA	Shearings	R962XVM	Stagecoach Manchester
R512UWL	Stagecoach Manchester	R753DRJ	Stagecoach Manchester	R918XVM	Stagecoach Manchester	R963XVM	Stagecoach Manchester
R513UWL	Stagecoach Manchester	R754DRJ	Stagecoach Manchester	R918YBA	Shearings	R964XVM	Stagecoach Manchester
R571YNC	First Manchester	R755DRJ	Stagecoach Manchester	R919XVM	Stagecoach Manchester	R965XVM	Stagecoach Manchester
R572ABA	Dennis's	R756DRJ	Stagecoach Manchester	R919YBA	Shearings	R966XVM	Stagecoach Manchester
R572SBA	First Manchester	R757DRJ	Stagecoach Manchester	R920XVM	Stagecoach Manchester	R967XVM	Stagecoach Manchester
R573ABA	Dennis's	R758DRJ	Stagecoach Manchester	R920YBA	Shearings	R968XVM	Stagecoach Manchester
R573SBA	First Manchester	R759DRJ	Stagecoach Manchester	R921XVM	Stagecoach Manchester	R969XVM	Stagecoach Manchester
R574ABA	Dennis's	R760DRJ	Stagecoach Manchester	R921YBA	Shearings	R970XVM	Stagecoach Manchester
R574SBA	First Manchester	R761DRJ	Stagecoach Manchester	R922XVM	Stagecoach Manchester	R971XVM	Stagecoach Manchester
R575ABA	Dennis's	R762DRJ	Stagecoach Manchester	R922YBA	Shearings	R972XVM	Stagecoach Manchester
R575SBA	First Manchester	R763DRJ	Stagecoach Manchester	R923XVM	Stagecoach Manchester	R973XVM	Stagecoach Manchester
R576SBA	First Manchester	R765DRJ	Stagecoach Manchester	R923YBA	Shearings	R974XVM	Stagecoach Manchester
R577SBA	First Manchester	R776PRM	Ken Routledge	R924XVM	Stagecoach Manchester	R975XVM	Stagecoach Manchester
R578SBA	First Manchester	R791NEC	Travellers	R924YBA	Shearings	R976XVM	Stagecoach Manchester
R579SBA	First Manchester	R791PAO	Stagecoach Cumberland	R925XVM	Stagecoach Manchester	R977XVM	Stagecoach Manchester
R580SBA	First Manchester	R792PAO	Stagecoach Cumberland	R925YBA	Shearings	R978XVM	Stagecoach Manchester
R581SBA	First Manchester	R793URM	Stagecoach Cumberland	R926XVM	Stagecoach Manchester	R979XVM	Stagecoach Manchester
R582SBA	First Manchester	R794URM	Stagecoach Cumberland	R926YBA	Shearings	R980XVM	Stagecoach Manchester
R583SBA	First Manchester	R795URM	Stagecoach Cumberland	R927XVM	Stagecoach Manchester	R981XVM	Stagecoach Manchester
R584SBA	First Manchester	R801WJA	Bu-val	R927YBA	Shearings	R982XVM	Stagecoach Manchester
R585SBA	First Manchester	R805WJA	Bu-val	R928XVM	Stagecoach Manchester	R983XVM	Stagecoach Manchester
R586SBA	First Manchester	R807WJA	Universal	R928YBA	Shearings	R984XVM	Stagecoach Manchester
R587SBA	First Manchester	R808WJA	Universal	R929XVM	Stagecoach Manchester	R985XVM	Stagecoach Manchester
R588SBA	First Manchester	R809WJA	Universal	R929YBA	Shearings	R986XVM	Stagecoach Manchester
R589SBA	First Manchester	R810WJA	Universal	R930XVM	Stagecoach Manchester	R987XVM	Stagecoach Manchester
R590SBA	First Manchester	R811WJA	Universal	R930YBA	Shearings	R988XVM	Stagecoach Manchester
R591SBA	First Manchester	R812WJA	Universal	R931XVM	Stagecoach Manchester	R989XVM	Stagecoach Manchester
R621CVR	First Manchester	R813WJA	Universal	R931YBA	Shearings	R990XVM	Stagecoach Manchester
R622CVR	First Manchester	R814LFV	Phoenix	R932XVM	Stagecoach Manchester	R991ANB	Shearings
R623CVR	First Manchester	R814WJA	Universal	R932YBA	Shearings	R991XVM	Stagecoach Manchester
R624CVR	First Manchester	R815LFV	Phoenix	R933XVM	Stagecoach Manchester	R992XVM	Stagecoach Manchester
R625CVR	First Manchester	R815WJA	Universal	R933YBA	Shearings	R993XVM	Stagecoach Manchester
R626CVR	First Manchester	R816LFV	Phoenix	R934XVM	Stagecoach Manchester	R994XVM	Stagecoach Manchester
R627CVR	First Manchester	R816WJA	Universal	R934YBA	Shearings	R995XVM	Stagecoach Manchester
R628CVR	First Manchester	R817WJA	Universal	R935XVM	Stagecoach Manchester	R996XVM	Stagecoach Manchester
R629CVR	First Manchester	R818WJA	Universal	R935YNF	Shearings	RAZ5171	Mayne
R630CVR	First Manchester	R819WJA	Universal	R936XVM	Stagecoach Manchester	RAZ5172	Mayne
R631CVR	First Manchester	R845VEC	Fishwick	R936YNF	Shearings	RAZ7353	Brownrigg's
R632CVR	First Manchester	R846VEC	Fishwick	R937XVM	Stagecoach Manchester	RAZ8627	Dennis's
R633CVR	First Manchester	R847VEC	Fishwick	R937YNF	Shearings	RAZ8628	Dennis's
R634CVR	First Manchester	R848VEC	Fishwick	R938XVM	Stagecoach Manchester	RFS584V	Stagecoach Ribble
R635CVR	First Manchester	R853WRM	Sim's Travel	R938YNF	Shearings	RGV36W	Stagecoach Ribble
R636CVR	First Manchester	R895XVM	Stagecoach Manchester	R939XVM	Stagecoach Manchester	RGV37W	Stagecoach Ribble
R637CVR	First Manchester	R896XVM	Stagecoach Manchester	R939YNF	Shearings	RGV38W	Stagecoach Ribble
R638CVR	First Manchester	R897XVM	Stagecoach Manchester	R940XVM	Stagecoach Manchester	RGV40W	Stagecoach Ribble
R638OTN	Shearings	R898AVM	Stagecoach Manchester	R940YNF	Shearings	RHG95T	Blackpool
R639CVR	First Manchester	R898XVM	Stagecoach Manchester	R941XVM	Stagecoach Manchester	RHG884X	Stagecoach Cumberland
R639OTN	Shearings	R899AVM	Stagecoach Manchester	R941YNF	Shearings	RHL174X	Brownrigg's
R640CVR	First Manchester	R899XVM	Stagecoach Manchester	R942XVM	Stagecoach Manchester	RIB4089	Blackpool
R641CVR	First Manchester	R901AVM	Stagecoach Manchester	R942YNF	Shearings	RIL1026	Kirby Lonsdale
R641MBV	Springfield Coachways	R901WEC	Battersby	R943XVM	Stagecoach Manchester	RIL5084	Stagecoach Cumberland
R641OBV	Blackburn	R901XVM	Stagecoach Manchester	R943YNF	Shearings	RJA719R	Archway
R641OTN	Shearings	R901YBA	Shearings	R944XVM	Stagecoach Manchester	RJA809R	Archway
R642CVR	First Manchester	R902WEC	Battersby	R944YNF	Shearings	RJI2161	Blue Bus
R642MBV	Springfield Coachways	R902XVM	Stagecoach Manchester	R945XVM	Stagecoach Manchester	RJI2162	Stainton
R642OBV	Blackburn	R902YBA	Shearings	R945YNF	Shearings	RJI8722	Rossendale
R643CVR	First Manchester	R903XVM	Stagecoach Manchester	R946XVM	Stagecoach Manchester	RJI8723	Rossendale
R643MBV	Springfield Coachways	R903YBA	Shearings	R946YNF	Shearings	RJI8918	Hulme Hall
R643OBV	Blackburn	R904XVM	Stagecoach Manchester	R947XVM	Stagecoach Manchester	RRM384X	Stagecoach Ribble
R644CVR	First Manchester	R904YBA	Shearings	R947YNF	Shearings	RRM386X	Stagecoach Ribble
R644OBV	Blackburn	R905XVM	Stagecoach Manchester	R948AMB	South Lancs Travel	RRM915M	Wright Bros
R645CVR	First Manchester	R905YBA	Shearings	R948XVM	Stagecoach Manchester	RRP858R	Stagecoach Ribble
R646CVR	First Manchester	R906XVM	Stagecoach Manchester	R948YNF	Shearings	RUT842	Stagecoach Cumberland
R647CVR	First Manchester	R906YBA	Shearings	R949AMB	South Lancs Travel	RXJ318	Springfield Coachways
R648CVR	First Manchester	R907XVM	Stagecoach Manchester	R949XVM	Stagecoach Manchester	RYV77	Finglands
R649CVR	First Manchester	R907YBA	Shearings	R949YNF	Shearings	S2BLU	Bluebird
R650CVR	First Manchester	R908XVM	Stagecoach Manchester	R950XVM	Stagecoach Manchester	S3BLU	Bluebird
R651CVR	First Manchester	R908YBA	Shearings	R950YNF	Shearings	S3JPT	J P Travel
R652OTN	Shearings	R909XVM	Stagecoach Manchester	R951XVM	Stagecoach Manchester	S4BLU	Bluebird
R661GCA	South Lancs Travel	R909YBA	Shearings	R951YNF	Shearings	S4HWD	Holmeswood
R668LFV	Stagecoach Ribble	R910XVM	Stagecoach Manchester	R952XVM	Stagecoach Manchester	S5BLU	Bluebird
R669LFV	Stagecoach Ribble	R910YBA	Shearings	R952YNF	Shearings	S6BLU	Bluebird
R670LFV	Stagecoach Ribble	R912XVM	Stagecoach Manchester	R953XVM	Stagecoach Manchester	S6JPT	J P Travel
R671LFV	Stagecoach Ribble	R912YBA	Shearings	R953YNF	Shearings	S9BLU	Blue Bus

Springfield Coachways operate three Optare Excel low-floor buses in Easylink livery. Pictured on route 630 to Billinge is R642MBV. *Cliff Beeton*

S18RED	Redline Coaches	S117TRJ	Stagecoach Manchester	S149TRJ	Stagecoach Manchester	S516LHG	Blackpool		
S43BLU	Blue Bus	S118KRN	Rossendale	S150TRJ	Stagecoach Manchester	S517LHG	Blackpool		
S45BLU	Blue Bus	S118TRJ	Stagecoach Manchester	S151TRJ	Stagecoach Manchester	S518LHG	Blackpool		
S57TNA	Mayne	S119KRN	Rossendale	S152TRJ	Stagecoach Manchester	S651RNA	First Manchester		
S63TNA	Mayne	S119TRJ	Stagecoach Manchester	S153TRJ	Stagecoach Manchester	S652RNA	First Manchester		
S101TNB	First Manchester	S120KRN	Rossendale	S154TRJ	Stagecoach Manchester	S653RNA	First Manchester		
S101TRJ	Stagecoach Manchester	S120TRJ	Stagecoach Manchester	S156TRJ	Stagecoach Manchester	S654NUG	First Manchester		
S102TNB	First Manchester	S121KRN	Rossendale	S157TRJ	Stagecoach Manchester	S654RNA	First Manchester		
S102TRJ	Stagecoach Manchester	S121TRJ	Stagecoach Manchester	S158TRJ	Stagecoach Manchester	S655NUG	First Manchester		
S103TNB	First Manchester	S122KRN	Rossendale	S159TRJ	Stagecoach Manchester	S655RNA	First Manchester		
S103TRJ	Stagecoach Manchester	S122TRJ	Stagecoach Manchester	S190RAO	Stagecoach Cumberland	S656NUG	First Manchester		
S104TNB	First Manchester	S123KRN	Rossendale	S191RAO	Stagecoach Cumberland	S656RNA	First Manchester		
S104TRJ	Stagecoach Manchester	S124TRJ	Stagecoach Manchester	S192RAO	Stagecoach Cumberland	S657NUG	First Manchester		
S105TNB	First Manchester	S125TRJ	Stagecoach Manchester	S193RAO	Stagecoach Cumberland	S657RNA	First Manchester		
S105TRJ	Stagecoach Manchester	S126TRJ	Stagecoach Manchester	S193UAO	Ken Routledge	S658NUG	First Manchester		
S106TNB	First Manchester	S127TRJ	Stagecoach Manchester	S194RAO	Stagecoach Cumberland	S659NUG	First Manchester		
S106TRJ	Stagecoach Manchester	S128TRJ	Stagecoach Manchester	S195RAO	Stagecoach Cumberland	S660NUG	First Manchester		
S107TNB	First Manchester	S129TRJ	Stagecoach Manchester	S196RAO	Stagecoach Cumberland	S661NUG	First Manchester		
S107TRJ	Stagecoach Manchester	S130TRJ	Stagecoach Manchester	S258JFR	Robinsons	S662NUG	First Manchester		
S108TNB	First Manchester	S131TRJ	Stagecoach Manchester	S259JFR	Robinsons	S663NUG	First Manchester		
S108TRJ	Stagecoach Manchester	S132TRJ	Stagecoach Manchester	S260JFR	Robinsons	S669SVU	First Manchester		
S109TNB	First Manchester	S133KRM	Stagecoach Cumberland	S269KHG	Stagecoach Ribble	S670SVU	First Manchester		
S109TRJ	Stagecoach Manchester	S133TRJ	Stagecoach Manchester	S270KHG	Stagecoach Ribble	S671SVU	First Manchester		
S110TNB	First Manchester	S134KRM	Stagecoach Cumberland	S299JRM	Ken Routledge	S672SVU	First Manchester		
S110TRJ	Stagecoach Manchester	S134TRJ	Stagecoach Manchester	S369SND	Finglands	S673SVU	First Manchester		
S111FML	First Manchester	S135TRJ	Stagecoach Manchester	S395HVV	First Manchester	S738RNE	Vale of Manchester		
S112TNB	First Manchester	S136TRJ	Stagecoach Manchester	S396HVV	First Manchester	S739RNE	Vale of Manchester		
S112TRJ	Stagecoach Manchester	S137TRJ	Stagecoach Manchester	S397HVV	First Manchester	S764RNE	Springfield Coachways		
S113TNB	First Manchester	S138TRJ	Stagecoach Manchester	S505LHG	Blackpool	S764SVU	Stagecoach Manchester		
S113TRJ	Stagecoach Manchester	S139TRJ	Stagecoach Manchester	S506LHG	Blackpool	S765RNE	Springfield Coachways		
S114KRN	Rossendale	S140TRJ	Stagecoach Manchester	S507LHG	Blackpool	S766RNE	Springfield Coachways		
S114TNB	First Manchester	S141TRJ	Stagecoach Manchester	S508LHG	Blackpool	S766SVU	Stagecoach Manchester		
S114TRJ	Stagecoach Manchester	S142TRJ	Stagecoach Manchester	S509LHG	Blackpool	S767SVU	Stagecoach Manchester		
S115KRN	Rossendale	S143TRJ	Stagecoach Manchester	S510LHG	Blackpool	S768SVU	Stagecoach Manchester		
S115TNB	First Manchester	S144TRJ	Stagecoach Manchester	S511LHG	Blackpool	S769RVU	Stagecoach Manchester		
S115TRJ	Stagecoach Manchester	S145TRJ	Stagecoach Manchester	S512LHG	Blackpool	S770RVU	Stagecoach Manchester		
S116KRN	Rossendale	S146TRJ	Stagecoach Manchester	S513LHG	Blackpool	S771RVU	Stagecoach Manchester		
S116TRJ	Stagecoach Manchester	S147TRJ	Stagecoach Manchester	S514LHG	Blackpool	S772RVU	Stagecoach Manchester		
S117KRN	Rossendale	S148TRJ	Stagecoach Manchester	S515LHG	Blackpool	S773RVU	Stagecoach Manchester		

Reg	Operator	Reg	Operator	Reg	Operator	Reg	Operator
S774RVU	Stagecoach Manchester	SND442X	First Manchester	T115JBA	Shearings	T341NBV	Rossendale
S775RVU	Stagecoach Manchester	SND444X	First Manchester	T116JBA	Shearings	T342NBV	Rossendale
S776RVU	Stagecoach Manchester	SND446X	First Manchester	T117JBA	Shearings	T343NBV	Rossendale
S778RVU	Stagecoach Manchester	SND447X	First Manchester	T118JBA	Shearings	T344NBV	Rossendale
S779RVU	Stagecoach Manchester	SND448X	First Manchester	T119JBA	Shearings	T370JVR	Finglands
S780RVU	Stagecoach Manchester	SND449X	UK North	T120JBA	Shearings	T436EBD	Lakeland
S781RVU	Stagecoach Manchester	SND451X	Stagecoach Manchester	T122JBA	Shearings	T486CCK	Lakeland
S782RVU	Stagecoach Manchester	SND452X	Stagecoach Manchester	T124JBA	Shearings	T487CCK	Lakeland
S796KRM	Stagecoach Cumberland	SND454X	UK North	T125JBA	Shearings	T506JNA	First Manchester
S797KRM	Stagecoach Cumberland	SND455X	Stagecoach Manchester	T126JBA	Shearings	T507JNA	First Manchester
S798KRM	Stagecoach Cumberland	SND456X	First Manchester	T127JBA	Shearings	T508JNA	First Manchester
S799KRM	Stagecoach Cumberland	SND458X	First Manchester	T128JBA	Shearings	T509JNA	First Manchester
S903JHG	Stagecoach Ribble	SND459X	First Manchester	T129JBA	Shearings	T510JNA	First Manchester
S903LHG	Battersby	SND460X	First Manchester	T130JBA	Shearings	T511JNA	First Manchester
S904JHG	Stagecoach Ribble	SND461X	First Manchester	T131JBA	Shearings	T512JNA	First Manchester
S904LHG	Battersby	SND464X	First Manchester	T132JBA	Shearings	T513JNA	First Manchester
S905JHG	Stagecoach Ribble	SND469X	First Manchester	T160MVM	Stagecoach Manchester	T514JNA	First Manchester
S905LHG	Battersby	SND471X	First Manchester	T161MVM	Stagecoach Manchester	T515JNA	First Manchester
S906JHG	Stagecoach Ribble	SND472X	Stagecoach Manchester	T162MVM	Stagecoach Manchester	T522JCA	Manchester Airport
S920SVM	Universal	SND473X	UK North	T163MVM	Stagecoach Manchester	T612MNF	Stagecoach Manchester
S925SVM	Universal	SND474X	First Manchester	T164MVM	Stagecoach Manchester	T613MNF	Stagecoach Manchester
S933SVM	Bu-val	SND475X	First Manchester	T165MVM	Stagecoach Manchester	T614DJA	Stagecoach Manchester
S934SVM	Bu-val	SND486X	First Manchester	T166MVM	Stagecoach Manchester	T615DJA	Stagecoach Manchester
S957URJ	R Bullocks	SND490X	First Manchester	T167MVM	Stagecoach Manchester	T616DJA	Stagecoach Manchester
S958URJ	R Bullocks	SND491X	First Manchester	T168MVM	Stagecoach Manchester	T617DJA	Stagecoach Manchester
S959URJ	R Bullocks	SND497X	First Manchester	T169MVM	Stagecoach Manchester	T618DJA	Stagecoach Manchester
S960URJ	R Bullocks	SND498X	First Manchester	T172MVM	Stagecoach Manchester	T619DJA	Stagecoach Manchester
S979TBA	J P Travel	SND499X	First Manchester	T173MVM	Stagecoach Manchester	T620DJA	Stagecoach Manchester
S989EEC	Travellers	SND502X	First Manchester	T174MVM	Stagecoach Manchester	T621DJA	Stagecoach Manchester
S992UJA	First Manchester	SND503X	First Manchester	T178MVM	Stagecoach Manchester	T622DJA	Stagecoach Manchester
S993UJA	First Manchester	SND504X	First Manchester	T179MVM	Stagecoach Manchester	T623DJA	Stagecoach Manchester
S994UJA	First Manchester	SND506X	UK North	T180MVM	Stagecoach Manchester	T644DJA	Stagecoach Manchester
S995UJA	First Manchester	SND507X	First Manchester	T181MVM	Stagecoach Manchester	T701PND	First Manchester
SAO466X	Wright Bros	SND508X	First Manchester	T182MVM	Stagecoach Manchester	T702PND	First Manchester
SAO467X	Wright Bros	SND509X	First Manchester	T183MVM	Stagecoach Manchester	T703PND	First Manchester
SBV16X	Blackburn	SND516X	First Manchester	T184MVM	Stagecoach Manchester	T704PND	First Manchester
SBV17X	Blackburn	SND517X	First Manchester	T185MVM	Stagecoach Manchester	T705PND	First Manchester
SCK224X	Stagecoach Ribble	SND522X	First Manchester	T186MVM	Stagecoach Manchester	T706PND	First Manchester
SCK225X	Stagecoach Ribble	SND523X	First Manchester	T187MVM	Stagecoach Manchester	T707PND	First Manchester
SCK226X	Stagecoach Ribble	SND524X	First Manchester	T188MVM	Stagecoach Manchester	T708PND	First Manchester
SHH387X	Stagecoach Ribble	SND529X	First Manchester	T189MVM	Stagecoach Manchester	T789JAO	Titterington
SHH388X	Stagecoach Ribble	SNS831W	Stagecoach Ribble	T190MVM	Stagecoach Manchester	T916SSF	First Manchester
SHH390X	Stagecoach Ribble	SPR35	Shearings	T191MVM	Stagecoach Manchester	T917SSF	First Manchester
SIA6180	Finglands	SRJ744R	Border	T192MVM	Stagecoach Manchester	T918SSF	First Manchester
SIB1832	Springfield Coachways	SRJ756R	Blackpool	T193MVM	Stagecoach Manchester	T919SSF	First Manchester
SIB2014	Hulme Hall	SRJ757R	Blackpool	T194MVM	Stagecoach Manchester	T953JAO	Sim's Travel
SIB2633	Stainton	SRN103P	Fishwick	T195MVM	Stagecoach Manchester	T965PVM	Dennis's
SIB6614	Finglands	SSU780W	Lancaster Bus	T196MVM	Stagecoach Manchester	TAO154R	Titterington
SIB6615	Finglands	SSV269	Mayne	T197JBA	Shearings	TAZ5004	Brownrigg's
SIB8405	Blackpool	SWS768S	Robinson's	T197MVM	Stagecoach Manchester	TAZ5284	Kirby Lonsdale
SIW2805	Brownrigg's	T2BLU	Bluebird	T198JBA	Shearings	TAZ5284	Kirby Lonsdale
SIW6251	Mayne	T3FWS	Stainton	T198TND	Stagecoach Manchester	TCK841	Stagecoach Cumberland
SJI2054	Stagecoach Manchester	T9RED	Redline Coaches	T199JBA	Shearings	TCW868T	Blackburn
SJI4558	Stagecoach Manchester	T10BLU	Blue Bus	T199TND	Stagecoach Manchester	TET746S	Mayne
SJI8113	Wright Bros	T10VCC	Border	T201TND	Stagecoach Manchester	TET747S	Mayne
SND101X	First Manchester	T11BLU	Blue Bus	T202TND	Stagecoach Manchester	THX303S	Mayne
SND102X	First Manchester	T11SLT	South Lancs Travel	T203TND	Stagecoach Manchester	THX555S	Mayne
SND103X	First Manchester	T11VCC	Border	T204TND	Stagecoach Manchester	THX594S	Mayne
SND104X	First Manchester	T12VCC	Border	T205TND	Stagecoach Manchester	THX601S	Mayne
SND112X	First Manchester	T13VCC	Border	T206TND	Stagecoach Manchester	TJI6878	J P Travel
SND114X	First Manchester	T58AUA	Fishwick	T207TND	Stagecoach Manchester	TJI7514	Pilkington
SND115X	First Manchester	T58JDB	Mayne	T208TND	Stagecoach Manchester	TJN505R	Blackburn
SND120X	Stagecoach Manchester	T59AUA	Fishwick	T209TND	Stagecoach Manchester	TKU462K	Blackpool
SND122X	First Manchester	T61LEC	Travellers	T210TND	Stagecoach Manchester	TKU465K	Blackpool
SND126X	First Manchester	T62LEC	Travellers	T211HCW	Blackpool	TKU466K	Blackpool
SND129X	First Manchester	T63LEC	Travellers	T211TND	Blackpool	TKU469K	Blackpool
SND130X	First Manchester	T64JDB	Mayne	T212HCW	Blackpool	TKU540	Mayne
SND131X	First Manchester	T64LEC	Travellers	T212TND	Stagecoach Manchester	TND102X	First Manchester
SND133X	First Manchester	T65JDB	Mayne	T213HCW	Blackpool	TOF694S	Blackburn
SND136X	First Manchester	T68FBN	R Bullocks	T213TND	Stagecoach Manchester	TRN481V	Stagecoach Ribble
SND137X	First Manchester	T69FBN	R Bullocks	T214HCW	Blackpool	TRN810V	Stagecoach Cumberland
SND138X	First Manchester	T101JBA	Shearings	T214TND	Stagecoach Manchester	TSD571S	Blackpool
SND139X	First Manchester	T102JBA	Shearings	T215HCW	Blackpool	TSK736	Cumbria Classic Coaches
SND140X	First Manchester	T103JBA	Shearings	T215TND	Stagecoach Manchester	TSU613	Wright Bros
SND147X	First Manchester	T104JBA	Shearings	T216HCW	Blackpool	TSU639W	Blackburn
SND148X	First Manchester	T105JBA	Shearings	T217HCW	Blackpool	TSU640W	Blackburn
SND149X	First Manchester	T106JBA	Shearings	T218HCW	Blackpool	TSU641W	Blackburn
SND150X	First Manchester	T107JBA	Shearings	T223JND	Mayne	TSV807	Wright Bros
SND288X	Hulme Hall	T108JBA	Shearings	T224JND	Mayne	TVN585	Lancaster Bus
SND416X	First Manchester	T109JBA	Shearings	T284PVM	Manchester Airport	TYT653	Titterington
SND419X	First Manchester	T110JBA	Shearings	T291ROF	Jim Stones	UCE665	Mayne
SND432X	Stagecoach Ribble	T112JBA	Shearings	T292ROF	Jim Stones	UCW315X	Travellers
SND438X	First Manchester	T113JBA	Shearings	T293ROF	Jim Stones	UDX921	Wright Bros
SND441X	First Manchester	T114JBA	Shearings	T294ROF	Jim Stones	UGE807W	Wright Bros

Reg	Operator	Reg	Operator	Reg	Operator	Reg	Operator
UHG141V	Preston	V122DND	First Manchester	V320DBU	First Manchester	WPH137Y	Blackburn
UHG142V	Preston	V124DND	First Manchester	V330DBU	First Manchester	WPH138Y	Blackburn
UHG143V	Preston	V125DJA	Mayne	V428DND	Finglands	WPH141Y	Blackburn
UHG144V	Preston	V125DND	First Manchester	V429DND	Finglands	WRH294J	Blackpool
UHG145V	Preston	V126DJA	Mayne	V801DFV	Stagecoach Cumberland	WRN139V	Blackburn
UHG147V	Preston	V126DND	First Manchester	V802DFV	Stagecoach Cumberland	WRN412V	Fishwick
UHG148V	Preston	V127DJA	Mayne	V803DFV	Stagecoach Cumberland	WRN413V	Fishwick
UHG149V	Preston	V127DND	First Manchester	V804DFV	Stagecoach Cumberland	WXI5865	Sim's Travel
UHG150V	Preston	V128DJA	Mayne	V806DFV	Stagecoach Cumberland	XAP956	Titterington
UHG351Y	Blackpool	V128DND	First Manchester	V807DFV	Stagecoach Cumberland	XAU701Y	Blackpool
UHG352Y	Blackpool	V129DJA	Mayne	V808DFV	Stagecoach Cumberland	XAU702Y	Blackpool
UHG353Y	Blackpool	V129DND	First Manchester	V809DFV	Stagecoach Cumberland	XAU703Y	Blackpool
UHG354Y	Blackpool	V130DND	First Manchester	V811DFV	Stagecoach Cumberland	XAU704Y	Blackpool
ULS318T	Blue Bus	V131DND	First Manchester	V812DFV	Stagecoach Cumberland	XAU705Y	Blackpool
ULS329T	Blue Bus	V132DND	First Manchester	VAZ2619	Dennis's	XAU706Y	Blackpool
ULS663T	Mayne	V133DND	First Manchester	VBV18Y	Blackburn	XBF58S	Springfield Coachways
ULS666T	Mayne	V134DND	First Manchester	VBV19Y	Blackburn	XCW957R	Fishwick
UNA822S	UK North	V135DND	First Manchester	VBV20Y	Blackburn	XDL521	Travellers
UNA829S	UK North	V136DND	First Manchester	VBV21Y	Blackburn	XDO32	Travellers
UOL337	Mayne	V137DND	First Manchester	VBV22Y	Blackburn	XHG96V	Blackpool
URM801Y	Stagecoach Cumberland	V138DND	First Manchester	VDV105S	Stagecoach Cumberland	XJF386	Travellers
URM802Y	Stagecoach Cumberland	V139DND	First Manchester	VEX291X	Hulme Hall	XJI1301	East Lancashire
URN166Y	Preston	V140DND	First Manchester	VFV907R	Abbotts	XJI1302	East Lancashire
URN167Y	Preston	V141DND	First Manchester	VJI6850	Hulme Hall	XJI1303	East Lancashire
URN168Y	Preston	V142DND	First Manchester	VJI6855	Hulme Hall	XOU692	Titterington
URN169Y	Preston	V190EBV	Preston	VLF578	Stagecoach Cumberland	XPG188T	Border
URN170Y	Preston	V191EBV	Preston	VOY182X	Rossendale	XPW876X	Border
URN171Y	Preston	V192EBV	Preston	VRM73S	Wright Bros	XRN44V	Stagecoach Ribble
URN172Y	Preston	V193EBV	Preston	VRN827Y	Stagecoach Ribble	XRN45V	Stagecoach Ribble
URN322V	Blackpool	V194EBV	Preston	VRN828Y	Stagecoach Ribble	XRN47V	Stagecoach Ribble
URN323V	Blackpool	V195EBV	Preston	VRN829Y	Stagecoach Cumberland	XRN48V	Stagecoach Ribble
URN324V	Blackpool	V196EBV	Preston	VRN830Y	Stagecoach Ribble	XRN49V	Stagecoach Ribble
URN325V	Blackpool	V206EBV	Blackburn	VRR447	Stagecoach Cumberland	XRR175S	Stagecoach Cumberland
URN326V	Blackpool	V207EBV	Blackburn	VUA472X	Hulme Hall	XSU905	Border
URN327V	Blackpool	V208EBV	Blackburn	WAO396Y	Stagecoach Ribble	XSU907	Border
URN328V	Blackpool	V209EBV	Blackburn	WAO645Y	Stagecoach Cumberland	XSU908	Border
URN329V	Blackpool	V210EBV	Blackburn	WAZ3866	Lancaster Bus	XSU909	Border
URN330V	Blackpool	V301DBU	First Manchester	WBN955L	First Manchester	XYS596S	Pilkington
UWV610S	Stagecoach Cumberland	V302DBU	First Manchester	WEC768Y	East Lancashire	YAE516V	Stagecoach Manchester
UWV612S	Stagecoach Cumberland	V303DBU	First Manchester	WEX827X	Border	YAZ7315	Mountain Goat
UWV618S	Stagecoach Cumberland	V304DBU	First Manchester	WFR167K	Abbotts	YCS93T	Blue Bus
UWV620S	Stagecoach Cumberland	V305DBU	First Manchester	WFS141W	Blue Bus	YDG616	Stagecoach Cumberland
UWV622S	Stagecoach Cumberland	V306DBU	First Manchester	WG2373	Cumbria Classic Coaches	YEV317S	Blackburn
UWW5X	Blackpool	V307DBU	First Manchester	WIB1366	East Lancashire	YEV324S	Blackburn
UWW11X	Blackpool	V308DBU	First Manchester	WIB4053	Blue Bus	YFG333	Travellers
UWW15X	Blackpool	V309DBU	First Manchester	WIB4054	Blue Bus	YPD129Y	Brownrigg's
V2SLT	South Lancs Travel	V310DBU	First Manchester	WJI2823	Hulme Hall	YPD133Y	Brownrigg's
V3BLU	Bluebird	V311DBU	First Manchester	WJI9072	Blue Bus	YPL764	Mayne
V3SLT	South Lancs Travel	V312DBU	First Manchester	WJI9073	Blue Bus	YRN507R	Abbotts
V4HWD	Holmeswood	V313DBU	First Manchester	WJI9074	Blue Bus	YRN815V	Pilkington
V21BLU	Bluebird	V314DBU	First Manchester	WLT697	The Coachmasters	YRN817V	Stagecoach Ribble
V22BLU	Bluebird	V315DBU	First Manchester	WLT706	Stagecoach Cumberland	YSE666Y	Lancaster Bus
V41DTE	First Manchester	V316DBU	First Manchester	WLT824	Stagecoach Cumberland	YSU991	Holmeswood
V42DTE	First Manchester	V317DBU	First Manchester	WLT980	Stagecoach Cumberland	YTY867	Holmeswood
V42PVM	Blue Bus	V318DBU	First Manchester	WPC316X	Stagecoach Ribble	YXI7923	Holmeswood
V43DTE	First Manchester	V319DBU	First Manchester	WPH134Y	Blackburn		

1 897990 48 0

blished by *British Bus Publishing Ltd*

Vyne, 16 St Margaret's Drive, Wellington, Telford, TF1 3PH

www.britishbuspublishing.co.uk   E-mail: sales@britishbuspublishing.co.uk

"I've been there, done that, and I've got the tee-shirt, 'cause I'm a member of ..."

≡OMNIBUS
S O C I E T Y

The enthusiasts with the
professional touch -
* regular depot visits
* day & weekend tours
* meetings & slide shows
* top speakers
* monthly local bulletin
* national magazine
* extensive library & archive
* nationwide associations

Can you afford not to be a
member? For more details,
a free bulletin and magazine,
write to the Secretary,
North Western &
    Yorkshire Branch,
10 Bradley Close, Timperley,
Altrincham WA15 6SH

THERE ARE MANY BUS SOCIETIES
BUT ONLY ONE OMNIBUS SOCIETY
(The tee-shirt is optional)